D1116498

CONTEMPORARY MATHEMATICS

FOR ELEMENTARY TEACHERS

CONTEMPORARY MATHEMATICS

FOR ELEMENTARY TEACHERS

HOWARD F. FEHR
Teachers College
Columbia University

THOMAS J. HILL
Montclair State College

D. C. HEATH AND COMPANY · BOSTON
SAN FRANCISCO
CHICAGO ENGLEWOOD ATLANTA DALLAS

Library of Congress Catalog Card Number: 66–18438

PRINTED IN THE UNITED STATES OF AMERICA
Printed January 1967

PREFACE

This book is a book on mathematics. It is written to serve as a professional subject matter textbook either for collegiate study or for in-service study, and as such it presents the foundations of arithmetic and geometry which are necessary for the conceptual teaching of a contemporary mathematics program in the elementary school.

The traditional mathematics program in the elementary school was for many years a course in computational arithmetic, based largely on the theory of learning which emphasizes associative skills. In the past twenty years, there has been a shift toward a more meaningful approach to the teaching of arithmetic in the schools of the United States. During the last ten years there has been a decided emphasis on a structural, conceptual point of view with much geometry, or the study of space, included as an integral part of the elementary school curriculum.

Because of the growing importance of mathematics in all endeavors of our society, most school systems have been allotting an increased amount of time to the study of mathematics. To make the proper use of this time, teachers must understand not only the basic ideas of number, number systems, and numeration, but also the basic concepts of the nature of the space we live in. All these ideas and concepts are essential for dealing effectively with everyday problems, and they contribute to a liberal education that is to include an understanding of science.

With these considerations in mind, the authors have had as their goal a presentation which has two general characteristics:

1. It permits the reader to construct for himself or herself the mathematical foundation of the arithmetic content that is useful in many everyday and scientific applications.
2. It reveals through simple, nonrigorous, but correct examples a few elementary and basic structures in mathematics that will help the student to feel and admire the deep unity of mathematical thought.

The authors have included only the material that is necessary for a thorough background for elementary school teachers. It is difficult to know where to draw the line, but at all times the authors have weighed the material as to its usefulness and feasibility in a responsible program. No unnecessary new vocabulary has been injected into this book. All the material is presented from a contemporary mathematical viewpoint as exemplified in the writings of SMSG (School Mathematics Study Group) and CUPM (Committee on the Undergraduate Program in Mathematics of the Mathematical Association of America).

There are many possible ways to develop the structure of the number systems of elementary school mathematics. To present all these ways would require a voluminous treatise, and some of them would not be appropriate for our purpose. For instance, one might start from a purely logical foundation using Peano's axioms. This book does not follow that method; first, because the Peano treatment is very abstract, and second, because it is far removed from the classroom work of the elementary teacher. Here, instead, the authors use the *set* approach because it requires very little preparatory knowledge and it is closely related to the way arithmetic is used in ordinary problem solving. Insofar as possible, the authors have tried to give a presentation that is sound mathematically, and yet as close as possible to the needs of classroom teaching.

Although there is no actual prerequisite other than a year each of high school algebra and high school geometry, nevertheless a course in college mathematics of some sort may provide a stronger background for the study of this book. The authors assume on the part of the reader some degree of maturity together with a sufficiently motivated interest to enable him to work through the text, examples, and exercises.

The book can serve as the basis for a full year course if taken at a moderate pace. Depending on the previous knowledge that a student has and on the depth of training desired, by a judicious choice of exercises the book may be covered in a half year of study.

The materials of this book have been class-tested in both in-service and regular university courses over the last four years. It is well established that they are presented in easily understandable form and are genuinely helpful to elementary school teachers.

The authors are indebted to many people, especially classroom teachers, for valuable suggestions that have gone into the writing of the book. They also express their appreciation to the editorial staff of D. C. Heath and Company, from which many suggestions for improvement have come.

HOWARD F. FEHR
THOMAS J. HILL

CONTENTS

1 SETS AND MAPPINGS

THERE ARE CERTAIN CONCEPTS *that are fundamental to the whole of mathematics from its very beginning in arithmetic, through algebra and geometry, into calculus and vector spaces, continuing in function theory and topology, and so on. These fundamental ideas, called* sets, mappings, relations, *and* functions, *appear first very simply in the study of number, but they are developed more deeply and abstractly in the higher branches of mathematics. Because of their importance in unifying the entire study of mathematics, it is essential that they be built correctly in the mind of the child as soon as he starts his thinking about number in the kindergarten and the elementary grades. To accomplish this, it is necessary that the teacher have a correct and usable knowledge of these concepts.*

We shall begin by studying sets, operations on sets, mappings, and relations.

1.1 WHAT IS A SET?

In mathematics we do not attempt to give a definition of the concept of *set*. A set is to be thought of intuitively as a collection of objects considered as an entity. By giving examples, illustrations, and applications, we attempt to develop a naive feeling for the concept of set. From this concept, we shall then be able to give definitions of the specific sets with which we shall deal.

EXAMPLE 1. In the front row of a class there are three persons. These persons are the *elements* (or *members*) of a "*set* of three persons." They are also said to *belong to* the set. Looking at the elements of this set, I notice three pairs of eyes. Do these three pairs of eyes *belong to* the set of three persons? The answer is *NO*, because the elements in the set referred to are persons, not pairs of eyes. It is always necessary to distinguish between the elements of a set and the set of features of each element of the set.

EXAMPLE 2. Bill has a collection of miniature automobiles, which he keeps in a bag. We represent this collection by writing a little cross to represent each automobile and drawing a closed line around them. Bill has a label on his bag, and we

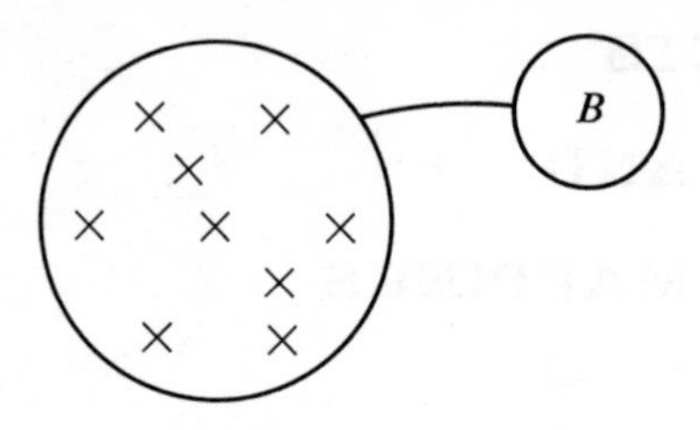

represent this in the figure by adding a tag with a letter, say B. Then we can say, "B is the set of Bill's miniature automobiles."

Example 2 shows one way of representing a *collection* or a *class* of things which we shall call a *set*. Note that in this representation, each element of the set is represented by a small cross. In general,

one element of a set cannot be represented by two symbols,

and

one symbol cannot denote two distinct elements of the set.

Note also that the position of the symbols is immaterial in depicting a set. The automobiles in Bill's bag can be shifted around in any position, but the set is still the same.

1.2 LANGUAGE AND SYMBOLS

While we can sometimes represent sets by drawings, we shall generally have to use other methods to convey what we have in mind concerning sets. So we create a special vocabulary and a special symbolism.

One way of naming a set is to use a single capital letter as in Example 2. Thus, if the set of Bill's miniature automobiles is designated by B, we may say:

$$\text{The set}\left\{\begin{array}{c}\text{named}\\ \text{or}\\ \text{referred to}\end{array}\right\}\text{by the letter } B$$

$$\left\{\begin{array}{c}\text{is the same as}\\ \text{or}\\ \text{is identical to}\end{array}\right\}\text{the set of Bill's automobiles.}$$

Such a label permits us to recognize one set among many sets.

Similarly, we use a single lowercase letter to designate each element of a set. Thus, if we represent Bill's collection of miniature automobiles as follows,

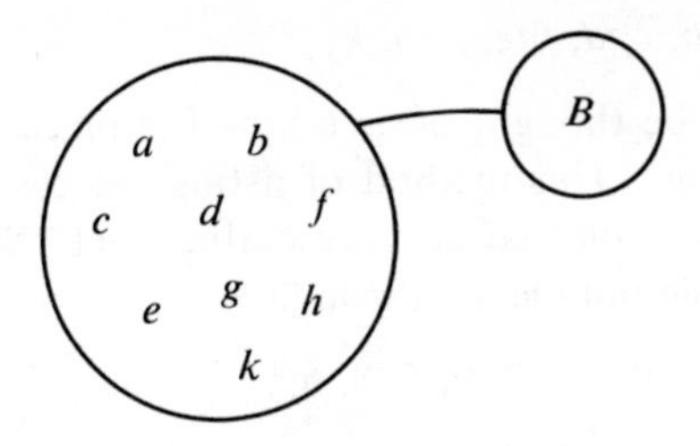

we may say:

$$\text{The automobile} \left\{ \begin{array}{c} \text{named} \\ \text{or} \\ \text{referred to} \end{array} \right\} \text{by the letter } c$$

$$\left\{ \begin{array}{c} \text{is an element of} \\ \text{is a member of} \\ \text{or} \\ \text{belongs to} \end{array} \right\} \text{the set } B \text{ of Bill's automobiles.}$$

Thus, using c gives us a way of identifying one special element among all the elements of the set. Moreover, since the letter p does not appear in the representation of the set, it is evident that p is not an element of B.

Furthermore, we represent

$$\left\{ \begin{array}{c} \text{is the same as} \\ \text{or} \\ \text{is identical to} \end{array} \right\} \text{by "="; and} \left\{ \begin{array}{c} \text{is an element of} \\ \text{is a member of} \\ \text{or} \\ \text{belongs to} \end{array} \right\} \text{by "}\in\text{."}$$

The negatives of these are represented by "$\neq$" and "$\notin$," respectively.

Thus, we now have three ways of referring to sets:

I. Ordinary language
The object c is one of Bill's automobiles.
The object p is not one of Bill's automobiles.

II. Mathematical language
The element c *belongs to* the set B.
The element p *does not belong to* the set B.

III. Symbolic representation
$c \in B$.
$p \notin B$.

We now turn to the actual representation of sets. If a set has only a few elements, we may simply list them enclosed in braces. Thus, to represent the set of Bill's automobiles, we may write

$$B = \{a, b, c, d, f, e, g, h, k\},$$

where the braces may be thought of as taking the place of the closed line used in the previous drawing. This method of listing the elements of a set between braces is called the *roster method* of representing a set. Similarly, we can represent the set of the whole numbers 5 through 9 as

$$\{5, 6, 7, 8, 9\} \text{ or } \{7, 9, 5, 8, 6\},$$

where any other arrangement of the *numerals* would denote the same set.

If, however, there are a great many elements in a set, we find it cumbersome to use the roster method, as, for example, for the set of male citizens of the United States over 21 years of age. How much paper that would take! For sets with many elements we may use either of two methods of representation. The first is a condensed roster method, where the listing of a few elements serves to convey the idea of all the other elements. Thus,

$$X = \{\mathrm{a}, \mathrm{b}, \mathrm{c}, \ldots, \mathrm{z}\}$$

may represent the set of all the letters of the alphabet.

The second method of representing a set is called the *set-selector* (*set-builder* or *set-abstractor*) or the *characterization method.* In this method we use a *variable* designated by a symbol such as x and some *characterization* or *defining property* which tells which substitutions for x are in the set designated. We shall illustrate this with the set of consonants selected out of the entire alphabet. Thus we write:

$$P = \{\underset{\text{variable}}{\underset{\downarrow}{x}} \quad \underset{\text{such that}}{\underset{\downarrow}{:}} \quad \underset{\text{characterization}}{\underset{\downarrow}{x \text{ is a consonant}}}\}$$

This is read, "P is the set of all those x, x a letter of the alphabet, such that x is a consonant." The set of possible substitutions we can make for x is called the *domain*, the *universe* (*of discourse*), or the *universal set.* In a given situation, this set is usually known or understood. If there is a possibility of misunderstanding the universe of discourse, we then name it, as in the phrase, "x a letter of the alphabet." Here the domain is the set X above. The set P then consists of those elements of the domain that are characterized as consonants.

EXAMPLE 3. Find the set of whole numbers which divide 60 exactly. Here the domain of x is the set of whole numbers. The phrase "divides 60 exactly" is the characterization. Thus we write:

$$D = \{x : 60 \div x \text{ is a whole number}\}$$

By actual division we find that the set can be exhibited by the roster method:

$$D = \{1, 2, 3, 4, 5, 6, 10, 12, 15, 20, 30, 60\}$$

As was noted earlier, a definition of the concept of set cannot be given. The concept of set can only be described by the way we use the term, as shown in the preceding sections. However, a *specific set* can be defined by giving the characterization of its elements.

Any set exists at first only in the mind of the observer. He can then find some characterization property by which he can define his set for others to comprehend. To do this, he may use a common name if the elements are well known, as, for example, the set of books on a particular desk. If the set is not well known, he uses the roster method or the characterization method. Thus there is a real difference between the *creating of a set* and the *defining of a set*, the latter needing language and symbols.

In defining a set it is essential that the definition make clear to all observers whether a particular object belongs to the set or does not belong to the set. Then the set is said to be *well-defined.* If this is not the case, there is no set. Some examples of descriptions that do not define sets are:

(a) blond pupils (what is blond?)
(b) wise senators (what is wise?)
(c) features of an individual (what are features?)

"Blond," "wise," and "features" are too vague to be characterizations for a set.

In writing the names of the elements of a set, repeating the name of an element does not increase the membership of the set. Thus, the set

{Bob, Bob, Bob, Sue, Dick}

is the same as the set

{Bob, Sue, Dick}.

If there were different elements in the set having the same name, we would add a subscript to the name as

$\{\text{Bob}_1, \text{Bob}_2, \text{Bob}_3, \text{Sue}, \text{Dick}\}$.

As another example, consider the name Barbara. The set of different letters occurring in this name is

{b, a, r}.

Can you find any other letters in this name? On the other hand, the set of symbols in this name could be designated as

$\{b_1, a_1, r_1, b_2, a_2, r_2, a_3\}$

because each symbol is, in a sense, an element of the word.

When two sets contain exactly the same elements, we say that they are *equal*. Thus the set $A = \{a, b, c\}$ is not equal to the set $X = \{x, y, z\}$ because the elements are different. However, the set $X = \{x, y, z\}$ is equal to the set $Z = \{z, x, y\}$ because the elements are exactly the same and their order of occurrence is immaterial. Thus we may write

$$X = Z.$$

In essence two equal sets are really one and the same set. Why then do we even speak of equal sets? We do because sometimes two quite different definitions produce the same set. For example, the set of whole numbers exactly divisible by 5 and the set of whole numbers for which the usual Hindu-Arabic notation ends in a "0" or a "5" are exactly the same; they are equal.

Now consider a set described as "the set of round desks in this room." But it so happens that there are no round desks in this room. Very well! *The set is empty.* Yet its elements have been characterized and it is a well-defined set. We designate the *empty set* by the symbol "$\emptyset$" or "{ }." As we shall see later, the number of elements in the empty set is zero, but the set $\{0\}$ is not the empty set, as it contains the number zero.

The distinction between a set and its elements must always be made, even when a set is so small that it contains a single element, e.g., the set of presiding presidents of the United States. If j is the presiding president, then $\{j\}$ represents the set of presiding presidents, and we must distinguish between the set containing a single element,

$$P = \{j\},$$

and the element j which is not a set. Thus it is correct to say

$$j \in \{j\}$$

even though j is the only member of the set, but it would be incorrect to say that j is the same as $\{j\}$. Furthermore, if the United States should decide to have a monarchy, the person j would be unchanged, but the set P would become the empty set.

1.4 EXERCISES

1. Create three different sets, and name them by the roster method.
2. Make a set representation for a class of pupils following the procedure for Bill's automobiles in section 1.2. Put a name tag on the set. Give a roster and a set-selector representation for the set. Is the teacher a member of the set?
3. Construct a problem similar to Exercise 2 for the set of classrooms in a school. Are there rooms in the building not in the set?

4. (a) What is the set of letters used to write the word "horse"?
   (b) What is the set of letters that occur
   (1) in the word "banana"? (2) in the word "Mississippi"?

5. For each of the following the domain of x is the set of whole numbers *greater than* 0 and *less than* 10. Write each set by the roster method.
   (a) $\{x : x \text{ is less than } 6\}$ (b) $\{x : x \text{ is greater than } 5\}$
   (c) $\{x : x + 2 \text{ is less than } 7\}$ (d) $\{x : x - 2 \text{ is greater than } 5\}$
   (e) $\{x : x \text{ is less than } 9 \text{ and } x \text{ is greater than } 5\}$
   (f) $\{x : 3x \text{ is less than } 9\}$ (g) $\{x : x + 3 = 3 + x\}$
   (h) $\{x : x + 1 = x\}$ (i) $\{x : x + 0 = x\}$

6. Give an illustration of
   (a) a well-defined set. (b) a description that does not define a set.

7. For $S = \{a, e, i, o, u\}$ which of the following are true statements?
   (a) $i \in S$ (b) $o \notin S$ (c) $b \in S$ (d) $y \in S$
   (e) $e \in \{e\}$ (f) $u = \{u\}$ (g) $a \in \emptyset$ (h) $a \notin \emptyset$

Write each of the following sets by the roster method:

8. The living past presidents of the United States.
9. The symbols used in the Hindu-Arabic decimal notation.
10. The states of the United States bordering on the Gulf of Mexico.
11. The numbers which can be represented by using one, two, or three of the digits 2, 3, 4, no digit occurring twice in a number.
12. The fractions less than 1 with denominators that are whole numbers ($\neq 0$) less than 5.
13. The squares of the whole numbers from 1 through 10.
14. The members of your family who are sisters or brothers.
15. The possible outcomes of a football game.
16. The ways in which two tossed coins can fall.

Write each of the following sets by the set-selector method:

17. The set of vowels in the English alphabet.
18. The set of consonants in the English alphabet.
19. The set of consonants that sometimes act as vowels.
20. The set of whole numbers greater than 10 but less than 100.
21. The set of symbols used to write Roman numerals.
22. Give three examples of
   (a) the empty set. (b) a set having a single element.
23. Distinguish the number zero from the empty set.

At times it is desirable to talk about a *part* of a set, as, for example, the set of boys, B, in a given class, A, containing both boys and girls. As another example, suppose that

$$A = \{0, 1, 2, 3, 4, 5, 6, 7, 8, 9\}$$

and

$$B = \{0, 2, 4, 6, 8\}.$$

In both cases, every element of B is also an element of A. We say that

B is a *subset* of A

and write

$$B \subset A,$$

where the symbol "$\subset$" is read "is a subset of" or "is included in" and is called the *inclusion* symbol.

Formally, we define a subset as follows:

DEFINITION: *If A and B are sets, then set B is a* subset *of set A if every element of set B is also an element of set A.*

Let us examine the consequences of this definition. Certainly the set

$$C = \{5, 6, 7, 8, 9, 10\}$$

is *not* a subset of A above, for $10 \in C$ but $10 \notin A$. On the other hand, if we consider the set A with respect to itself, we see that every element of A is an element of A. Hence, by our definition

$$A \subset A;$$

that is, *every set is a subset of itself.* It is called the *improper* subset. In contrast, such a subset as set B that does not contain all the elements of A is called a *proper* subset of set A.

Now let us consider the empty set $\emptyset$. It has no elements. Hence, it is impossible for $\emptyset$ to have elements that are *not* elements of A. Then it does not violate the definition to say that

$$\emptyset \subset A;$$

that is, *the empty set is a subset of every set.*

Suppose that $A \subset B$ and $B \subset A$ hold simultaneously. From $A \subset B$ we know that every element of A is included in B. From $B \subset A$ we know that every element of B is included in A. Since both conditions hold, the two sets must be equal, for there can be no element of one set not contained in the other set.

We may write this conclusion as

$$(A \subset B \quad \text{and} \quad B \subset A) \quad \text{implies that} \quad A = B.$$

[Some books use the symbol "$\supset$," read "includes"; thus, if $B \subset A$,

$$A \supset B.$$

However, there is no need for this symbol since the statement can always be expressed as $B \subset A$. Also, some books use the symbol "$\subseteq$" to include both proper and improper subsets. Then the symbol "$\subset$" may mean "is a proper subset of." In this book we shall not use the symbols "$\supset$" and "$\subseteq$."]

Notice, in particular, the difference between the symbols "$\subset$" and "$\in$." The first represents a relation of one set to another set, called "inclusion"; the second represents a relation of an element to its set and is called "belonging." Thus,

$$3 \in A \qquad \text{and} \qquad B \subset A$$

are correct usages of the symbols.

To say $a \subset \{a, b\}$ is false. Since a is not a set, it cannot possibly be a subset. However, to say

$$\{a\} \subset \{a, b\}$$

is true, for $\subset$ is a relation between *sets*.

Again, to say $\{a\} \in \{a, b\}$ is false. The set $\{a, b\}$ has two elements, a and b; it does not have the set $\{a\}$ as an element. But to say

$$a \in \{a, b\}$$

is true, for $\in$ is a relation between an *element* and a *set* to which it belongs.

A set is a collection of objects, but then it is in itself a new object and may become an element of a set. Thus we may have a set of sets.

EXAMPLE 4. Consider the set L of letters of the alphabet. Then the set of vowels V is a subset of L, and we write

$$V \subset L.$$

The set of consonants C is also a subset of L, and we write

$$C \subset L.$$

We can now form a new set S for which the elements are the sets V and C:

$$S = \{V, C\}$$

This is *not* the set L, for L has 26 elements. The set S has only two elements, each element a set.

An interesting case is the set of all possible subsets of a given set. Consider the set

$$M = \{x, y, z\}.$$

Then the possible subsets of M form a new set R as follows:

$$R = \{\{x, y, z\}, \{x, y,\}, \{x, z\}, \{y, z\}, \{x\}, \{y\}, \{z\}, \emptyset\}$$

These *eight* subsets include three sets with a single element and the empty set.

So far in this book we have dealt only with *finite* sets, that is, sets in which the elements can be counted, arriving at a last element. However, several of the finite sets of numbers that we have used as examples are subsets of the set of whole numbers

$$W = \{0, 1, 2, 3, \ldots\},$$

which is an example of an *infinite* set, a set that has no last element. It is important to understand the difference between an infinite set and a set that is very large but, nevertheless, finite. For example, the set of words in the English language is a finite set, but it takes a large dictionary to list the elements of the set.

1.6 EXERCISES

1. Give at least three examples of an important subset of a given set.
2. Consider the set B of American League baseball players and the set A of the ten American League teams:
   (a) Is a member of B a member of A?
   (b) Is a member of A a member of B?
   (c) Is a member of an element of A a member of B?
   (d) Is a member of B a member of an element of A?
   (e) Are the sets A and B equal?
3. (a) Write out the set of all subsets of the set $\{a, b\}$.
   (b) Write out the set of all subsets of the set $\{a\}$.
   (c) Considering your answers to (a) and (b) and the discussion of the subsets of set $M = \{x, y, z\}$ given in section 1.5, estimate the number of subsets you would expect from the set $\{a, b, c, d\}$. Prove your answer.
   (d) Generalize the answer to parts (a), (b), and (c).
4. Given a collection of children in a classroom, tell if it is possible to designate a particular child as a member of a subset characterized as follows:
   (a) Weighs more than 70 pounds.
   (b) Has fair complexion.
   (c) Is a boy.
   (d) Is a bright pupil.

5. (a) List the ways in which you can trace the adjoining figure without lifting your pencil or retracing any segment.

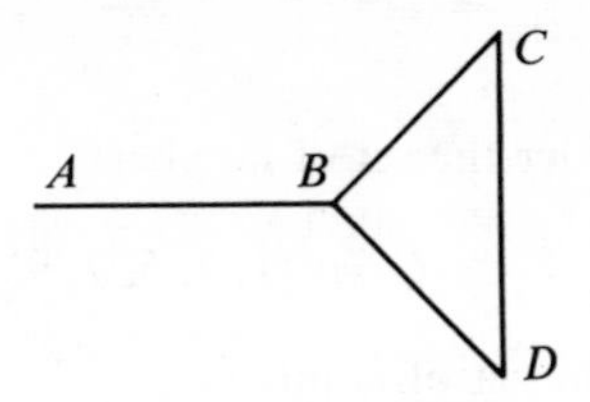

(b) The same as part (a) for the adjoining figure.

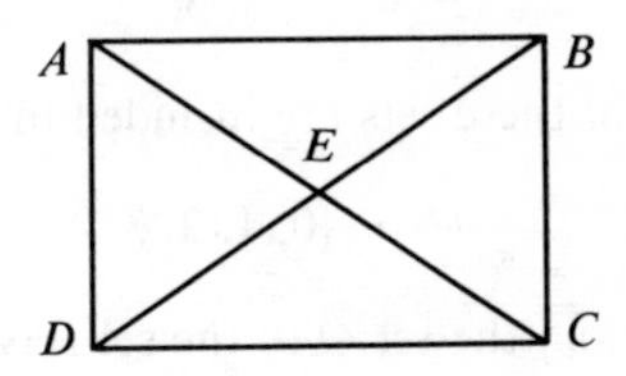

6. How many subsets does the set $\emptyset$ have?

7. List at least three important subsets of the set of the states of the United States of America.

8. (a) List a few numbers of a set for which the Hindu-Arabic numeral ends in a "1," "3," "5," "7," or "9."

   (b) List a few numbers of a set of whole numbers which when divided by 2, give a remainder of 1.

   (c) Are the sets in (a) and (b) equal? Is each a subset of the other?

9. Is the set of human beings alive on earth at the time you are reading this finite or infinite? Explain your answer.

10. Give at least three examples each of

    (a) very large finite sets.

    (b) infinite sets.

11. Given the numbers 6 and 7 we can write the fractions $\frac{6}{7}$ and $\frac{7}{6}$. You know that $\frac{6}{7}$ is less than 1 and $\frac{7}{6}$ is greater than 1. Form all possible fractions from the numerals 1, 2, 3, 4, 5, and find the subset of these fractions for which the values are less than 1.

12. There are four children in a set, designated by a, b, c, d. A subset of three children is to be selected from this set of four. Write the set of all possible subsets that could be chosen.

13. (a) Using the set

$$A = \{a, b\}$$

write the set S of all possible subsets.

   (b) Using the symbols $\in, \subset, =, \not\subset$ (meaning "is not a subset of"), write four true statements and four false statements relating the elements of set A and set S.

Consider the set of numbers

$$O = \{1, 3, 5, 7, 9\}$$

and the set of numbers

$$P = \{2, 3, 5, 7\}.$$

Both of these sets are included in the set

$$C = \{0, 1, 2, 3, 4, 5, 6, 7, 8, 9\}.$$

If we join the set O to the set P, we obtain the set

$$M = \{1, 2, 3, 5, 7, 9\},$$

which is also included in the set C. Note that while the elements 3, 5, and 7 belong to both O and P, they are listed only once in the set M, since they are identical (see section 1.3). The set M is called the *union* of sets O and P, and the operation of combining them is also called *union*. The symbol for the union operation is "∪," and we write

$$O \cup P = M.$$

This type of operation is called a *binary operation*, since *two* sets are combined to form a new set.

In general, we have the following definition:

DEFINITION: *Let A and B be two sets which are subsets of a universal set E. Form the set which contains all the elements that belong to A or to B. The result is called the* union *of sets A and B. In symbols:*

$$A \cup B = \{x : x \in A \text{ or } x \in B\}.$$

To understand the implications of this definition, we must understand the use of the logical term "or." This word may be used in two senses. One is the *exclusive* sense as in, "Either you will pass the course or you will repeat it." In this case the occurrence of one of the conditions *excludes* the occurrence of the other. The word "or" may also be used in the *inclusive* sense as in, "Either students or teachers will receive a discount." This means that students may get the discount, teachers may get a discount, or a graduate student, who is both a student and a teacher, may get the discount. That is, if one of these classes of persons gets the discount, the persons in the other classes are not precluded from getting a discount also. It is the *inclusive* sense of "or" that is applied in the definition of union.

Earlier we used symbols surrounded by a closed curve to represent a set and its elements. Now we introduce another representation, in which we use a *bounded region*, considering points in the region as elements of the set (as A)

without actually marking them. Such a representation is the basis of the so-called *Venn diagrams*, named for an English mathematician and logician, John Venn, who first used them.

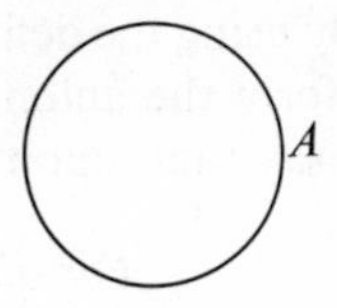

We can use a Venn diagram to illustrate the union of two sets. Let A be the set of coffee drinkers in a restaurant and B the set of pie eaters. Then the set of coffee drinkers *or* pie eaters is the union of the two sets. This is shown by the

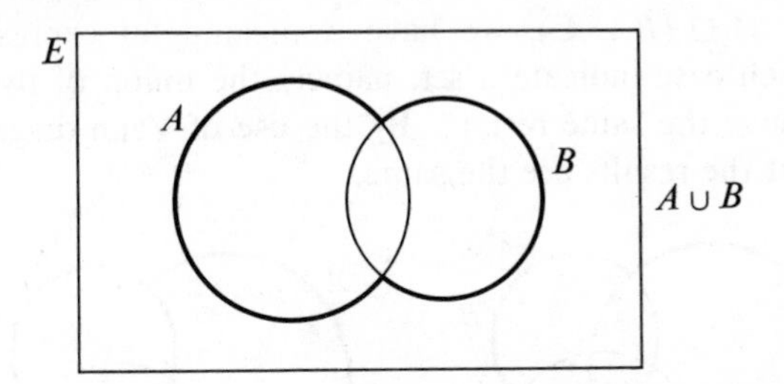

Venn diagram where the circles bound the regions A and B, respectively, and the heavy line bounds the union of A and B, that is, $A \cup B$.

If two sets have no elements in common, they are said to be *disjoint*. Thus, in a class of pupils the set of boys and the set of girls are disjoint sets, and their union is the class. Can you give other illustrations of disjoint sets?

EXAMPLE 5. Let M_3 be the set of numbers which are divisible by 3. Then

$$M_3 = \{0, 3, 6, 9, 12, 15, 18, 21, \ldots\}.$$

Let M_7 be the set of numbers which are divisible by 7. Then

$$M_7 = \{0, 7, 14, 21, \ldots\}.$$

The union of these two sets gives the numbers which are divisible by 3 *or* by 7:

$$M_3 \cup M_7 = \{0, 3, 6, 7, 9, 12, 14, 15, 18, 21, 24, \ldots\}$$

EXAMPLE 6. In the drawing below are represented two intersecting lines, CA and DB, in the plane p. The region H_1, shaded in solid lines, is the portion of plane p on the side of line CA that does not contain point B. The region H_2, shaded in dashed lines, is the portion of plane p on the side of line DB that does not contain point A. The union of the two shaded regions, H_1 and H_2, is the *exterior* of angle AOB.

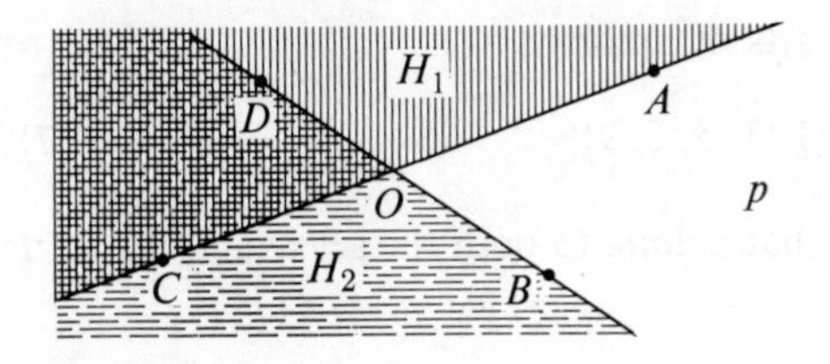

By using the definition of union or Venn diagrams, it is easy to see that whether we form the union of A and B or the union of B and A, we get the same result. We say that union is *commutative* and write:

For all sets A and B

$A \cup B = B \cup A.$ COMMUTATIVITY OF $\cup$

If we write $A \cup B \cup C$, the expression has no meaning because we have defined union as an operation involving only two sets. However, if we write $(A \cup B) \cup C$ or $A \cup (B \cup C)$, we have a meaningful expression, since the parentheses in each case indicate a set, namely the union of two sets. Do the two expressions give the same result? By the use of Venn diagrams it is again easy to verify that the results are the same.

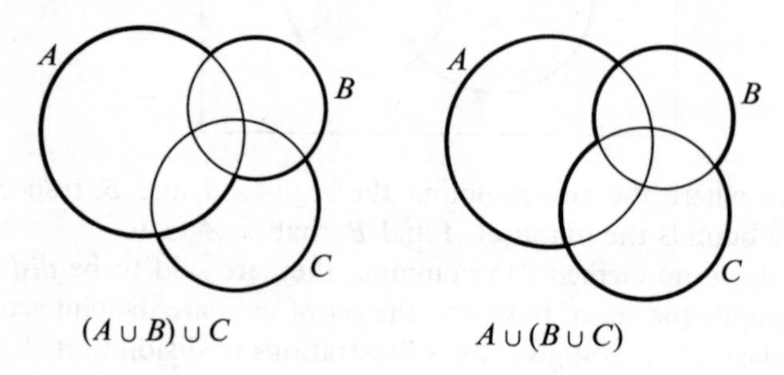

We say that union is *associative* and write:

For all sets A, B, and C

$(A \cup B) \cup C = A \cup (B \cup C).$ ASSOCIATIVITY OF $\cup$

And now, without ambiguity, $A \cup B \cup C$ means either union.

There is one set whose union with any other set is always the other set. This is the empty set. We say that the set $\emptyset$ is the *identity element* for the union operation and write:

For all sets A

$A \cup \emptyset = \emptyset \cup A = A.$ IDENTITY PRINCIPLE FOR $\cup$

The above three properties of union will be used when we consider the operations on whole (cardinal) numbers in Chapter 3.

1.8 INTERSECTION OF SETS

Consider again the sets of numbers

$$O = \{1, 3, 5, 7, 9\} \quad \text{and} \quad P = \{2, 3, 5, 7\}.$$

There are numbers that belong to both the set O and the set P. This set of numbers is called the *intersection* of sets O and P, and the operation is also called *intersection*. The symbol for the intersection operation is "$\cap$," and we write

$$O \cap P = \{3, 5, 7\}.$$

In general, we have the following definition:

DEFINITION: *Let A and B be two sets which are subsets of a universal set E. Form the set which contains all the elements that belong to A and to B. The result is called the* intersection *of sets A and B. In symbols:*

$$A \cap B = \{x : x \in A \text{ and } x \in B\}.$$

To understand the implications of this definition, we must understand the use of the logical term "and." This connective asserts that both the sentences which flank it must hold (or be true) if the entire compound sentence is to be true. Thus, in the above definition, each x in the intersection must be *both* a member of set A *and* a member of set B. Why are the numbers 1, 2, and 9 not members of the intersection $O \cap P$?

The intersection of two sets can also be represented by a Venn diagram. If sets A and B are, respectively, the coffee drinkers and the pie eaters of section 1.7, then the shaded region in the diagram below represents the intersection of these sets, that is, the set of persons who are both drinking coffee and eating pie.

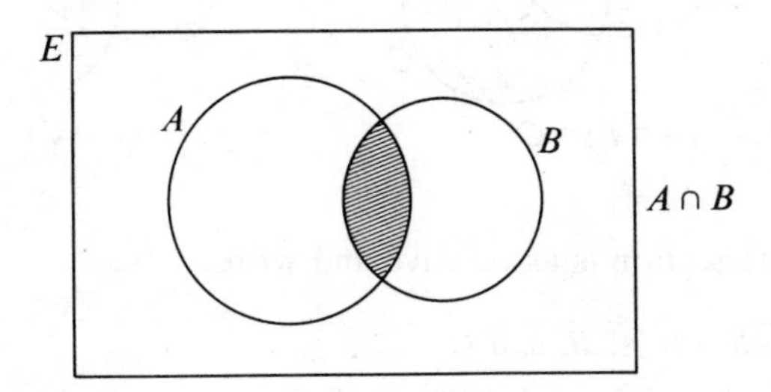

If two sets are disjoint, there are no elements common to both sets. However, we still speak of the intersection of these two sets and say that it is the empty set. This shows another generalization made possible by the empty set.

If $A \cap B = \emptyset$,

then the sets are disjoint, and conversely.

EXAMPLE 7. Consider the sets M_3 and M_7 of Example 5 in section 1.7. The intersection of these two sets is

$$M_3 \cap M_7 = \{0, 21, 42, \ldots\}.$$

Note that the intersection is the set of numbers that are divisible by both 3 *and* 7.

EXAMPLE 8. Consider the drawing in Example 6 in section 1.7. The region H_1, shaded in solid lines, is the portion of the plane p on the side of line CA that contains point D. The region H_2, shaded in dashed lines, is the portion of plane p on the side of line DB that contains point C. The intersection of the two shaded regions, H_1 and H_2, is the *interior* of angle COD.

The definition of intersection and the Venn diagram illustrate the fact that the intersection operation is commutative. We write:

For all sets A and B

$A \cap B = B \cap A.$ COMMUTATIVITY OF $\cap$

Again, if we write $A \cap B \cap C$, the expression has no meaning. However, $(A \cap B) \cap C$ and $A \cap (B \cap C)$ are meaningful, since each parenthetical expression represents a set. Do the two expressions give the same result? The following diagrams illustrate that they do give the same set.

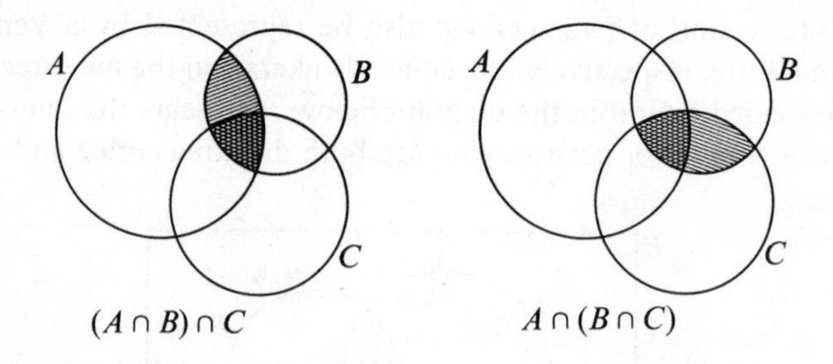

We say that intersection is associative and write:

For all sets A, B, and C

$(A \cap B) \cap C = A \cap (B \cap C).$ ASSOCIATIVITY OF $\cap$

Thus, without ambiguity, $A \cap B \cap C$ means either expression.

Is there an identity element for the intersection operation? That is, is there a set whose intersection with any other set is the other set? In symbols, is there a set X such that for any set A, $A \cap X = X \cap A = A$? Yes; it is the universal set E of which a set A is a subset. This is shown by the following Venn diagram where for any A in E the intersection of the two sets is A.

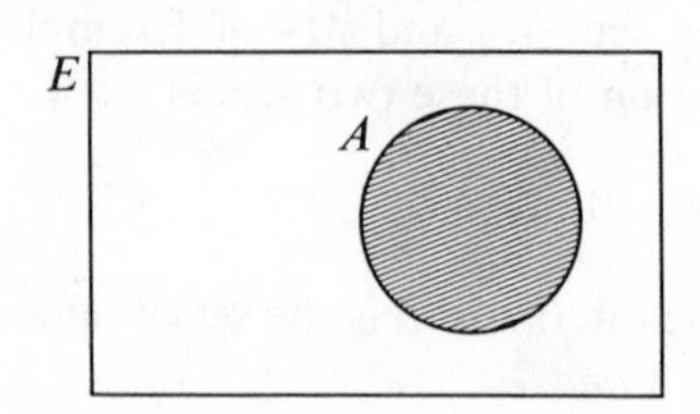

Thus, we say that the universal set E is the *identity element* for the intersection operation and write:

For all sets A

$A \cap E = E \cap A = A.$ IDENTITY PRINCIPLE FOR $\cap$

1.9 EXERCISES

1. Given the sets $N = \{1, 2, 3, 4, 5, 6, 7, 8, 9\}$, $E = \{2, 4, 6, 8\}$, $O = \{1, 3, 5, 7, 9\}$, and $P = \{2, 3, 5, 7\}$, write a representation of:
   (a) $O \cap P$ (b) $O \cup P$ (c) $E \cap O$
   (d) $E \cup O$ (e) $E \cup P$ (f) $E \cap P$
   (g) $E \cup O \cup P$ (h) $N \cap P$ (i) $N \cup P$
2. Let M_2 be the set of whole numbers which are multiples of 2 and M_5 be the set of those which are multiples of 5. Find $M_2 \cup M_5$ and $M_2 \cap M_5$.
3. If two sets have at least one element in common, they are said to *intersect*. If this is true, distinguish between the use of "intersect" and "intersection."
4. Describe the intersection and the union of the set of boys and the set of girls in a classroom.
5. Let A be the set of multiples of 3, B the set of numbers giving a remainder 1 when divided by 3, and C the set of numbers giving a remainder 2 when divided by 3. Describe the sets:
   (a) $A \cup B$ (b) $A \cup C$ (c) $A \cup B \cup C$ (d) $A \cap B \cap C$
6. Draw a Venn diagram to represent the fact that there are a set of 20 students taking algebra, a set of 30 students taking history, and 10 students taking both algebra and history. How many students are there in the union of the two sets?
7. If $A \subset B$, what can you say about $A \cup B$? About $A \cap B$?
8. Considering streets to be paved surfaces, describe:
   (a) The intersection of two crossing streets
   (b) The union of two crossing streets
9. Let A be the set of whole numbers whose units digit is 0, 4, or 8. (Some of the numbers are 0, 14, 68, 244, 1258, etc.) Let B be the set of whole numbers for which the units digit is 2 or 6. (Some numbers of B are 6, 26, 212, etc.) Describe the sets:
   (a) $A \cup B$
   (b) A set C where $C \subset A$ and C contains only those elements of A that are exactly divisible by 4
   (c) A set D where $D \subset B$ and D contains only those elements of B that are exactly divisible by 4
   (d) The set $C \cup D$
   (e) The set $C \cap D$

Consider a class of boys and girls. The girls form a subset of the class. The set of boys then consists of all the other elements of the class, those that are not in the set of girls in the class. We can refer to the set of boys as the set of not-girls. This set is called the *complement* of the set of girls with respect to the set of students in the class.

Similarly, if from a squad S of 25 football players 11 are selected to be the team on the field, the complement of the team is the set of players on the bench. If we designate the set of players on the field by A, then the complement of A, that is, the set of players on the bench (not playing), is designated by A'. Thus, we have

$$A \cup A' = S \quad \text{and} \quad A \cap A' = \emptyset,$$

where S is the universal set, or the set of all players, and $\emptyset$ is the empty set. The operation of finding the complement is called *complementation.*

Just as A' is the complement of A, A is the complement of A'; thus,

$$(A')' = A.$$

In general, we have the following definition:

DEFINITION: *Let U be a universal set and let A be a subset of U. Then the set of elements of U which are* not *elements of A is called the* complement *of A with respect to U. In symbols:*

$$A' = \{x : x \in U \text{ and } x \notin A\}.$$

This is illustrated by the following Venn diagram:

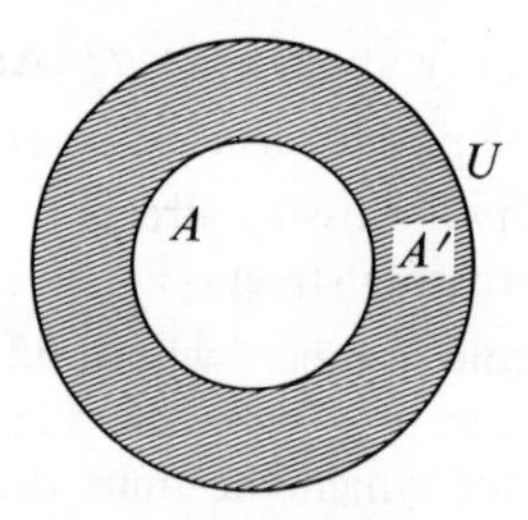

In the definition of complement we used another logical concept, that of *negation* as designated by the word "not." This word implies that a property or characteristic can be applied to elements or things in such a precise way that all intelligent persons can tell whether an element does or does not have the property, and further that it is impossible *for any element to have and not have the property simultaneously.* The word "not," therefore, excludes those elements that have the property.

Note the correspondence between operations on sets and their logical equivalents:

Union	or (inclusive)
Intersection	and
Complementation	not

There is one more operation that is defined on sets; this is called *subtraction* of sets because in one sense it is related to the taking away of elements. Consider again the set A of coffee drinkers and the set B of pie eaters introduced in section 1.7. Suppose that from all the coffee drinkers we take away those who are also eating pie. Then we say that we have "subtracted the pie eaters from the coffee drinkers" and write

$$A \setminus B \quad \text{(read "}A\text{ slash }B\text{")},$$

where the bar "\" indicates a subtraction of sets (not numbers). The shaded section in the Venn diagram below shows the *difference* $A \setminus B$. What region would represent $B \setminus A$?

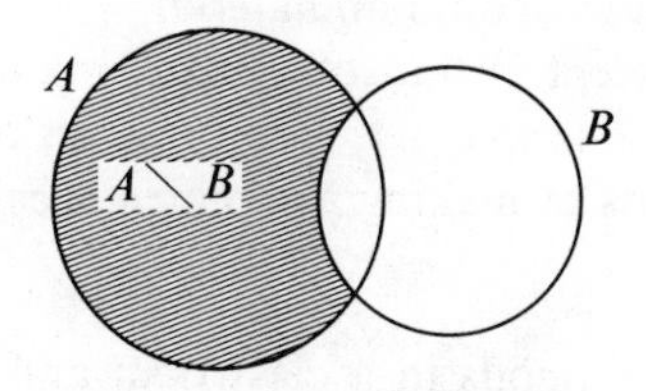

In general, we have the following definition:

DEFINITION: *Given two sets A and B, the set of elements of A that are not in B is called the* difference *of sets A and B. In symbols:*

$$A \setminus B = \{x : x \in A \text{ and } x \notin B\}.$$

If B is a subset of A, then $A \setminus B$ is also the complement B' with respect to A if A is regarded as a universal set. If A and B are disjoint sets, then $A \setminus B = A$. Illustrate each of these cases by appropriate Venn diagrams.

EXAMPLE 9. Given the sets $N = \{1, 2, 3, 4, 5, 6, 7, 8, 9\}$, $E = \{2, 4, 6, 8\}$, $O = \{1, 3, 5, 7, 9\}$, and $P = \{2, 3, 5, 7\}$, find the sets E', O', and P' with respect to N. Also find $N \setminus O$, $N \setminus P$, $O \setminus P$, and $E \setminus O$.

Solution: $E' = \{1, 3, 5, 7, 9\} = O$; $O' = \{2, 4, 6, 8\} = E$;
$P' = \{1, 4, 6, 8, 9\}$.
$N \setminus O = E$; $N \setminus P = \{1, 4, 6, 8, 9\} = P'$; $O \setminus P = \{1, 9\}$;
$E \setminus O = E$, since no elements of O belong to E.

One of the most important ideas in contemporary expositions of mathematics is that of an *ordered pair* of elements. While this idea can be explained rigorously, we shall use only a naive understanding of it. By a *first element* we shall mean a thing which precedes in time of speaking, or of writing its name from left to right, another thing called the *second element*. Thus, if we write 3 and then 4, as "3, 4," we say that 3 "comes before" 4 and that the *order* of "3, 4" is different from the order of "4, 3." Such a set of two elements which occur in a specified order is called an *ordered pair* of elements and is symbolized by

$$(a, b).$$

The element a is selected first, then the element b. Generally,

$$(a, b) \neq (b, a).$$

When would $(a, b) = (b, a)$? Only when a and b are the same element.

Notice that an ordered pair (a, b) is different from a set $\{a, b\}$, for in a set the order in which the elements occur is immaterial.

Another important concept is that of a matching or assignment of elements of one set to elements of a second set, forming a set of ordered pairs. We first study three special methods of making assignments, called *mappings*.

EXAMPLE 10. Consider the pupils in a classroom and the pupils' chairs. Now each pupil usually has a chair assigned as his or her chair. We shall consider that the pupil comes *first* and then a chair is assigned to the pupil. Thus we have an ordered pair

(Pupil, Chair).

If there are as many chairs as pupils or more chairs than pupils, then every pupil will be assigned a chair and there will be as many ordered pairs as there are pupils. Each chair that is selected occurs only once in the ordered pairs, but not all chairs may be used. If there are chairs left unassigned, one feels that the set of chairs is in some way "larger" or "greater" than the set of pupils. The mapping may be illustrated by the adjoining diagram.

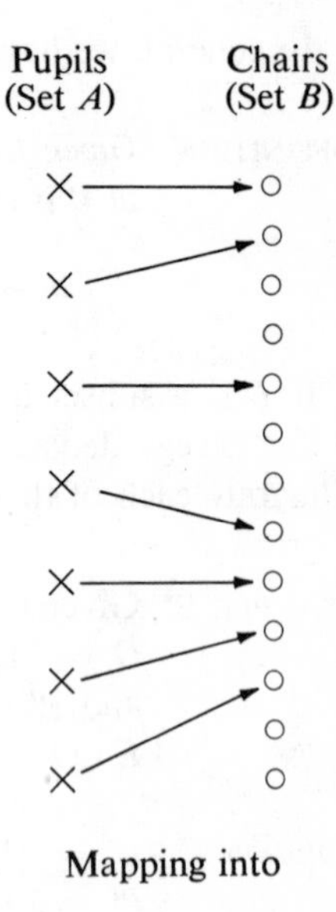

Mapping into

The above example illustrates one way of matching or *mapping* elements of one set (Pupils) with another set (Chairs). In general, we have this definition:

DEFINITION: *When every element of the first set, set A, has assigned to it one and only one element of the second set, set B, and an element of set B is assigned to only one element of set A, but some elements of the second set may be unassigned, the mapping is called a*

mapping *of set A* into *set B.*

It is also called an injection; *that is, set A is* injected into *set B.*

EXAMPLE 11. In a classroom there are working tables. Each of the pupils has assigned to him a table that is his working table. All the tables are assigned, but several pupils may be matched with the same table. Here we have a set of ordered pairs

(Pupil, Table)

in which the same table may occur in a number of the ordered pairs, but a pupil will occur only once in all the ordered pairs. In this case, where a table is assigned to several pupils and all tables are assigned, one feels that the set of tables is in some way "smaller" or "less" than the set of pupils.

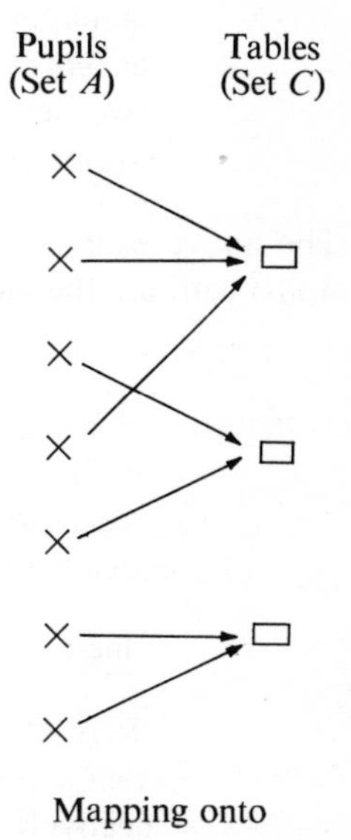

Mapping onto

The above example illustrates a second way of matching elements of one set (Pupils) with another set (Tables). In general, we have this definition:

DEFINITION: *When every element of the second set, set C, is assigned, and perhaps assigned to more than one element of the first set, set A, and every element of set A has assigned to it just one element of set C, the mapping is called a*

mapping *of set A* onto *set C.*

It is also called a surjection *because set A covers all the elements of set C.*

EXAMPLE 12. For the class of pupils there is a set of arithmetic books. Each pupil has a book assigned to him, and after all the assignments have been made, there are no books left unassigned. Here we have a set of ordered pairs

(Pupil, Book)

in which no pupil nor book occurs more than once in the set of ordered pairs. The set of pupils is mapped *into* the set of books, but the set of books is also mapped *into* the set of pupils. Since all the books are assigned, the set of pupils is mapped *onto* the set of books as well as *into* it. In this case, one feels that the two sets, though not equal, have the "same size."

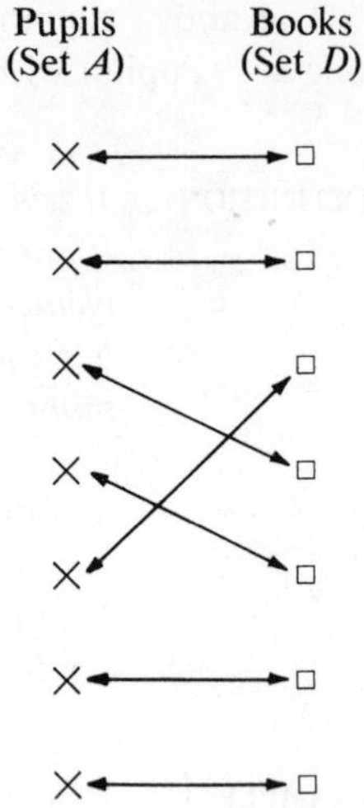

Pupils (Set A) | Books (Set D)

Mapping one-to-one

The above example illustrates a third way of matching elements of one set (Pupils) with another set (Books). In general, we have this definition:

DEFINITION: *When one and only one element of the second set, set D, is assigned to an element of the first set, set A, all elements of set D are assigned, and every element of set A has an assignment, the mapping is called a*

one-to-one reversible mapping *of set A onto set D.*

It is also called a bijection *because it is both an injection and a surjection. Also we say that set A can be mapped* bijectively to *set D.*

This type of mapping is described by various names. Often the word "reversible" is dropped, and the mapping is called briefly "one-to-one." It is very common in elementary mathematics to say that two sets have been placed in "one-to-one correspondence." When we say this, we mean that *the mapping is one-to-one.*

In making a mapping, it is not necessary that the two sets be distinct. A set can be mapped into itself. For example, we can map the set of whole numbers into itself by the ordered pair (Number, Number plus 3). One element is (5, 8). Write out ten of the ordered pairs that exhibit this mapping. What kind of mapping is it?

In a mapping, the first set, that is, the set of first elements, is called the *domain*, and the subset of elements of the second set that are assigned is called the *range*.

1.12 EXERCISES

1. Using sports squads, give at least two illustrations of the complement of a set.
2. From a set of 12 dolls, 4 are taken to school for display. Describe the set remaining at home in terms of complementation.
3. Draw Venn diagrams to illustrate A' and $A \setminus B$. Which of these ideas is related to subtraction in arithmetic?
4. Call the entire set of dots shown in the adjoining figure, E; the set of dots on the square, S; and the set of dots inside the square, I.

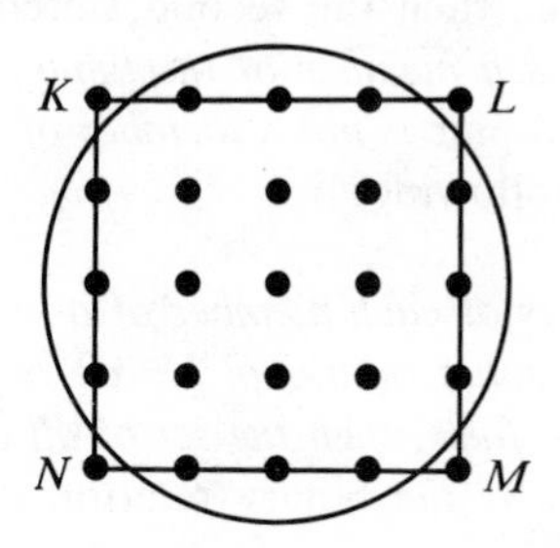

With respect to the set E, find the complement of:

(a) Set S (b) Set I

(c) The set of dots outside the circle

(d) The set of dots inside the circle

(e) The set of dots on the circle

5. Illustrate a mapping of the set of whole numbers into the set of whole numbers where the ordered pair is (Number, Square of the number).
6. Map a class of students onto their ages.
7. Map the set $A = \{1, 2\}$ into the set $B = \{3, 4, 5\}$ in all possible ways. Can set A be mapped onto set B?
8. Map the set B of Exercise 7 onto the set A in all possible ways. Can set B be mapped into set A?
9. Map the set $C = \{a, b, c\}$ one-to-one to the set $D = \{x, y, z\}$ in every possible way. How many ways are there?
10. Give two examples each of

    (a) an injection. (b) a surjection. (c) a bijection.
11. Explain why it is impossible to map an overflow audience into the seats of the theater. Can the seats be mapped into the overflow audience?

Consider the verbal phrase "is the father of" and two ordered pairs, (John, John-junior) and (John-junior, John). If the phrase is flanked by the elements of the first ordered pair in the order given, we obtain the statement

John is the father of John, Jr.

However, if we flank the phrase by the members of the second ordered pair, we obtain the statement

John, Jr., is the father of John.

If the first statement is true, then the second statement is false. We then say that the first ordered pair *is a member of the binary relation* "is the father of," and that the second ordered pair *is not a member of the relation.*

In general, we have the following:

DEFINITION: *If the elements of each member of a set of ordered pairs are connected by some relational phrase to form a sentence that can be true or false, then the set of all ordered pairs yielding true sentences is the* binary relation *described by the relational phrase.*

To determine a binary relation, we do the following:

(1) Define a *set* whose elements are to be related.
(2) Consider all possible *ordered pairs* of these elements.
(3) Write a *relational phrase*, such as, "is the father of" or "is less than."
(4) *Flank* this relational phrase on the left by the first element and on the right by the second element of an ordered pair.
(5) Determine whether the statement thus obtained is *true* or *false*.
(6) If it is true, accept the ordered pair as a member of the relation.
(7) Proceed in the same manner with every other ordered pair.
(8) The set of ordered pairs for which the statements are true is the relation.

EXAMPLE 13. For the set $\{0, 1, 2, 3, 4, 5\}$ the set of all possible ordered pairs contains 36 elements:

$$\{(0, 0), (0, 1), (0, 2), (0, 3), (0, 4), (0, 5),$$
$$(1, 0), (1, 1), (1, 2), (1, 3), (1, 4), (1, 5),$$
$$. \quad . \quad . \quad . \quad . \quad . \quad . \quad . \quad . \quad . \quad . \quad .$$
$$(5, 0), (5, 1), (5, 2), (5, 3), (5, 4), (5, 5)\}$$

Find the relation described by the relational phrase "is the square of."

Solution: Testing the ordered pairs, we find

"0 is the square of 0"—true;
"0 is the square of 1"—false;
. . . .
"1 is the square of 1"—true; and so on.

The set of ordered pairs for which the statement is true will be found to be

$\{(0, 0), (1, 1), (4, 2)\}$.

Thus this set is the relation "is the square of" over the given set. We can illustrate this by the graph at the right where the values of the first elements of the ordered pairs are plotted horizontally and the values of the second elements are plotted vertically. The three points representing the relation are indicated by solid dots.

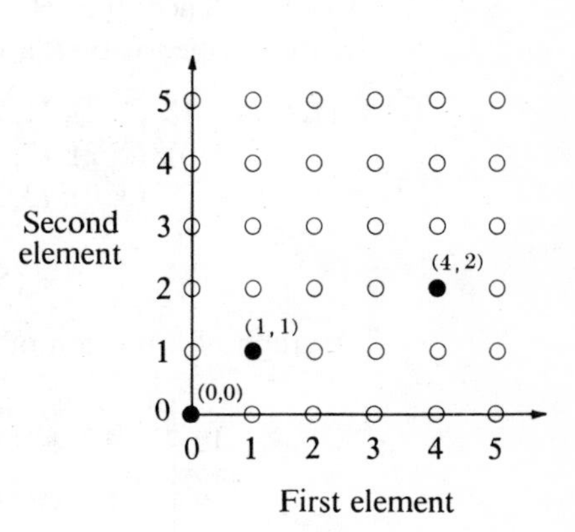

EXAMPLE 14. Using the same set as in Example 13, find the relation described by the relational phrase "has for its square."

Solution: If we use R to symbolize the relational phrase (that is, R is to be read as "has for its square" in the following expressions), we find

$0\ R\ 0$ (true); $1\ R\ 1$ (true); $2\ R\ 4$ (true);
$4\ R\ 2$ (false); $3\ R\ 1$ (false); and so on.

The set of ordered pairs for which the statement is true is

$\{(0, 0), (1, 1), (2, 4)\}$,

which is different from that found in Example 13.

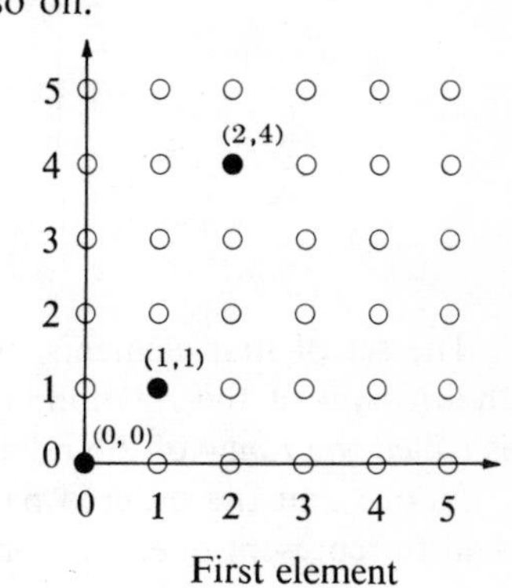

EXAMPLE 15. Let the set under consideration be all the whole numbers less than 100,

$$S = \{0, 1, 2, \ldots, 99\}.$$

Find the relation described by "is an exact divisor of."

Solution: Again we symbolize the relational phrase by R. There are 100×100, or 10,000, possible ordered pairs that can be formed with elements of S. Note first that 0 is not a divisor of any number, and so all ordered pairs $(0, n)$ are not in the relation. However, the pairs $(n, 0)$ are. Again note that 1 is an exact divisor of every number, 2 is an exact divisor of the even numbers, 3 is an exact divisor of 3, 6, 9, . . . ; and so on. Hence, the set of ordered pairs for which the sentences formed with R are true is

$$\{(1, 0), (1, 1), (1, 2), (1, 3), \ldots, (1, 99),$$
$$(2, 0), (2, 2), (2, 4), \ldots, (2, 98),$$
$$(3, 0), (3, 3), \ldots, (3, 99),$$
$$\cdot \quad \cdot \quad \cdot \quad \cdot \quad \cdot \quad \cdot \quad \cdot \quad \cdot$$
$$(50, 0), (50, 50)\}.$$

A graph of a portion of this relation is shown below.

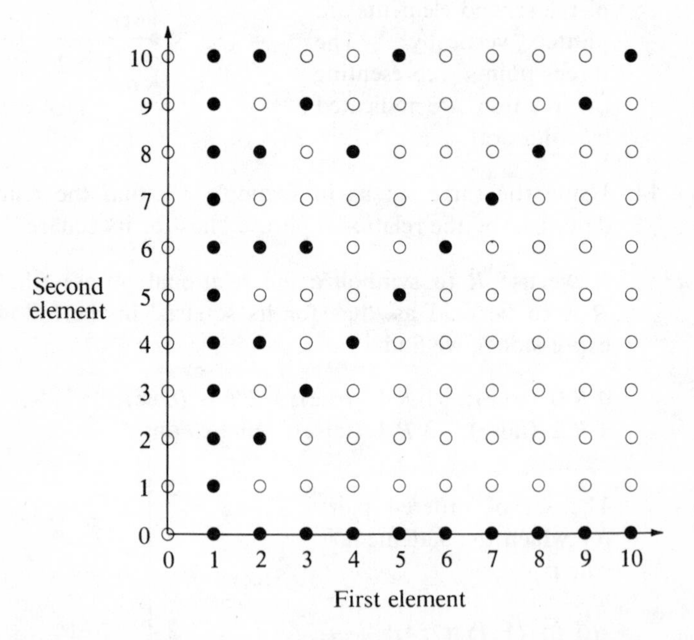

The set of first elements of the ordered pairs selected as a relation is called the *domain* of the relation; the set of second elements corresponding to these is called the *range* of the relation.

Notice that the ordered pairs in the relations of Examples 13 and 14 may be said to represent one-to-one mappings of set $A = \{0, 1, 4\}$ to set $B = \{0, 1, 2\}$

and set B to set A. Neither relation represents a mapping of set $E = \{0, 1, 2, 3, 4\}$ into itself because not all the elements of E have elements assigned to them. Moreover, the relation of Example 15 does not represent a mapping of the set $\{1, 2, \ldots, 50\}$ into the set $\{0, 1, 2, \ldots, 99\}$ because more than one element is assigned to each first element. On the other hand, any set of ordered pairs obtained in a mapping is a relation.

There are three properties that a relation may or may not have. These properties are important and are given special names.

If each element of a set S has the relation to itself, the relation is said to be *reflexive*. For example, "is equal to" ("is the same as," represented by "$=$") is a reflexive relation, for surely $x = x$ for any element x of a given set. Formally, the condition is:

For all $x \in S$

$x \; R \; x$. REFLEXIVITY

On the other hand, for "is less than," represented by "$<$," over the set of whole numbers, $x < x$ is false, as $2 \not< 2$ (2 is not less than 2) and $8 \not< 8$. If a relation of an element to itself always gives a false statement, the relation is said to be *irreflexive*.

If for every ordered pair (x, y) for which $x \; R \; y$ gives a true statement, the statement $y \; R \; x$ is also true, the relation is said to be *symmetric*. For example, "is parallel to" defines a symmetric relation for the set of lines in a plane, for if line x is parallel to line y, then line y is also parallel to line x. Similarly, "is perpendicular to" is a symmetric relation. [Is it reflexive?] Formally, the condition is:

For all $x, y \in S$

if $x \; R \; y$, *then* $y \; R \; x$. SYMMETRY

On the other hand, the relation "is less than" over the set of whole numbers is not symmetric, for if $2 < 4$, then $4 \not< 2$. A relation for which $x \; R \; y$ is true but $y \; R \; x$ is false is said to be *ir-symmetric*.

A relation is said to be *transitive* if when x is related to y and y is related to z, it is also true that x is related to z. For example, "is less than" defines a transitive relation on the set of whole numbers; $2 < 4$ and $4 < 5$ and $2 < 5$. Formally, the condition is:

For all $x, y, z \in S$

if $x \; R \; y$ *and* $y \; R \; z$, *then* $x \; R \; z$. TRANSITIVITY

Is "is parallel to" over the set of lines of a plane transitive? Yes. Is "is perpendicular to" over the set of lines of a plane transitive? No. Illustrate both these situations. When the statements $a \; R \; b$ and $b \; R \; c$ are true but $a \; R \; c$ is false, the relation is said to be *ir-transitive*.

DEFINITION: *A relation that has all the above three properties, that is, is reflexive, symmetric, and transitive, is called an* equivalence relation.

EXAMPLE 16. Let the set be a pile of assorted artists' color sheets with six different colors. Let the relation be "is the same color as," which we again designate as R. Then it is easy to verify:

$a \; R \; a$.
If $a \; R \; b$, then $b \; R \; a$.
If $a \; R \; b$ and $b \; R \; c$, then $a \; R \; c$.

Thus the relation "is the same color as" is reflexive, symmetric, and transitive and so is an equivalence relation. It separates, or *partitions*, the set into subsets by colors such that in each subset all elements have the same color. Thus no element of one of these subsets is an element of any other subset. Schematically, this is illustrated below, where the set S of artists' color sheets has its elements in any position, but the set denoted by S/R is a set of six subsets into which the elements have been partitioned.

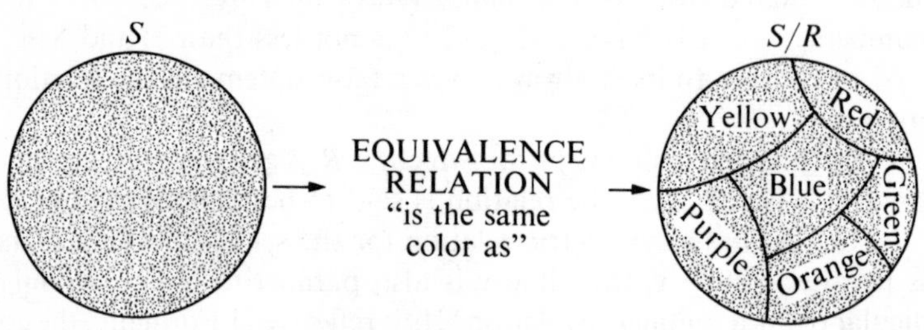

The above Example illustrates a general theorem, which we state now and shall use without giving a formal proof.

EQUIVALENCE THEOREM: *An equivalence relation over a set partitions the set into nonempty disjoint subsets.*

The disjoint subsets resulting from a *partition* are called *equivalence classes*. The set of all equivalence classes is called the *quotient set* and is denoted by S/R.

EXAMPLE 17. Let S be the set of all pupils in a school. Let the relational phrase be "is in the same grade as." This is an equivalence relation, since for each pupil $a \; R \; a$, $a \; R \; b$ implies $b \; R \; a$, and $a \; R \; b$ and $b \; R \; c$ imply $a \; R \; c$. This relation over the set of all the pupils partitions them into equivalence classes, which are the grades.

1.14 EXERCISES

1. Let $S = \{0, 1, 2, \ldots, 25\}$. Let the relational phrase be "is the square root of."
   (a) How many ordered pairs are possible?
   (b) Give several ordered pairs for which the relational statement is false.
   (c) Give the set of ordered pairs that form the relation.

2. Two numbers are said to be *relatively prime* if they have no common divisor other than 1. Thus 4 is relatively prime to 3, but not to 2. Let S be the set of whole numbers greater than 1 and less than 10. Find the relation given by the phrase "is relatively prime to."

3. Is the phrase "is in love with" precisely defined over a set of persons? Can this phrase be used to determine a relation?

4. At an alumni reunion at a university for men only, a father and son banquet was held. Is a binary relation over the set of alumni defined by "is the father of"? Is it reflexive, symmetric, transitive? Can (a, b) and (a, c) both be elements of the relation?

5. The relation "is less than or equal to," where "or" is used in the inclusive sense, is the union of the relations "is less than" and "is equal to." It is represented by "$\leq$." Over the set of whole numbers is this relation reflexive, symmetric, transitive? Is it an equivalence relation?

6. Let the set S be the set of whole numbers, including zero. Let a relational phrase be "gives the same remainder when divided by 3 as." Is this relation reflexive, symmetric, transitive? If it is an equivalence relation, what are the equivalence classes?

7. Let S be the set of regular playing cards. Let a relation be defined by "is the same suit as." Discuss this relation.

8. Consider a set of sets. Let the phrase relating the elements of the set be "can be mapped bijectively to." Show that this is an equivalence relation and describe the equivalence classes.

1.15 SUMMARY

In this chapter we studied the concept of a set of elements; the property of belonging to a set, designated by $\in$; the universal set; the null set, designated by $\emptyset$; the representation of sets by the roster method and by the set-selector method, which uses a variable and a characteristic property; the meaning of equal sets; subsets of a given set and the concept of inclusion, designated by $\subset$.

Three important operations on sets were defined, namely union ($\cup$), intersection ($\cap$), and complementation (A') with the corresponding logical words, "or," "and," and "not," respectively. A type of subtraction of sets was defined. The commutative, associative, and identity properties of union and intersection were discussed.

The mappings of a set "into," "onto," and "one-to-one" were illustrated, developing from the concept of ordered pairs. The chapter ended with a treatment of binary relations, especially the equivalence relation and its properties.

All these properties of sets will be used in subsequent chapters to construct the number systems, the systems of numeration, and the fundamental properties of space.

1.16 REFERENCE QUESTIONS

1. Recall and list the three properties which define an *equivalence relation.* (See section 1.13.) For a discussion of the role of this important kind of relation in mathematics education, see

   Félix, Lucienne. "Modern Mathematics Begins in the Elementary School," *The Arithmetic Teacher*, 9: 32–36; 1962.

2. In this chapter, a binary relation over a set was defined. What is this definition? For another treatment of binary relations, see

   College Entrance Examination Board. *Appendices* (Report of the Commission on Mathematics). New York: College Entrance Examination Board, 1959. Chapter 2.

2 THE CARDINAL NUMBERS

NUMBER IS AN ABSTRACTION. *It is a property of sets. In this chapter we shall develop the concept of one kind of number as the property of the size of a set, that is, the manyness, numerosity, or plurality of its elements, and we shall discuss briefly another kind of number that is the property of order in a set.*

2.1 EQUIVALENT SETS; CARDINAL NUMBERS

While the sets $A = \{a, b, c\}$ and $X = \{x, y, z\}$ are not equal (they do not have the same elements), there is something they do have in common; that is, each can be mapped one-to-one, or bijectively, to the other (section 1.11).

The relation described by the relational phrase

"can be mapped bijectively to"

can be shown to be an equivalence relation (section 1.13) as follows:

Surely a set A can be mapped bijectively to itself by assigning each element to itself as shown in the adjoining diagram.† (There are also five other ways of mapping the set A bijectively to itself.) Thus the relation is reflexive.

$$\begin{aligned} a &\rightarrow a \\ b &\rightarrow b \\ c &\rightarrow c \end{aligned}$$

Secondly, the relation is symmetric, as can be seen by reversing the elements of each ordered pair of the bijection of sets A and X.

$$\begin{aligned} a &\leftrightarrow x \\ b &\leftrightarrow y \\ c &\leftrightarrow z \end{aligned}$$

† The symbol "→" is read "has assigned to it"; thus, "a has a assigned to it" and, on the next page, "a has x assigned to it and x has 5 assigned to it."

Finally, suppose that the set X is mapped bijectively to the set $N = \{1, 3, 5\}$. Then the relation can be shown to be transitive by assigning the second element of the second mapping to the first element of the first mapping:

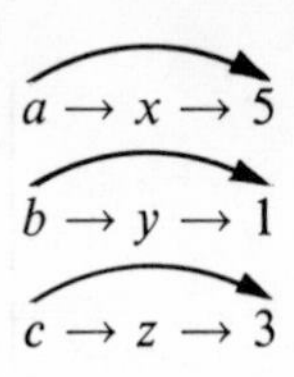

$$\text{If } a \to x \text{ and } x \to 5, \text{ then } a \to 5.$$

Now we apply the equivalence theorem of section 1.13 to a set S of sets, using the relation R, "is mapped bijectively to." The initial set S consists of elements that are sets of the type $\emptyset$, $\{a\}$, $\{a_1, a_2\}$, $\{b\}$, $\{a_1, a_2, a_3\}$, and so on. The relation R on this set gives a quotient set consisting of equivalence classes. These classes are disjoint, and in any equivalence class all the sets can be mapped bijectively to each other.

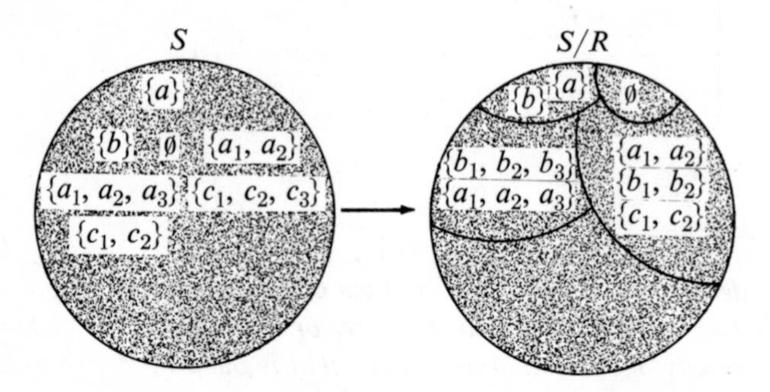

All the sets of a given equivalence class are said to be *equivalent sets*. They have the property of having the "same size" (compare Example 12 of Chapter 1). This property that all the sets of an equivalence class have in common is called the *cardinal number* of the class. Any one of the sets in the class can be used to represent this property. We distinguish between the (cardinal) number of a set from the set itself by writing

"$\mathrm{n}\{a, b, c\}$" for the number of the set $\{a, b, c\}$ †
or "$\mathrm{n}(A)$" for the number of the set A.

Thus, all sets in an equivalence class have the *same cardinal number;* for example,

$$\mathrm{n}\{a, b, c\} = \mathrm{n}\{x, y, z\} = \mathrm{n}\{b_1, b_2, b_3\} = \cdots,$$

where "=" means "is the same as" or "is equal to" and is called the *equals sign*. Formally, we have:

DEFINITION: *Those sets which can be mapped bijectively are called* equivalent sets, *and a* cardinal number *is the property that is possessed by all members of a class of equivalent sets.*

The cardinal number tells the "size," or "manyness," of the set of elements. This property has also been called the *power* or the *strength* of the set.

---

† The symbol "$|\{a, b, c\}|$" is also sometimes used to designate the number of set $\{a, b, c\}$.

In order to study the cardinal numbers, we shall construct a particular set, called a *standard set*, for each equivalence class. First, we define the *successor* of a set $M = \{a, b\}$ to be the set which contains the same elements as M, together with the set M itself as a new element. We denote the successor of M by M^+ and write

$$M^+ = \{a, b, \{a, b\}\} = \{a, b, M\}.$$

Also, the set M is said to be the *predecessor* of M^+.

Similarly, if $K = \{a\}$, then $K^+ = \{a, K\}$, where the set K itself has been placed with the element a to form the successor set to K. Note that a and K are distinct elements, for a is an element of a set K, while K is a set with a single element a.

Now consider $\emptyset$, the empty set. Then the successor of $\emptyset$ is

$$\emptyset^+ = \{\emptyset\},$$

and this set is distinct from $\emptyset$, since $\{\ \}$ and $\{\emptyset\}$ are different. Let us call the set $\emptyset^+$ by the Roman numeral I; that is,

$$\emptyset^+ = \{\emptyset\} = \mathrm{I}.$$

Then the successor of I is

$$\mathrm{I}^+ = \{\emptyset, \mathrm{I}\}, \text{ which we name II},$$

that is, the set $\{\emptyset\}$ to which the set itself is adjoined as a new element. We could also have written $\mathrm{I}^+ = \{\emptyset, \{\emptyset\}\}$.

Now the successor of II is

$$\mathrm{II}^+ = \{\emptyset, \mathrm{I}, \mathrm{II}\} = \mathrm{III}.$$

Continuing in this manner, we create the following set of sets, called *standard sets:*

$$\begin{array}{cccccc} \emptyset, & \{\emptyset\}, & \{\emptyset, \mathrm{I}\}, & \{\emptyset, \mathrm{I}, \mathrm{II}\}, & \{\emptyset, \mathrm{I}, \mathrm{II}, \mathrm{III}\}, & \ldots \\ \emptyset, & \mathrm{I}, & \mathrm{II}, & \mathrm{III}, & \mathrm{IV}, & \ldots \end{array}$$

The (cardinal) numbers of these sets, with the corresponding number symbols and names, are:

$$\begin{array}{cccccc} n\{\ \}, & n\{\emptyset\}, & n\{\emptyset, \mathrm{I}\}, & n\{\emptyset, \mathrm{I}, \mathrm{II}\}, & n\{\emptyset, \mathrm{I}, \mathrm{II}, \mathrm{III}\}, & \ldots \\ 0, & 1, & 2, & 3, & 4, & \ldots \\ \text{zero}, & \text{one}, & \text{two}, & \text{three}, & \text{four}, & \ldots \end{array}$$

Thus, zero is the number of an empty set; its successor set, containing a single element, that is, a *singleton*, has the number one; two is the number of the successor set to a singleton; and so on.

If we have five persons in a family, we can arrange these persons in a row according to some rule. Then we say that the persons are *ordered*, or arranged *in order*, by an *order relation*. Different order relations will give different orders. Some order relations that we could use are "is taller than," "is smaller than," "weighs more than," "is older than," and so on. If we agree to arrange the persons from left to right according to one of these relations, we shall have the five persons in a row in such an order that each person except the last "comes before" one or more of the others, and all ordered pairs that satisfy the relational phrase constitute the order relation (see section 1.13). In general, an order relation can be symbolized by "$\prec$," which is read "comes before."

Now consider the set of standard sets of section 2.2. Each of these sets has a finite number of elements. Let an order relation be designated by $\prec$ and defined as follows:

A set A "comes before" B if A can be mapped bijectively to a proper subset of B.

Under this definition any standard set "comes before" its successor, since the successor contains an element not in the predecessor. Thus

$$\{a, b\} \prec \{a, b, \{a, b\}\}.$$

Note that for an order relation:

1. $A \nprec A$. (For example, no set can come before itself.) Order is not reflexive; it is irreflexive.
2. If $A \prec B$, then $B \nprec A$. Order is ir-symmetric.
3. If $A \prec B$ and $B \prec C$, then $A \prec C$. Order is transitive.

Now applying the order relation defined above to the set of standard sets, we see that they can be arranged in the order

$$\emptyset, \ \mathrm{I}, \ \mathrm{II}, \ \mathrm{III}, \ \mathrm{IV}, \ \mathrm{V}, \ \ldots,$$

where the order of the names of the sets is from left to right.

We can now order the (cardinal) numbers of these sets, using the symbol "$<$," which is read "is less than," as follows:

$$\mathrm{n}(A) < \mathrm{n}(B) \quad \text{if} \quad A \prec B$$

Hence

$$\mathrm{n}(\emptyset) < \mathrm{n}(\mathrm{V}), \quad \mathrm{n}(\mathrm{III}) < \mathrm{n}(\mathrm{IV}), \quad \mathrm{n}(\mathrm{II}) < \mathrm{n}(\mathrm{III}), \quad \ldots.$$

With the usual number symbols we have the order

$$0, 1, 2, 3, \ldots, n, \ldots,$$

where any number *is less than* any number to its right.

Note that in this ordering of the cardinal numbers, there is a smallest number, or first number, namely zero. Further, if any finite number of cardinals are selected at random, they can be arranged in order, and there will be a first element. For this reason, the set of cardinals is said to be *well-ordered.*

2.4 EXERCISES

1. Distinguish between equal sets and equivalent sets.
2. Give three illustrations of equivalent sets.
3. Distinguish between a set and the number of a set.
4. What is the successor of the set $\{a, b, c\}$? What is the predecessor of the set $\{a, b, c, \{a, b, c\}\}$?
5. Does every set have a successor? Illustrate your answer.
6. Does every set have a predecessor? Illustrate your answer.
7. Give the possible bijections of the set $\{a, b, c\}$ to the set $\{x, y, z\}$.
8. Prove that no set is equivalent to its successor.
9. How many mappings of $\{a, b, c, d\}$ onto itself are possible? Write several possible mappings.
10. Without counting, how can you tell in a class whether or not the set of boys is equivalent to the set of girls?
11. Give a set for which the cardinal number is 5. Is 10. Is greater than 200,000,000.
12. (a) Write the set of cardinal numbers less than 10.
    (b) Use the roster method to indicate $\{n : 5 < n < 14\}$.
13. What is $n(\emptyset)$? $n\{\emptyset\}$? $|\emptyset|$? $|\{\emptyset\}|$? $|\{\emptyset, 1\}|$?
14. Discuss the statement: "A relation is an order relation if it is transitive."
15. Beginning with the set $\{\ \}$ and its successor $\{\{\ \}\}$, write the five sets for which the cardinal numbers are 0, 1, 2, 3, 4.
16. How can a six-year-old use equivalent sets to learn the concept of the cardinal number 3? Can this child learn 3 before knowing 2?
17. Two people each choose a cardinal number. What possible order relation can exist between the chosen numbers?
18. Tell under what conditions a number n is between x and y.
    Hint: Consider the numbers 2, 5, 7 and the numbers 8, 3, 1. Then tell what you mean by "between."

2.5 CARDINAL, WHOLE, AND NATURAL NUMBERS

Many different names are used to classify the numbers used in the elementary school. Among these are "cardinal," "whole," "natural," "counting," and "ordinal." If one understands to which set of numbers these names are applied, no confusion can result, but unfortunately different writers apply the names in different manners.

We have developed in sections 2.1–2.3 a set of numbers to which all writers apply the same name, that is, the *cardinal numbers:*

$$C = \{0, 1, 2, 3, \ldots, n, \ldots\}$$

Most writers, and we shall follow their example, refer to this set also as the *whole numbers.* The word "whole" comes from the use of numbers in measuring quantities, where there often is a number of whole units and then a fractional part of a unit more. The whole numbers have the same property as the cardinal numbers, that is, the property of the "manyness" of equivalent sets. There really is no need for the use of the adjective "whole" except for its common usage in everyday affairs.

The word "natural" comes largely from tradition and is most commonly applied to the set of numbers

$$N = \{1, 2, 3, \ldots, n, \ldots\}.$$

It took the human race a long time to consider 1 as a number, for it was considered by the ancient Greeks to be the source of number with 2 as the first number. About A.D. 1140 Rabbi Ben Ezra wrote a book in which he argued that 1 should also be considered as a number, but it was not generally accepted as such until the late 1500's.

In the period from 1880 to 1900, when mathematicians were first discovering that all mathematics can be developed logically by making certain assumptions about certain elements of a set, it was quite common to assume the existence of the numbers in the set N and to develop all other types of numbers from these. Thus the numbers in the set N were referred to as the *natural numbers.* One mathematician, Leopold Kronecker, said, "God created the natural numbers; the rest is the work of man."

While people have often recorded the number of things they possessed, they have less often felt the need to represent the number of the empty set. It was not considered "natural" to speak of the number of things which constitute the empty set. Yet today it has become quite natural to speak of zero runs or zero elements of a set. There is nothing "unnatural" about the number zero, and some mathematicians have called the set C above by the name "natural numbers." It would seem appropriate to discard the word "natural" as an unnecessary adjective, especially in the elementary school.

If you were asked to *count* the number of circular desks in your classroom, it could be that the number would be zero, since there are no circular desks in your room. In this sense, 0 could be considered as a "counting" number, but this is a rather sophisticated idea, especially for young children, since in everyday life we are usually concerned with counting nonempty sets of objects. Thus, if we delete 0 from the ordered set of cardinal numbers C, we obtain the ordered set N, called *natural numbers* in section 2.5, and call the set N also the *counting numbers.*

Counting is accomplished by mapping a set of objects into the ordered set N of counting numbers. Thus, we have, first, a set of objects, O, in which the order is immaterial, and second, the ordered set of counting numbers, N. An object is selected from O and $1 \in N$ is assigned to it; another object is selected and $2 \in N$ is assigned to it; and so on:

$$O = \{0, \triangle, \sqsubset\!\sqsupset, \times, \square, +, *, \cdot\}$$

$$N = \{1, 2, 3, 4, 5, 6, 7, 8, \ldots\} \qquad \text{Thus, } \mathrm{n}(O) = 8.$$

or, in general,

$$O = \{0, \triangle, \sqsubset\!\sqsupset, \times, +, \ldots, \nabla\}$$

$$N = \{1, 2, 3, 4, 5, \ldots, n, \ldots\} \qquad \text{Thus, } \mathrm{n}(O) = n.$$

After every object has been assigned, the last number assigned is the (cardinal) number of objects in the set O. Why? Because the set of ordered cardinals from 1 to n has the cardinal number n:

$$\mathrm{n}\{1\} = 1, \qquad \mathrm{n}\{1, 2\} = 2, \qquad \ldots, \qquad \mathrm{n}\{1, 2, 3, \ldots, n\} = n$$

Any order of the objects of O will give the same (cardinal) number.

Note that after the objects of set O have been counted, we can rearrange them in the order of the counting numbers assigned to each object. In doing so, when the counting comes to an end, the objects of O are in *an order:*

$$\begin{array}{rcccccccc} O = \{ & \triangle, & \times, & 0, & +, & \sqsubset\!\sqsupset, & \square, & \cdot, & *\} \\ & \downarrow & \downarrow & \downarrow & \downarrow & \downarrow & \downarrow & \downarrow & \downarrow \\ N = \{ & 1, & 2, & 3, & 4, & 5, & 6, & 7, & 8\} \end{array}$$

In this order we know that $+$ comes before $\cdot$ because 4 comes before 7. We also know that $\sqsubset\!\sqsupset$ comes before $\square$ because 5 comes before 6. Both the objects and the numbers are now ordered, and the two sets are said to be *similar*. In general, two sets are said to be *similar* if, first, they are in one-to-one correspondence and, second, if in one set an element a comes before an element b, then in the other set the element a' mapped to a comes before the element b' mapped to b.

In discussing counting and the ordering of sets, it is natural to think of sets that are nonempty. Although a mathematician may speak of a 0th draft of a speech as the one that comes before the first one, nevertheless in ordinary discourse we would refer to these as the first and second drafts. Let us, therefore, list the standard sets of section 2.2 beginning with the set whose only element is the empty set:

$$\{\emptyset\}, \qquad \{\emptyset, \text{I}\}, \qquad \{\emptyset, \text{I}, \text{II}\}, \qquad \{\emptyset, \text{I}, \text{II}, \text{III}\}, \qquad \ldots$$

Next we construct sets *similar* to each of these sets by mapping them into the set of counting numbers N in the same order. Thus the following sets are obtained:

$$\{1\}, \qquad \{1, 2\}, \qquad \{1, 2, 3\}, \qquad \{1, 2, 3, 4\}, \qquad \ldots$$

These sets may be used as representatives, or *standard types* (*ordinal types*), of all similar sets. The last element in the standard type is defined as the *ordinal number* of the set and all sets *similar* to it.

Thus, in the ordered set $\{1, 3, 5, 7\}$ we may say that 7 is the fourth element or element number 4. Since $\{1, 3, 5, 7\}$ is ordered, we know that $\{1, 3, 5\}$ is an ordered subset, and hence 3 is the ordinal number of this set, and 5 is element number 3. Of course, the ordered subset $\{3, 5, 7\}$ also has the ordinal number 3, and in this case 7 is the third element or element number 3. Similarly, the ordered subset $\{1, 3\}$ tells us that element 3 is the second element.

Remember that "similar" applies to ordered sets. Thus while a *cardinal number* tells how many elements are in a set (and all *equivalent* sets) independent of the order of the elements, an *ordinal number* tells the position or place of the terminal object in an ordered set (and all *similar* sets).

EXAMPLE 1. Consider the ordered set of letters of the alphabet,

$$\{a, b, c, \ldots, z\}.$$

How many elements does it contain? The answer is 26, and it is a *cardinal number*. *What is the number* of element "e"? The answer is 5, and it is an *ordinal number*. If the letters are arranged in reverse order, the cardinal number of the set is still 26. However, the (ordinal) number of the letter "e" is 22 (it is the 22d letter in the ordered set), while "v" is the 5th letter or letter number 5.

DEFINITION: *Those sets which can be mapped bijectively with the order preserved are called* similar sets, *and an* ordinal number *is the property that is possessed by all members of a class of similar sets.*

In the process of counting a set of objects, the counting numbers are a well-ordered set (section 2.3) but the set of objects need not be ordered. In finding the ordinal number of an object by "counting off," we put the set of objects in order, and hence the two sets are similar.

Recall that in section 1.7 when we were given two sets A and B and formed a new set $A \cup B$, the elements of the union were the same kind of things as the elements of sets A and B. We shall now construct a new set from the sets A and B, in which the elements of the new set are also new things, different from the elements of A or of B. To do this, we shall use the idea of an ordered pair (section 1.11).

EXAMPLE 2. Let $A = \{a, b, c\}$ be the set of pitchers of a baseball team. Let $B = \{p, q\}$ be the set of catchers of the same team. A battery is an ordered pair (pitcher, catcher). We now form the set of all possible batteries from sets A and B. It is the set of ordered pairs:

$$\{(a, p), (a, q), (b, p), (b, q), (c, p), (c, q)\}$$

DEFINITION: *The set of ordered pairs formed by pairing the elements of a set A with each element of a set B is called the* product set *of sets A and B and is designated by $A \times B$, read "A cross B." In symbols, we write:*

$$A \times B = \{(x, y) : x \in A \text{ and } y \in B\}$$

In Example 2, you will note that $n(A) = 3$, $n(B) = 2$, and $n(A \times B) = 6$. When multiplication of cardinal numbers is defined in section 3.6, it will be seen that

$$n(A) \cdot n(B) = n(A \times B).$$

This explains why $A \times B$ is called the "product" set.

We can illustrate the product set graphically as follows: On squared paper, select three vertical parallel lines to represent a, b, and c, respectively. Select two horizontal lines to represent p and q. The points of intersection can represent the ordered pairs (vertical line, horizontal line) or, for Example 2, the ordered pairs (pitcher, catcher). Thus each point represents an ordered pair, and the totality of points of intersection represents the product set.

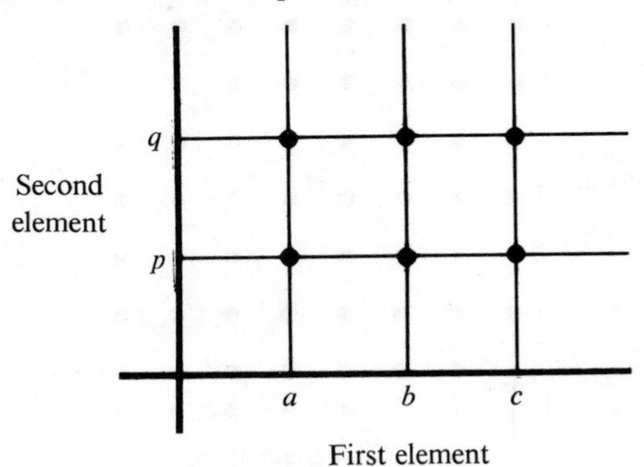

The product set is also called a *Cartesian product* in honor of a French mathematician, René Descartes, who first suggested such an approach to geometry. Since the symbol for the operation is a cross, $\times$, the product set is sometimes called a *cross product*.

Note that the product set $A \times B$ is not equal to the product set $B \times A$ when $A \neq B$. In Example 2 we would have

$$B \times A = \{(p, a), (p, b), (p, c), (q, a), (q, b), (q, c)\},$$

which is not the same as the set $A \times B$. Are the two sets equivalent? Yes, and the reader should verify this.

We can form the product set of a set with itself. Thus,

$$S \times S = \{(x, y) : x \in S \text{ and } y \in S\}.$$

For the set A in Example 2

$$A \times A = \{(a, a), (a, b), (a, c), (b, a), (b, b), (b, c), (c, a), (c, b), (c, c)\}.$$

To develop a *number system*, as we shall do later in this book, it will be necessary to use the product set of the set of cardinal numbers with itself:

$$C = \{0, 1, 2, 3, \ldots, n, \ldots\}$$
$$C \times C = \{(x, y) : x \in C \text{ and } y \in C\}$$

If we try to write out $C \times C$ by the roster method, we can exhibit only some of the elements:

$$\begin{aligned} C \times C = \{&(0, 0), (0, 1), \ldots, (0, n), \ldots \\ &(1, 0), (1, 1), \ldots, (1, n), \ldots \\ &(2, 0), (2, 1), \ldots, (2, n), \ldots\} \end{aligned}$$

Thus $C \times C$ is the set of all possible ordered pairs of cardinal numbers. This set can be represented graphically as follows:

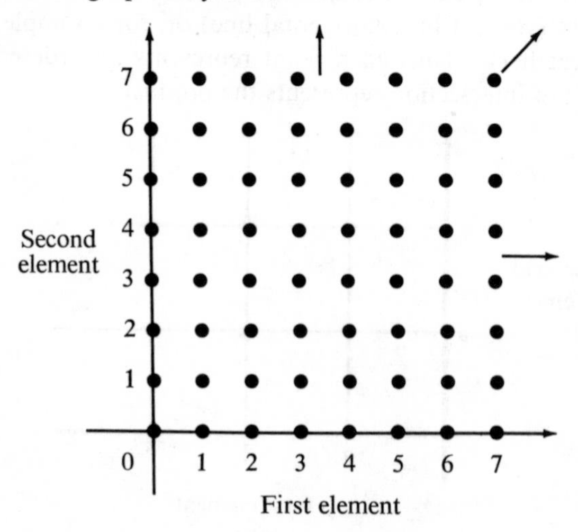

Each point represents an ordered pair of numbers, and to any ordered pair of numbers there is assigned only one point. These points are called *lattice points.*

Look again at Examples 13, 14, and 15 in section 1.13 and compare their graphs with the ones in this section. Observe that *a relation on a set S may be defined as a subset of the product set S × S.*

We are now in a position to consider the three relations

$$a < b, \qquad a = b, \qquad a > b$$

where "$>$" means "greater than," and "$a > b$" means "$b < a$." These relations may be seen to be disjoint subsets of the product set as follows:

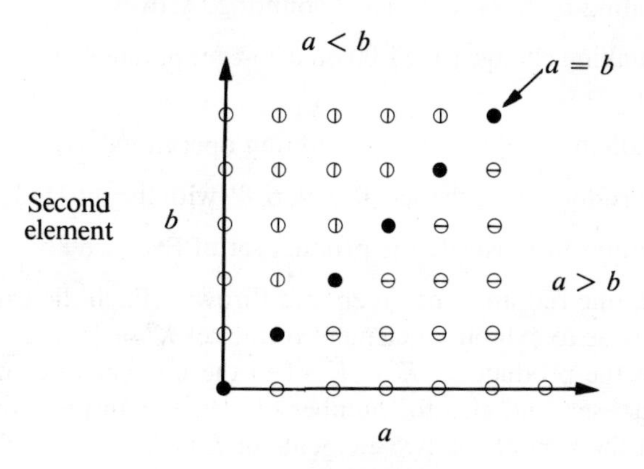

The relation $a = b$ is the set of ordered pairs

$$Q = \{(0, 0), (1, 1), (2, 2), \ldots\}.$$

The relation $a < b$ is the set of ordered pairs

$$L = \{(0, 1), (0, 2), \ldots, (1, 2), (1, 3), \ldots, (2, 3), \ldots\}.$$

The relation $a > b$ is the set of ordered pairs

$$G = \{(1, 0), (2, 0), \ldots, (2, 1), (3, 1), \ldots, (3, 2), \ldots\}.$$

The relation $a \leq b$ is $Q \cup L$ and means that a may be less than *or* equal to b, where "or" is used in the *inclusive* sense. This is equivalent to $a \not> b$. Similarly, $a \geq b$ is $Q \cup G$ and means that a may be greater than *or* equal to b. This is equivalent to $a \not< b$. Also, $L \cup Q \cup G = C \times C$.

Since L, Q, and G are disjoint sets, any given ordered pair (a, b) will be an element of only one of these sets. That is, for any given numbers a and b, we shall have

$$a < b \quad \textit{or} \quad a = b \quad \textit{or} \quad a > b,$$

where "or" is used in the *exclusive* sense. This is called the *law of trichotomy.*

2.8 EXERCISES

1. Explain the meaning of the ordinal word "third." What is meant by referring to the "8th" article?
2. In how many ways can you count the fingers on one hand?
3. Could you count starting from zero? Explain your answer.
4. The alphabet is usually presented as an ordered set. Give two ordered subsets of the alphabet. Is the alphabet well-ordered?
5. Explain the meaning of

   (a) "counting by fives"; (b) "counting by twos."
6. Explain making change for $1.00 on a 33-cent purchase as a counting operation.
7. Explain tallying (𝍸 . . .) as a counting operation.
8. Find the product set of the set $\{0, 2, 4, 6, 8\}$ with the set $\{1, 3, 5, 7, 9\}$.
9. Draw a graph to illustrate the product set of Exercise 8.
10. Two dice, one red and one green, are thrown. Each die can fall in such a way as to exhibit an element of the set $K = \{1, 2, 3, 4, 5, 6\}$. Write out the product set $K \times K$. Tell the number of elements in the product set, and also the number of elements in the product set for which the sum of the two elements of K is 7.
11. A girl has 3 dresses and 2 pairs of shoes. Exhibit the possible outfits (dress, shoes) as a product set.
12. A penny can fall $\{H, T\}$. A die can fall $\{1, 2, 3, 4, 5, 6\}$. If both a penny and a die are thrown, exhibit the possible outcomes as a product set

    (a) if the penny is thrown first;
    (b) if the die is thrown first.
13. Explain how a mapping of certain students to their homeroom teacher could be represented by a subset of the product set of all students with all homeroom teachers.
14. Exhibit the product set of segments $\{|, -, /, \backslash, |\}$ with itself, and graph the set as in section 2.7. From the set and the graph select the subset of ordered pairs in which the two elements are the same or the first segment is parallel to the second. Draw the graph of this subset.
15. A basketball team consists of

    {right guard, left guard, center, left forward, right forward}

    in the order given. Opposing teams are in a huddle before the game starts. The whistle blows and the teams line up to start the game.

Use this situation to distinguish

(a) between equivalent and similar sets;

(b) between the cardinal and the ordinal number of the sets.

16. Tom, Dick, Sue, and Mary decide to play a game of Parcheesi. Explain how the ordinal number 4 helps them to get the game under way.

17. A group of students count off, saying one-two-three-four-five-six. In what manner is the person who says "six" using it as a cardinal number? As an ordinal number?

2.9 FUNCTIONALS AND FUNCTIONS

There is, among many others, a fourth way of assigning elements in a set B to elements of a set A that may be different from the three mappings defined in section 1.11. Since this type of assignment is used to define the operations in arithmetic, it is important for the purposes of this book. It is called a *functional* and is illustrated by the following example.

Consider a set of runners, $R = \{a, b, c, d, e, f, g\}$, in a race, and a set of numbers, $T = \{9, 10, 11, 12, 13\}$, which represent tentative running times in seconds. We shall assign to each runner the nearest number of seconds it took him to run the race. This is shown in the adjoining diagram. Note that to each runner except g, who dropped out, there is assigned one and only one time. However, this is not a mapping because not all members of set R are used. Moreover, the numbers 9 and 13 are not assigned, and so the assignment is not a mapping of the subset $D = \{a, b, c, d, e, f\}$ onto T. Note also that 10 and 11 are assigned to more than one runner, and so the assignment is not a mapping of D into T.

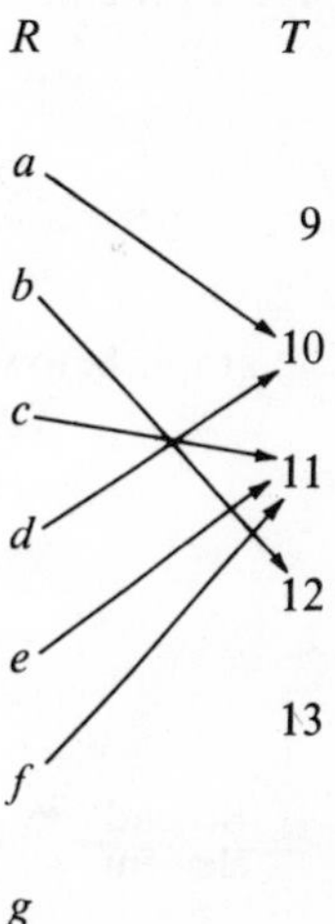

This assignment is an example of a *functional* (a noun here), which is defined as follows:

(a) Not every element of the first set (the set of runners) has to have an assignment (but all may have).

(b) Not every element of the second set (the set of times) has to be assigned (but all may be).

(c) Some elements of the second set may be assigned to several elements of the first set (but may not be).

(d) No element of the first set has assigned to it more than one element of the second set.

Thus all three mappings of section 1.11 are functionals, but there are functionals that are not mappings.

We say that we have

"a functional of the *second* set *on* the *first* set."

Recall that when we have a mapping, the language differs, and we say that we have

$$\text{“a mapping of the } \textit{first} \text{ set} \left\{\begin{matrix}\text{into}\\ \text{onto}\\ \text{one-to-one to}\end{matrix}\right\} \text{the } \textit{second} \text{ set.”}$$

For a functional the subset of the first set (set R above) which contains all the elements having an assignment is called the *domain*, and the subset of the second set (set T) which contains the assigned elements is called the *range*. In the foregoing example the domain is $\{a, b, c, d, e, f\}$, and the range is $\{10, 11, 12\}$.

The set of ordered pairs obtained in a functional is called a *function*. The *domain* and the *range of the function* are the same as the domain and the range of the functional. We say that we have a function *of* the range *on* the domain. Thus, in the above example:

$$\begin{aligned} \text{Function} &= \{(a, 10), (b, 12), (c, 11), (d, 10), (e, 11), (f, 11)\} \\ \text{Domain} &= \{a, b, c, d, e, f\} \\ \text{Range} &= \{10, 11, 12\} \end{aligned}$$

The graph below represents the function.

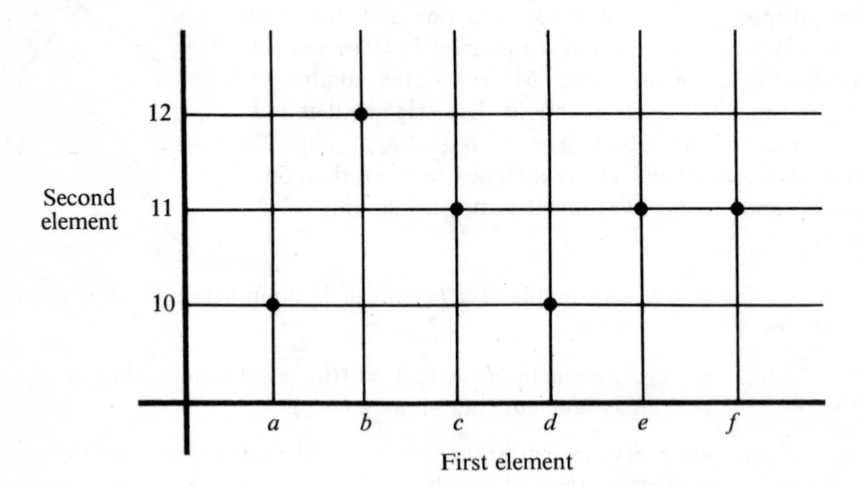

It will be observed that a mapping can be set up from the domain of a function to its range. In the above example it is a surjection but not a bijection. Thus, we have a mapping of the domain *onto* the range, but a function of the range *on* the domain.

Formally, we have:

DEFINITION: *Let A and B be two sets. Let some element of A have assigned to it one and only one element of B. Different elements of A may have assigned to them the same element of B. The set of ordered pairs thus formed is a relation called a* function. *In symbols:*

$$F = \{(x, y) : x \in A \rightarrow y \in B, \text{ and only one element of } B \text{ is assigned to an element of } A\}.$$

Thus, a function is the set of all ordered pairs for which the first element, belonging to a set A, has assigned to it a second element, belonging to a set B, and only one element of set B is assigned to an element of set A. If the domain of F is $D \subset A$, then F is said to be a *function on D*.

We are now in a position to combine the concepts of product set, relation, and function into a general idea. The concepts of relation and function involve ordered pairs, which can be exhibited as points on a graph. The easiest way to form ordered pairs is to use the product set. If all members of the product set are tested by flanking a relational phrase, the subset of the product set giving true statements is a relation. If the relation is such that each member of the first set occurs at most once as a first element in the relation, the relation is called a function. In section 1.13 it was noted that any set of ordered pairs obtained in a mapping is a relation. Now we see that such a set of ordered pairs is actually a function.

EXAMPLE 3. Consider the set $A = \{3, 4, 5, 6\}$ and the set $B = \{4, 5, 6, 7\}$. Then $A \times B = \{(3, 4), (3, 5), (3, 6), (3, 7), (4, 4), (4, 5), (4, 6), (4, 7), (5, 4), (5, 5), (5, 6), (5, 7), (6, 4), (6, 5), (6, 6), (6, 7)\}$.

(a) Test the relational phrase "is less than."

(b) Test the relational phrase "gives the sum 10 when added to."

Solution: (a) Testing all ordered pairs for "is less than," we find that the relation is

$$R = \{(3, 4), (3, 5), (3, 6), (3, 7), (4, 5), (4, 6), (4, 7), (5, 6), (5, 7), (6, 7)\}.$$

Since the first elements 3, 4, 5 occur more than once, this relation is not a function.

(b) Testing all ordered pairs for "gives the sum 10 when added to," we find that the relation is

$$F = \{(3, 7), (4, 6), (5, 5), (6, 4)\}.$$

This is a function on A, since all the members of A, 3, 4, 5, 6, occur once and only once as first elements in the ordered pairs.

EXAMPLE 4. Given the set

$$A = \{3, 4, 5, 6, 7\}.$$

(a) Show that "is less than" applied to $A \times A$ is a relation that is not a function.
(b) Show that "is the predecessor of" is a function.

Solution: (a) Testing all ordered pairs for "is less than," we obtain the relation

$$R = \{(3, 4), (3, 5), (3, 6), (3, 7), (4, 5), (4, 6), (4, 7), (5, 6), (5, 7), (6, 7)\}.$$

Since 3, 4, 5 occur more than once as first elements in the ordered pairs, it is not a function.
(b) Testing all ordered pairs for "is the predecessor of," we obtain the set of ordered pairs

$$F = \{(3, 4), (4, 5), (5, 6), (6, 7)\}.$$

This is a function on the domain $D = \{3, 4, 5, 6\}$ because each of these elements occurs as a first element once and only once. It is not a function on the set A because $7 \in A$ but 7 does not occur as a first element in any ordered pair.

2.10 EXERCISES

1. Using the sets $A = \{2, 4, 6\}$ and $B = \{3, 5, 7\}$, exhibit:
   (a) $A \times B$
   (b) The relation $a < b$, where $a \in A$ and $b \in B$
   (c) The function "is one less than"
2. Form at least three other relations in the set $A \times B$ of Exercise 1, and exhibit three other functions.
3. (a) Describe a function of state capitals on the set of states of the United States.
   (b) Describe a relation of cities of over 100,000 population on the states of the United States.
   (c) Describe a function of the average age in years of animals on a set of animals.
   (d) Describe the function of the whole numbers on the ordered pairs of whole numbers by addition.
4. Show that "is the square of" is a function of the whole numbers on the whole numbers. Describe the domain and the range of this function.
5. Show that "is the square root of" is a function of the whole numbers on a subset of the whole numbers. Describe the domain and the range.

6. Consider the set of cardinal numbers, C, and the product set $C \times C$. To each ordered pair of $C \times C$ assign the sum of the elements of this ordered pair. Is this relation a function? Explain your answer.

7. For each graph, tell

   (a) whether it is a relation or a function,
   (b) the domain, and
   (c) the range.

(I) (II) 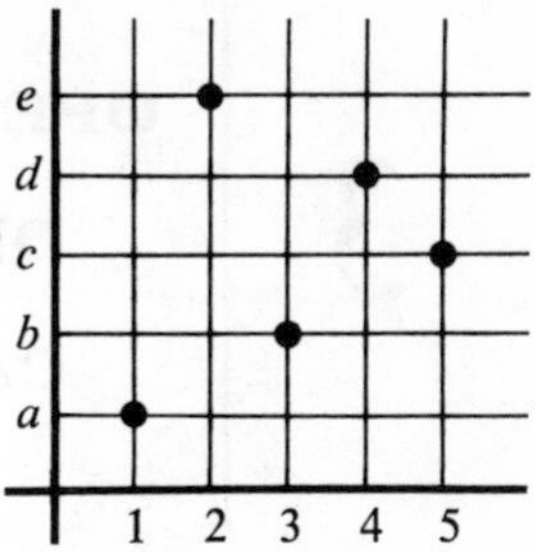 (III) 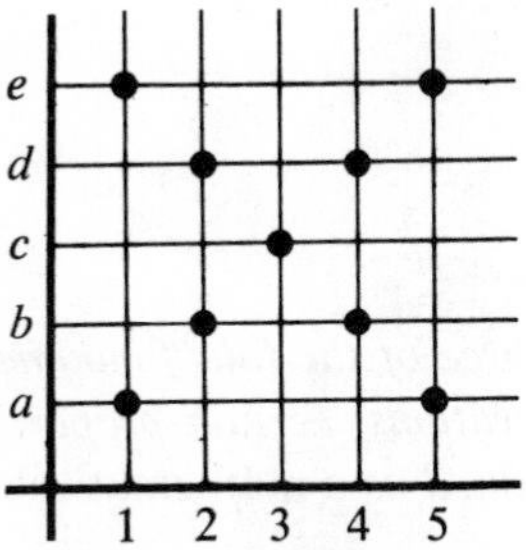 (IV)

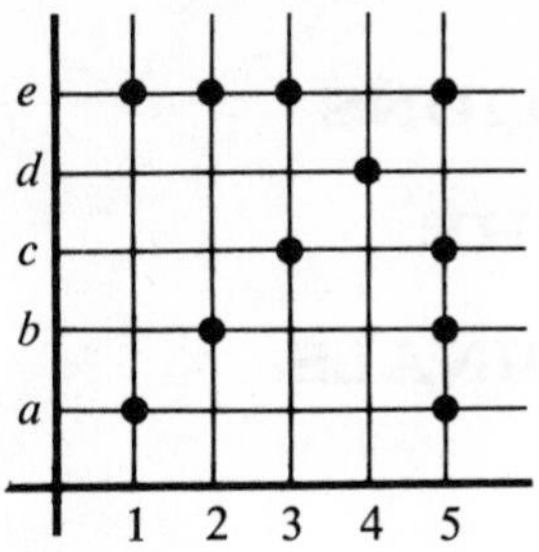

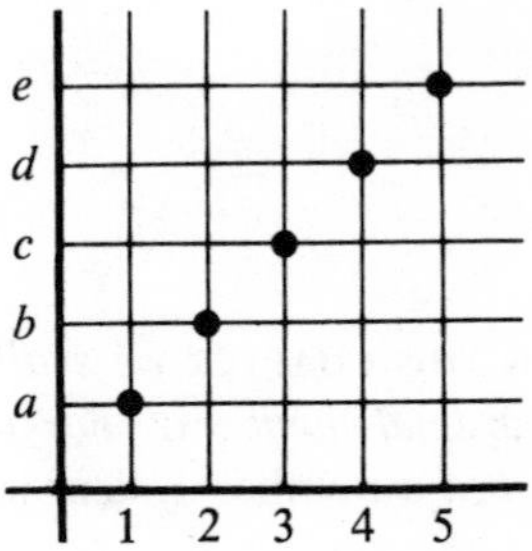

8. Show that a mapping of two equivalent sets is a function.

9. Can a function contain only one element, that is, only one ordered pair? Prove your reply.

10. Is the relation "is less than or equal to" applied to $C \times C$ a function? Explain your reply.

11. Is the relation "is one more than" applied to $C \times C$ a function? Explain your reply.

2.11 REFERENCE QUESTIONS

1. What were the sets developed as *standard sets* in this chapter? In this connection, see

   National Council of Teachers of Mathematics. *Topics in Mathematics for Elementary School Teachers* (29th yearbook). Washington, D.C.: NCTM, 1964. Pp. 11–15.

   What are the standard sets used in the above reference? Does it matter what the elements of the standard sets are?

2. Is one's weight a function of one's height? For a discussion of the answer to this question, as well as a general discussion of functions, see

   Brune, Irvin H. "Symbols and Functions," *The Arithmetic Teacher*, 4: 232–235; 1958.

3 OPERATIONS ON THE CARDINALS

IN THIS CHAPTER *we shall study three of the four fundamental operations on the cardinal numbers. For these operations, certain properties will be developed, and then a* number system *will be defined as a* máthematical structure.

3.1 INTRODUCTION

It is customary to call addition, subtraction, multiplication, and division the four fundamental *operations* of arithmetic. Since they deal with one number operated on by another number, thus involving two numbers, they are called *binary operations.*

For the present we limit our considerations to the set of cardinal numbers,

$$C = \{0, 1, 2, 3, \ldots\}.$$

If to *every* ordered pair of cardinal numbers it is possible to assign a definite cardinal number, as we shall see is the case for addition and multiplication, the operation is called an *internal law of composition*, and it may be described as a mapping of $C \times C$ onto C. However, in the case of subtraction and division, where to some ordered pairs (e.g., $2 - 6$ or $5 \div 3$) no cardinal number can be assigned, the operation is not internally possible, as we have a mapping of only a proper subset of $C \times C$ onto C. In other words, for addition and multiplication we have a function of C on $C \times C$, but for subtraction and division we have a function of C on a subset of $C \times C$. In general, all operations can be defined as functionals (recall section 2.9), and the ultimate goal in learning the fundamental arithmetic facts is to associate a definite functional with a definite operation.

All of this will become evident as we define the different ways the assignments are made for the four operations. Thus, if to (2, 3) we assign 5 and to (3, 8) we assign 11, and so on, we call the operation *addition*. If, however, to (2, 3) we assign 6 and to (3, 8) we assign 24, and so on, we call the operation *multiplication*.

To discover how to make these assignments of numbers for the different operations, we shall relate them to operations on disjoint sets. Note well that operations on sets are not operations on numbers, and that the latter are abstractions made from certain operations on sets.

3.2 ADDITION

Let A and B be two *disjoint* sets; that is, they have no elements in common. Recall (section 1.7) that the union of two sets was defined as an operation in which two sets were combined in a stated way to form a new set. Using the language of mappings, we may say that the ordered pair of sets (A, B) had assigned to it the set S containing all the elements of A or B:

Union operation on sets

$$\underbrace{\underbrace{(A, B)}_{\text{Ordered pair}} \longrightarrow \underbrace{S}_{\text{Union}}}_{A \cup B = S}$$

Now consider the numbers of the sets A, B, and S and let $\text{n}(A) = a$, $\text{n}(B) = b$, and $\text{n}(S) = s$. The operation *addition* is defined as the *assignment* of the number s to the ordered pair of numbers (a, b):

Addition operation of numbers

$$\underbrace{\underbrace{(a, b)}_{\text{Ordered pair}} \longrightarrow \underbrace{s}_{\text{Sum}}}_{a + b = s}$$

The number s is called the *sum*, and the numbers a and b are called *addends*. When we write $a + b = s$ we say, "b has been added to a, to yield the sum s." We also say "a plus b equals s." Similarly, $b + a$ represents the fact that a has been added to b.

If we consider the set of cardinal numbers

$$C = \{0, 1, 2, 3, \ldots, n, \ldots\}$$

and form the product set

$$C \times C = \{(a, b) : a \in C \text{ and } b \in C\},$$

then for *any* ordered pair (a, b) of $C \times C$ we can find two disjoint sets having the numbers a and b, form their union, and find the number of the union, $s \in C$. Thus to each ordered pair of cardinal numbers, we can *always* assign another cardinal number, called the *sum*, and the operation of addition is always possible for any two given cardinal numbers. Thus, we have a mapping of $C \times C$ onto C, and the operation is an internal law of composition as indicated in section 3.1;

we say that *the set of cardinal numbers is closed to addition.* This is well exhibited by an addition table where each cell represents the sum of the elements (a, b) and every cell is occupied by a number.

Addition Table

b

$+$	0	1	2	3	4	5	$\cdots$	b	$\cdots$
0	0	1	2	3	4	5	$\cdots$	b	$\cdots$
1	1	2	3	4	5	6	$\cdots$	$b+1$	$\cdots$
2	2	3	4	5	6	7	$\cdots$	$b+2$	$\cdots$
3	3	4	5	6	7	8	$\cdots$	$b+3$	$\cdots$
4	4	5	6	7	8	9	$\cdots$	$b+4$	$\cdots$
$\vdots$	$\vdots$	$\vdots$	$\vdots$	$\vdots$	$\vdots$	$\vdots$		$\vdots$	
a	a	$a+1$	$a+2$	$a+3$	$a+4$	$a+5$	$\cdots$	$a+b$	$\cdots$
$\vdots$	$\vdots$	$\vdots$	$\vdots$	$\vdots$	$\vdots$	$\vdots$		$\vdots$	

a

It is also evident from the table that we can conceive of addition as "counting on." If a is the number of one set, then beginning with the elements of the next set we can count $a + 1, a + 2, \ldots, a + b$, and this last cardinal is the sum of a and b.

Recall that in writing the expression $a + b$, we consider it to represent the result of *adding b to a.* Thus three added to four is written $4 + 3$. However, $b + a$ is the result of adding a to b. Thus $a + b$ and $b + a$ represent different addition operations. Does the order matter? If 3^2 and 2^3 are evaluated as will be done in Chapter 4, the results are 9 and 8, respectively, and the orders in which the numbers appear give different results. However, we know that $2 + 3 = 3 + 2$ and $8 + 7 = 7 + 8$, etc. How do we know it? Because the union of disjoint sets is commutative (see section 1.7) and hence $n(A) + n(B)$ is the same as $n(B) + n(A)$. We write this property of addition in the following form:

For each x and each y, where x and y are cardinal numbers,

$x + y = y + x.$ COMMUTATIVITY OF $+$

This is the *commutative principle of addition.* In the symbolic expression, or *formula*, if the x is replaced by any cardinal number and the y by any cardinal number, a *true statement* is produced. Thus we can think of the formula as representing millions and millions of statements, all true. We say that x and y are *variables* and their *domain* (section 1.2) is the set of cardinal numbers.

The expression $2 + 5 + 8$ has no meaning until we give it one, since addition has been defined for pairs of numbers only, while the given expression involves three numbers. Suppose that we look upon it as meaning

$$(2 + 5) + 8,$$

where 5 is added to 2, and then 8 is added to the result. We could also look upon it as

$$2 + (5 + 8),$$

where 8 is added to 5, and then the result is added to 2. If we consider disjoint sets having the numbers 2, 5, and 8, we know that the corresponding operation of union on the sets is associative (see section 1.7). From this we conclude that the operation of addition is also associative and write:

For each x, each y, and each z, where x, y, and z are cardinal numbers,

$$(x + y) + z = x + (y + z). \qquad \text{ASSOCIATIVITY OF } +$$

This is the *associative principle of addition.* It is another formula which we can think of as representing millions and millions of true statements, as we replace x, y, and z by cardinal numbers.

Since $(a + b) + c = a + (b + c)$, we define $a + b + c$ as meaning either one.

In combining two disjoint nonempty sets, the union is always greater than either set. However, if a set is combined with the empty set, the union has the same number as the given set. We can express the corresponding property for numbers by saying:

For each cardinal number x, there is an identity element of addition, *the number zero, such that*

$$x + 0 = 0 + x = x. \qquad \text{IDENTITY PRINCIPLE OF } +$$

This is the *identity principle of addition.*

By using the above properties, we can now prove that $2 + 2 = 4$, without the use of sets. To do this, we observe that the successor of a number, defined in section 2.2, can be obtained by adding 1 to the number. Hence the successor of 1 is $1 + 1$, which is another name for 2, and so on. So, we have:

$2 + 2 = 2 + (1 + 1)$	Substituting $1 + 1$ for 2
$= (2 + 1) + 1$	By the associative principle
$= 3 + 1$	Substituting 3 for $2 + 1$, the successor of 2
$= 4$	Substituting 4 for the successor of 3

Similarly, show that $5 + 2 = 7$ from $4 + 3 = 7$.

3.3 EXERCISES

By the use of mappings and disjoint sets X, Y, and Z, show the following:

1. If $n(X) = n(Y)$, then

$$n(X) + n(Z) = n(Y) + n(Z).$$

   This is called the *uniqueness law of addition.*

2. If $n(X) < n(Y)$, then

$$n(X) + n(Z) < n(Y) + n(Z).$$

3. If $n(X) > n(Y)$, then

$$n(X) + n(Z) > n(Y) + n(Z).$$

4. If a, b, and c are cardinal numbers, and

$$a + c = b + c, \text{ then}$$
$$a = b.$$

   This is called the *cancellation law of addition.*

5. Repeat Exercise 4 with $<$ substituted for $=$.

6. Using the properties of addition show that

$$a + b + c = c + a + b.$$

7. Show how the addition $a + b$ can be considered a result of counting b units beyond a.

8. Suppose sets A and B overlap. Let $n(A) = 20$, $n(B) = 18$, and $n(A \cap B) = 5$.
   (a) Find the $n(A \cup B)$.
   (b) Generalize the results in a formula.

9. Given the set of even numbers $\{0, 2, 4, 6, 8, \ldots, 2n, \ldots\}$. Show that addition is always possible within this set, and that it is commutative and associative. Is there an identity element?

10. Explain each step in the following:

$$(a + b) + c \overset{1}{=} c + (a + b) \overset{2}{=} c + (b + a) \overset{3}{=} (c + b) + a.$$

11. Prove:
   (a) $x + r + s = s + r + x$
   (b) $a + b + c + d = a + c + d + b$

Subtraction of whole numbers is related to finding the complement of a set, or of subtracting a subset of a set from the set. If

$$B \subset A,$$

then D is the complement of B with respect to A if

$$A \setminus B = D.$$

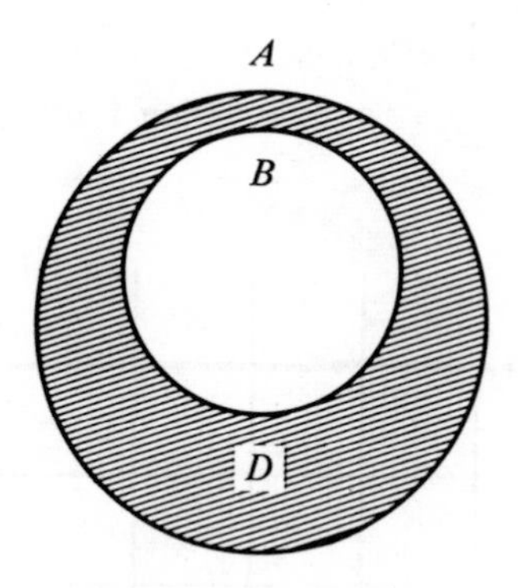

Let $n(A) = a$, $n(B) = b$, and $n(D) = d$. Then $n(B) \leq n(A)$, or $b \leq a$, since $B \subset A$ (section 2.3). Thus,

Subtraction of sets	Subtraction of numbers
$\underbrace{(A, B)}_{\text{Ordered pair}} \longrightarrow \underbrace{D}_{\text{Complement}}$	$\underbrace{(a, b)}_{\text{Ordered pair}} \longrightarrow \underbrace{d}_{\text{Difference}}$
$A \setminus B = D, \quad B \subset A$	$a - b = d, \quad b \leq a$

In the above illustration $n(A) = a$ is called the *minuend*, $n(B) = b$, the *subtrahend*, and the result $n(D) = d$, the *difference*. We also have

$$(a - b = d,\ b \leq a) \Rightarrow a = d + b,$$

where the symbol $\Rightarrow$ is read "implies." It is a logical shorthand for "if–then." Thus the expression means: "*If* $a - b = d$ and $b \leq a$, *then* $a = d + b$."

If B is the improper subset, then $B = A$ and

$$n(A) - n(B) = n(\emptyset) = 0 \qquad \text{or} \qquad a - b = 0.$$

If B is the empty set, then

$$n(A) - n(\emptyset) = a - 0 = a \qquad \text{and} \qquad n(A) = n(D).$$

The ordered pairs (a, b) of $C \times C$ with $a < b$ do not belong to the function. Thus the operation of subtraction is *not always* possible. Hence subtraction is not a mapping of $C \times C$ onto C, but rather a functional of C on $C \times C$. However, every number of C is assigned to some or several ordered pairs of $C \times C$, and so we have a mapping of a subset of $C \times C$ onto C. This is shown in the subtraction table, where the first column shows that every number of C is an answer to some subtraction. Also, in the table the cells corresponding to the ordered pairs (a, b) with $a < b$ are unoccupied. We say that *the set of cardinal numbers is open to subtraction.*

Subtraction Table

b

$-$	0	1	2	3	4	$\cdots$	$b < a$	$\cdots$	$b = a$
0	0					$\cdots$			
1	1	0				$\cdots$			
2	2	1	0			$\cdots$			
3	3	2	1	0		$\cdots$			
4	4	3	2	1	0	$\cdots$			
$\vdots$	$\vdots$	$\vdots$	$\vdots$	$\vdots$	$\vdots$		$\vdots$		
a	a	$a-1$	$a-2$	$a-3$	$a-4$	$\cdots$	$a-b$	$\cdots$	0
$\vdots$	$\vdots$	$\vdots$	$\vdots$	$\vdots$	$\vdots$		$\vdots$		$\vdots$

(a labels the rows.)

It is easy to verify that subtraction is not commutative, since if $a > b$, then $b < a$ and $a - b$ exists but $b - a$ is open. Similarly, subtraction is not associative, for

$$a - (b - c) \neq (a - b) - c.$$

For example, $8 - (5 - 4) = 8 - 1 = 7$, but $(8 - 5) - 4 = 3 - 4$ is open. Again, while $a - 0 = a$, it is not the case that $0 - a = a$, and hence there is no identity element for subtraction.

3.5 EXERCISES

1. (a) If the union of disjoint sets A and B gives a universal set E, show that B is the complement of set A.

   (b) Show that

$$E \setminus A = B,$$
$$E \setminus B = A,$$
$$A \cup B = E,$$
$$B \cup A = E.$$

   (c) Write the number operations corresponding to the set operations in (b).

   (d) Illustrate (b) and (c) using the numbers 7, 4, and 3.

2. A man has 4 dollar bills. A second man has 9 dollar bills. Can you subtract the first set of bills from the second set? If so, what is your answer? How do you explain the numerical difference between the two sets?

3. (a) Show why

$$\{a, b, c, d\} \setminus \{e, f, g\} = \{a, b, c, d\} \quad \text{is true.}$$

   (b) Show why

$$\mathrm{n}\{a, b, c, d\} - \mathrm{n}\{e, f, g\} = \mathrm{n}\{a\} \quad \text{is true.}$$

4. Show that the difference of any two given numbers can always be found. What agreement must be made on the order of the given numbers?

5. If $b > c$, then $a + (b - c) = (a + b) - c$. Explain why this is true. Hint: Let $x = a + (b - c)$, and add c to each side. Recall that by definition $(b - c) + c = b$.

6. Consider a set of numbers $a_0, a_1, a_2, a_3, \ldots, a_n$ where any a_i is greater than the immediately following a_{i+1}, and zero is not included. Also consider the following:

$$b_0 = a_0$$
$$b_1 = a_0 - a_1$$
$$b_2 = a_0 - a_1 + a_2$$
$$b_3 = a_0 - a_1 + a_2 - a_3$$

   (a) In the ordered sequence $b_0, b_1, b_2, b_3, \ldots, b_n$ show that $b_1, b_3, b_5, \ldots$ are, respectively, less than $b_0, b_2, b_4, \ldots$.

   (b) Illustrate with the set 10, 8, 7, 5, 3, 2, 1.

There are several ways in which *multiplication* can be defined, all important in their context. Here we shall give three definitions.

Perhaps the simplest and most widely used concept is that of using a cardinal number as an *operator*. First consider a collection of equivalent sets (each set has the same number) as, for example, a collection of dozens of eggs, or of rows of six chairs, or of boxes of ten pads of paper. Suppose that we desire to have a certain number of these equal-sized sets, for example, five dozen of eggs, seven rows of chairs, or three boxes of pads. We then form the union of the desired number of equal-sized sets. The number of this union is the sum of the numbers (sizes) of the equal-sized sets and is called the *product* obtained by multiplying the size of the set (*multiplicand*) by the number of sets desired (*multiplier*).

In the diagram, we have a collection of sets, all having the number 5. We form the union of 4 such sets:

$$\begin{array}{|cccc|ccc}
\times & \times & \times & \times & \times & \times & \times \ldots \\
\times & \times & \times & \times & \times & \times & \times \ldots \\
\times & \times & \times & \times & \times & \times & \times \ldots \\
\times & \times & \times & \times & \times & \times & \times \ldots \\
\times & \times & \times & \times & \times & \times & \times \ldots
\end{array}$$

The number of the union is $5 + 5 + 5 + 5 = 20$. We write

$$5 \cdot 4 = 20$$

and say "five *multiplied by* four is twenty." We can also write

$$4 \times 5 = 20$$

and say "four *times* five equals twenty." Note that "times" and "multiplied by" are different relations, and we designate them respectively by the symbols "$\times$" and "$\cdot$". In each case of the example given, 5 is the multiplicand and 4 is the multiplier. We also say 5 is the *operand* and 4 is the *operator*, and that 5 and 4 are *factors* of 20.

Since for any ordered pair of cardinals (a, b) it is possible to find a cardinal number that represents the product, the operation is defined as a mapping of $C \times C$ onto C, as shown in the following diagram.

Multiplication operation on numbers

$$\underbrace{\underbrace{(a, b)}_{\text{Ordered pair}} \longrightarrow \underbrace{(p)}_{\text{Product}}}_{a \cdot b = p}$$

A second common way to think of multiplication is to use a *replacement set.* Let A be a set of three cans of food. Now replace each can by its cost B of seven nickels, and form the union of the replacement sets, set P:

$$A = \{\square, \square, \square\}$$

$$B = \{\circ, \circ, \circ, \circ, \circ, \circ, \circ\}$$

$$P = \{\circ, \circ, \circ, \circ, \circ, \circ, \circ\} \cup \{\circ, \circ, \circ, \circ, \circ, \circ, \circ\} \cup \{\circ, \circ, \circ, \circ, \circ, \circ, \circ\}$$

The number of nickels in set P is $7 + 7 + 7 = 21$. We say that the price (7 nickels) of a can has been multiplied by the number (3) of cans bought to obtain the *product*

$$7 \cdot 3 = 21.$$

Can you give other examples of the daily use of this definition of multiplication?

Notice that forming the union of several sets of the same size, as is done in both these definitions, is equivalent to the "repeated addition" definition sometimes given for multiplication.

A third definition of multiplication makes use of the *product set* (section 2.7) and is useful in subsequent study of algebra, especially the topic of combinations. Consider two sets,

$$A = \{a, b, c\} \quad \text{and}$$
$$B = \{x, y\}.$$

Then the product set $A \times B$ consists of all possible ordered pairs:

$$A \times B = \{(a, x), (a, y), (b, x), (b, y), (c, x), (c, y)\}$$

The number $n(A \times B)$ is found by counting the number of ways each element of set B can be associated with each element of set A, and this number is called the *product* of the numbers of the two sets A and B:

$$n(A) \cdot n(B) = n(A \times B)$$

Note that in this definition, the elements of the set $A \times B$ are ordered pairs, while in the first two definitions, the elements of the set corresponding to the product were singletons. Note also that in forming the product set, each element of set A, in fact, has assigned to it the elements of set B, e.g., a has x and y assigned to it, b has x and y, and c has x and y, so that this definition of multiplication is similar to the second definition.

Using any of the definitions of multiplication, we can build a table. If the table were extended for both a and b, every cell would be occupied by a number, and hence *the set of cardinal numbers is closed to multiplication.* Thus, we have a mapping of $C \times C$ onto C, and the operation is an internal law of composition.

Multiplication Table

b

	$\cdot$	0	1	2	3	$\cdots$	b	$\cdots$
	0	0	0	0	0	$\cdots$	0	$\cdots$
	1	0	1	2	3	$\cdots$	$1 \cdot b$	$\cdots$
	2	0	2	4	6	$\cdots$	$2 \cdot b$	$\cdots$
a	3	0	3	6	9	$\cdots$	$3 \cdot b$	$\cdots$
	$\vdots$	$\vdots$	$\vdots$	$\vdots$	$\vdots$		$\vdots$	
	a	0	$a \cdot 1$	$a \cdot 2$	$a \cdot 3$	$\cdots$	$a \cdot b$	$\cdots$
	$\vdots$	$\vdots$	$\vdots$	$\vdots$	$\vdots$			

Using an *array* of objects as in the first definition of multiplication, it is easy to notice that the *commutative principle of multiplication* holds:

$$a \cdot b = b \cdot a$$

b columns

$a \cdot b$ [a in a column

× × × × × ×
× × × × × ×
× × × × × ×
× × × × × ×
× × × × × × a rows] $b \cdot a$

b in a row

Also, from the third definition, since $B \times A$ is obtained from $A \times B$ merely by interchanging the order of the two elements in each ordered pair, we have the fact that $n(A \times B) = n(B \times A)$ and thus $a \cdot b = b \cdot a$. In general:

For each x and each y, where x and y are cardinal numbers,

$$x \cdot y = y \cdot x. \qquad \text{COMMUTATIVITY OF } \cdot$$

If we write $3 \cdot 2 \cdot 5$, the expression has no meaning since multiplication is a binary operation. If, however, we define this to mean $(3 \cdot 2) \cdot 5$, where $3 \cdot 2$ is a product, then the expression has meaning, namely $6 \cdot 5$ or 30. It is also easy to verify that $3 \cdot (2 \cdot 5)$ gives the same result.

In general:

For each x, each y, and each z, where x, y, and z are cardinal numbers,

$$x \cdot (y \cdot z) = (x \cdot y) \cdot z. \qquad \text{ASSOCIATIVITY OF } \cdot$$

This is the *associative principle of multiplication.*

Since $(a \cdot b) \cdot c = a \cdot (b \cdot c)$, we define $a \cdot b \cdot c$ to be either expression.

The number 1 plays the same role in multiplication that 0 does in addition. Thus:

For each cardinal number x, there is an identity element of multiplication, *the number* 1, *such that*

$$1 \cdot x = x \cdot 1 = x. \qquad \text{IDENTITY PRINCIPLE OF } \cdot$$

This is the *identity principle of multiplication.*

Again, using any one of the definitions of multiplication, with one set being the empty set, it is a simple matter to show that

$$0 \cdot x = x \cdot 0 = 0. \qquad \text{ZERO PRINCIPLE OF } \cdot$$

We call this the *principle of multiplying by zero.*

Finally, using the fact that $0 = 0 \cdot x$ and the cancellation law, which follows in section 3.8, it is easy to show that

$$\textit{If } x \cdot y = 0, \textit{ then } x = 0 \textit{ or } y = 0. \qquad \text{ZERO PRODUCT PRINCIPLE}$$

3.7 FURTHER PROPERTIES OF ADDITION AND MULTIPLICATION

There is a very important property involving the two operations of addition and multiplication which we now consider. Suppose that we were asked to find the answer to $3 + 4 \cdot 6$. If no further information were given, we could do the operations in the order given, that is, add 4 to 3 to yield 7 and multiply by 6 to get 42. We could also multiply 4 by 6 to get 24 and add this to 3 to obtain 27. The two answers do not agree, so that certainly

$$(a + b) \cdot c \neq a + (b \cdot c).$$

Generally, it is agreed that $a + b \cdot c$ means "$a + (b \cdot c)$"; that is, we first multiply, then we add. Thus $3 + 4 \cdot 6 = 27$. Then what does $(a + b) \cdot c$ mean? That we first find the sum of a and b and multiply the sum by c. However, it is easy to verify that

$$(6 + 3) \cdot 4 = (6 \cdot 4) + (3 \cdot 4); \; (8 + 2) \cdot 5 = (8 \cdot 5) + (2 \cdot 5);$$

and, in general:

For each x, each y, and each z, where x, y, and z are cardinal numbers,

$$(x + y) \cdot z = (x \cdot z) + (y \cdot z). \qquad \text{DISTRIBUTIVITY FOR } \cdot \text{ OVER } +$$

This is called the *distributive principle of multiplication over addition.*

If we agree that in a series of indicated additions and multiplications, we first perform all multiplications from left to right in the order given, and then perform the additions on the results, we can write the distributive principle in the form

$$(x + y) \cdot z = x \cdot z + y \cdot z.$$

Since we have already accepted the commutative principle of multiplication, we can also write this in the form

$$z \cdot (x + y) = z \cdot x + z \cdot y.$$

Using these principles we have developed, we can now prove that $2 \cdot 2 = 4$ as follows:

$2 \cdot 2 = 2 \cdot (1 + 1)$	Writing $1 + 1$ for 2
$= 2 \cdot 1 + 2 \cdot 1$	By the distributive principle
$= 2 + 2$	By the identity principle
$= 4$	Since $2 + 2 = 4$ as proved in section 3.2

The associative and commutative laws of addition and multiplication can be generalized to show any order of occurrence of the numbers and to include three or more numbers. First (see section 3.2),

$$a + b + c = (a + b) + c.$$

Then

$$\underbrace{a+b+c = (a+b)+c}_{\text{Definition}} = \underbrace{a+(b+c)}_{\text{Associativity}} = \underbrace{a+(c+b)}_{\text{Commutativity}} = \underbrace{(a+c)+b}_{\text{Associativity}} = \underbrace{a+c+b}_{\text{Definition}}.$$

If "+" is replaced by "·" the resulting property is true.

Further, we define

$$a + b + c + d = [(a + b) + c] + d.$$

By repeated application of the associative and commutative laws we obtain:

$$\begin{aligned}[(a + b) + c] + d &= (a + b) + (c + d) = (a + b) + (d + c)\\ &= [(a + b) + d] + c = [a + (b + d)] + c\\ &= [a + (d + b)] + c = [(a + d) + b] + c\\ &= (a + d) + (b + c) = (a + d) + (c + b)\\ &= [(a + d) + c] + b = a + d + c + b\end{aligned}$$

(Tell which law was used in each step.) In the final expression, the b and d have changed places from those in the first expression. If "+" is replaced by "·" the resulting relation is true.

The examples given are illustrations of a general principle which we state as:

> *In an indicated addition (or multiplication) of three or more numbers, the sum (or product) remains constant if the order of occurrence of the numbers is rearranged.*

We can also generalize the distributive law which is given by the formula

$$a \cdot (b + c + e + \cdots) = a \cdot b + a \cdot c + a \cdot e + \cdots.$$

From now on we shall generally omit the "$\cdot$" for multiplication, and write, for example,

$a(b + c)$ for $a \cdot (b + c)$ and ab for $a \cdot b$.

Similarly we may write

$3(a + b)$ for $3 \cdot (a + b)$ and $2a$ for $2 \cdot a$.

3.8 UNIQUENESS AND CANCELLATION LAWS

In the exercises of section 3.3 the first five of the following laws were proved for cardinal numbers. The others can be proved similarly.

$a = b \Rightarrow a + c = b + c$: THIS IS THE UNIQUENESS LAW OF +
$a < b \Rightarrow a + c < b + c$
$a > b \Rightarrow a + c > b + c$

$$\left.\begin{array}{l} a + c = b + c \Rightarrow a = b \\ a + c < b + c \Rightarrow a < b \\ a + c > b + c \Rightarrow a > b \end{array}\right\} \quad \text{CANCELLATION LAWS OF } +$$

$(a < b \text{ and } c < d) \Rightarrow a + c < b + d$
$(a > b \text{ and } c > d) \Rightarrow a + c > b + d$

These laws can be used in making mental estimates of sums. For example, $48 + 69 < 50 + 70$ or 120; $41 + 32 > 40 + 30$ or 70.

There are corresponding laws for multiplication, which follow from any of its definitions:

$a = b \Rightarrow ac = bc$ UNIQUENESS LAW OF $\cdot$
$(a < b \text{ and } c \neq 0) \Rightarrow ac < bc$
$(a > b \text{ and } c \neq 0) \Rightarrow ac > bc$

Consider why the condition $c \neq 0$ is necessary in the last two statements.

We can also prove the following:

$$\left.\begin{array}{l} (ac = bc \text{ and } c \neq 0) \Rightarrow a = b \\ (ac < bc \text{ and } c \neq 0) \Rightarrow a < b \\ (ac > bc \text{ and } c \neq 0) \Rightarrow a > b \end{array}\right\} \quad \text{CANCELLATION LAWS OF } \cdot$$

As an example, we give a proof of

$$(ac > bc \text{ and } c \neq 0) \Rightarrow a > b.$$

We shall give an *indirect proof* in which we try to eliminate all possible cases that are consequences of assuming the contrary or negative of what we wish to prove. By the law of trichotomy (section 2.7), for any given a and b we must have $a < b$ *or* $a = b$ *or* $a > b$, where "or" is used in the exclusive sense. If $a \not> b$, then either $a = b$ or $a < b$. If $a = b$, then $ac = bc$; but we know that $ac > bc$, and so $a \neq b$. If $a < b$, then $ac < bc$; but we know that $ac > bc$, and so $a \not< b$. The only case remaining is $a > b$. The reader should prove the other two laws in a similar manner.

Notice that several of these laws have special names.

Some of these laws can be combined in pairs. For example, we can combine $a = b \Rightarrow a + c = b + c$ and $a + c = b + c \Rightarrow a = b$ as

$$a = b \Leftrightarrow a + c = b + c,$$

where the symbol "$\Leftrightarrow$" is a logical symbol which is read "if and only if" or "implies reciprocally."

It is often convenient to refer to a sentence such as

$$a + c = b + c$$

as an *equality* whether it is a true or a false statement, and to a sentence such as

$$a + c < b + c \qquad \text{or} \qquad a + c > b + c$$

as an *inequality* whether it is a true or a false statement. In these sentences, $a + c$ is the left side (or member) and $b + c$ is the right side (or member).

3.9 EXERCISES

1. Prove that $0 \cdot a = 0$, using $A = \emptyset$, $B = \{x, y, \ldots, z\}$.
2. Prove that $1 \cdot a = a$, using $A = \{x\}$, and B a set such that $\text{n}\{B\} = a$.
3. Show that replacing each element of $A = \{x, y, z\}$ by disjoint sets equivalent to $B = \{a, b, c, d\}$ gives a set equivalent to that given by replacing each element of B by disjoint sets equivalent to set A.
4. Using a rectangular solid made of cubes, a of them in the length, b in the width, and c in the height, prove that $a \cdot (b \cdot c) = (a \cdot b) \cdot c$.
5. If $a \cdot b \cdot c \cdot d$ means $[(a \cdot b) \cdot c] \cdot d$, show that $a \cdot b \cdot c \cdot d = d \cdot a \cdot c \cdot b$.
6. Show that in a continued multiplication, $a \cdot b \cdot c \cdot d \cdot e \cdot \cdots \cdot k$, any two factors can be interchanged without affecting the product.
7. If $b \geq c$, show that $a(b - c) = ab - ac$; i.e., that multiplication is distributed over a subtraction. Hint: $b - c = x \Rightarrow b = x + c$. Now multiply both sides of this expression by a, etc.
8. Show how, knowing a rule to multiply by 10, one can use the associative law to develop a rule for multiplying by 20, 30, . . . , or 90.
9. Give an illustration of each type of multiplication defined in the text.

10. If $1 + 2 + 3 + \cdots + n = \dfrac{n(n + 1)}{2}$, multiply both sides by 2, use the distributive law, and find a formula for the first n even numbers.

11. Use the distributive law to prove

$$(2 + 3)(2 + 3) = 2 \cdot 2 + 2 \cdot (2 \cdot 3) + 3 \cdot 3.$$

12. Using the successor of a number as 1 + the number, prove $2 \cdot 3 = 6$.

13. There are five differently colored flags in a set. Any two flags give a signal, the same signal regardless of the order in which they are waved. Find the total number of possible signals.

14. Using the multiplication table, call the main diagonal the set of cells from the upper left to the lower right, bisecting the table. These cells all have the products 1, 4, 9, 16, ...
   (a) Show that any two cells symmetric to this diagonal have the same number. What property does this show for multiplication?
   (b) Connect all the centers of the cells for which the product is 30 by a continuous line. Is this a straight line?

15. Prove: If for each x not equal to zero, $x \cdot a = x$, then a is 1. Hint: $x = x \cdot 1$.

3.10 A NUMBER SYSTEM

The cardinal numbers form a *number system*, that is, a set of elements, called *numbers*, for which the following characteristics must hold.

1. Two operations which are internal laws of composition, that is, such that the set of numbers is closed to the two operations, must be defined. We shall call these operations "addition" and "multiplication," and indicate them by the symbols $\oplus$ and $\odot$ to indicate that they need not be the precise operations defined in this chapter. Thus, for all x and all y, $x \oplus y$ and $x \odot y$ exist and are unique.

2. The operation $\oplus$ is commutative and associative; that is:

   For each x, each y, and each z

$$x \oplus y = y \oplus x,$$
$$(x \oplus y) \oplus z = x \oplus (y \oplus z).$$

3. The operation $\odot$ is commutative and associative; that is:

   For each x, each y, and each z

$$x \odot y = y \odot x,$$
$$x \odot (y \odot z) = (x \odot y) \odot z.$$

4. The operation $\odot$ is distributive over $\oplus$; that is:

   For each x, each y, and each z

$$\begin{aligned} x \odot (y \oplus z) &= (x \odot y) \oplus (x \odot z) \\ &= (y \oplus z) \odot x. \end{aligned}$$

These four requirements are the only ones needed to constitute a number system. Thus, under the usual rules of addition and multiplication, the set of even cardinal numbers

$$E = \{0, 2, 4, 6, 8, 10, \ldots, 2n, \ldots\}$$

form a number system. The reader should check that all four of these conditions hold on this set.

The cardinal numbers have additional properties, which, while useful, are not required for a number system. Thus, the cardinals have a 0, which is the identity element of addition. So does the set E of even numbers. The cardinals have a 1, which is the identity element of multiplication. The set E above does not have an identity element for multiplication. Again, as you learned in school, for each fraction there is another fraction called its *reciprocal* such that the product of the two fractions is 1. For example, for $\frac{2}{7}$ there is $\frac{7}{2}$; for $\frac{1}{3}$ there is $\frac{3}{1}$; etc. But neither the cardinals nor the set E above have this property. Only one cardinal number has a reciprocal. What is this number?

As we study further, we shall come across other sets of elements which form number systems. We shall also see other structures than that of a number system. But we are now in a position to get a first understanding of the meaning of a *mathematical structure*, which consists of:

1. A set of elements, the nature of which is undefined
2. One or more binary operations defined on the elements
3. Certain accepted properties (called axioms or postulates) on the defined operations
4. Further properties derived by logical deduction from the operations and the axioms

While the set of elements is undefined, the elements do have a meaning that is derived from the way the operations are defined, from the postulated properties the operations obey, and from the new properties the operations obey as derived by logical deduction. This can be visualized by thinking of the cardinal numbers just as symbolic forms, 0, 1, 2, etc., then realizing how these forms are related by the definitions of $+$ and $\cdot$, next visualizing the commutative, associative, and distributive properties, and finally recalling other inequalities which we established deductively for these two operations. This structure is an example of a number system.

Frequently in the foregoing pages we have replaced one expression by another having the same value. If one expression has the same value as a second expression for all replacements of the variables, then in any sentence or other expression it is permissible to replace one of these expressions by the other. For example, for all a, $a \cdot 0 = 0$. Now in the sentence $a \cdot b = 0$, we may replace the 0 by its equal and write $a \cdot b = a \cdot 0$. This process of replacing an expression by an equivalent expression is called *substitution*. Thus, since $5 = 3 + 2$ we can transform $5 \cdot 7$ into $(3 + 2)7$, by substitution.

We can prove still other properties for the cardinal numbers. For example, we can prove $c + a = a \Rightarrow c = 0$ as follows: We have $a = 0 + a$ by the identity principle of addition. Hence $c + a = 0 + a$ by substitution, and then by the cancellation law which we proved, the a's drop out and $c = 0$.

Also, we can prove that if $c \cdot a = c$ and $a \neq 1$, then c must be zero. We shall give an indirect proof based on the fact that either $c = 0$ or $c \neq 0$ because of the meaning of "not" (section 1.10). Notice that this is the exclusive use of "or."

(1) $c = c \cdot 1$	By the identity principle of multiplication
(2) $c \cdot a = c \cdot 1$	Substituting $c \cdot 1$ for c in $c \cdot a = c$
(3) $c = 0$ or $c \neq 0$	Meaning of "not"
(4) If $c \neq 0$; in (2), $a = 1$.	By the cancellation law of multiplication
(5) This is impossible.	Given $a \neq 1$
(6) Hence $c = 0$.	Only remaining possibility

We list below the important properties possessed by the cardinal numbers. Properties P_4 and P_{10} are left blank because, whatever they are (as developed later), the cardinal numbers do not have them. Later we shall develop other number systems which do possess properties P_4 and P_{10}, and then we shall state them. In writing the formulas for the principles, we introduce the following symbols:

"$\forall_x$" which is read, "For each x"

"$\exists_x :$ " which is read, "There is a value of x such that," or "There exists an x such that"

Thus, "$\forall_x \forall_y\ x \cdot y = y \cdot x$" is read, "For each x and for each y, x multiplied by y equals y multiplied by x." Recall that a formula can be thought of as representing millions and millions of true statements. This means that you can replace the variables x and y by any cardinals, and you will always get a true statement. Of course, you must replace the letter by the same number, every place the letter occurs in the formula. The reader should practice reading each formula and giving specific examples until the symbolism becomes almost automatic.

Let there be a set of elements on which there are defined two internal laws of composition $+$ and $\cdot$, called addition and multiplication. Then if the set is the cardinal numbers, all properties except P_4 and P_{10} are universally true.

*P_1	$\forall_x \forall_y\ x + y = y + x$	COMMUTATIVITY OF $+$
*P_2	$\forall_x \forall_y \forall_z\ x + (y + z) = (x + y) + z$	ASSOCIATIVITY OF $+$
P_3	$\exists_0 : \forall_x\ x + 0 = 0 + x = x$	IDENTITY PRINCIPLE OF $+$
P_4	. . . .	. . . .
*P_5	$\forall_x \forall_y\ x \cdot y = y \cdot x$	COMMUTATIVITY OF $\cdot$
*P_6	$\forall_x \forall_y \forall_z\ x \cdot (y \cdot z) = (x \cdot y) \cdot z$	ASSOCIATIVITY OF $\cdot$
P_7	$\exists_1 : \forall_x\ x \cdot 1 = 1 \cdot x = x$	IDENTITY PRINCIPLE OF $\cdot$
*P_8	$\forall_x \forall_y \forall_z\ x \cdot (y + z) = x \cdot y + x \cdot z$	DISTRIBUTIVITY FOR $\cdot$ OVER $+$
P_9	$x \cdot y = 0 \Rightarrow x = 0$ or $y = 0$	ZERO PRODUCT PRINCIPLE
P_{10}	. . . .	. . . .

The *P form a number system.

3.11 EXERCISES

1. Show that the set of counting numbers, $\{1, 2, 3, \ldots, n, \ldots\}$ forms a number system. Which of the properties P_1–P_{10} does it not have?
2. Prove that if $x \cdot y = 0$, then either $x = 0$ or $y = 0$ (Property P_9). Hint: Use the fact $x \cdot 0 = 0$.
3. Prove: if $c \cdot a = a$, and $a \neq 0$, then $c = 1$.
4. Show that the set of odd numbers $\{1, 3, 5, \ldots, 2n + 1\}$ under ordinary $+$ and $\cdot$ does not form a number system.
5. (a) The product of two cardinal numbers is 10. What are the numbers?
   (b) The product of two cardinal numbers is 1. What are the numbers?
   (c) The product of two cardinal numbers is 0. What is one number? The other number?
6. A set of elements consists of $\{0, 1, 2\}$ for which the $+$ and $\cdot$ are defined by the following tables:

$+$ (x \ y)	0	1	2
0	0	1	2
1	1	2	0
2	2	0	1

$\cdot$ (x \ y)	0	1	2
0	0	0	0
1	0	1	2
2	0	2	1

   Prove that the set is a number system and list all the properties P_1–P_{10} that hold for this system.
7. In Exercise 6 is subtraction an internal law of composition? That is, is there an answer to $1 - 2 = x$? If so, $1 = x + 2$. Make the subtraction table.
8. If we define the operation "ⓐⓥ" to mean "add two given numbers and divide the sum by two,"
   (a) show that this operation is commutative, that is,

$$a \circledcirc b = b \circledcirc a.$$

   (The symbol is "av" in a circle.)

   (b) is the operation associative? Prove your answer.
9. Consider the set of numbers $\{0, 1, 2, 3, 4, 5, 6, 7, 8, 9\}$. Define the sum for any two numbers of the set to be the units digit of ordinary addition. Define the product for any two numbers to be the units digit of ordinary multiplication. Show that this set forms a number system. Make the addition and multiplication table for this system.

3.12 REFERENCE QUESTIONS

1. How was a *number system* defined in this chapter? (Note that a number system must possess a basic *structure*.) For a more detailed discussion of structure, see

   Taylor, Howard E. and Wade, Thomas L. "On the Meaning of Structure in Mathematics," *The Mathematics Teacher*, LVIII: 226–231; 1965.

2. In this chapter, how were arrays used to illustrate the commutative property of multiplication? Interestingly enough, arrays may also be used for physical illustrations of the associative property of multiplication. In this connection, see

   Hannon, Herbert. "A New Look at the Basic Principles of Multiplication with Whole Numbers," *The Arithmetic Teacher*, 7: 357–361; 1960.

3. Some authors speak of subtraction as "the inverse of addition." For an explanation of this terminology, as well as a full discussion of operations with whole numbers, see

   National Council of Teachers of Mathematics. *Topics in Mathematics for Elementary School Teachers* (29th yearbook). Washington, D.C.: NCTM, 1964. Pp. 48–83.

4 POWERS AND DIVISION

IN THIS CHAPTER *we shall study two new operations defined on the cardinal numbers. One of these, raising to a power, will be an internal law of composition; that is, the operation will be defined in such a way as to be always possible for any two given numbers. The other, division, when defined in one sense is not always a possible operation, but we shall also give a more general definition so that this second operation will also become an internal law of composition.*

4.1 RAISING TO A POWER

A sum of like numbers can be considered as a product as shown in section 3.6. We can also proceed as follows. The expression

$$4 + 4 + 4 + 4 + 4$$

can be written in the form

$$4 \cdot 1 + 4 \cdot 1 + 4 \cdot 1 + 4 \cdot 1 + 4 \cdot 1$$

(since 1 is the identity element for multiplication). Using the generalized distributive law, we see that this expression becomes

$$4(1 + 1 + 1 + 1 + 1).$$

The expression in parentheses becomes 5 by using the definition of successor of a number. Hence, we have the form which is much simpler than the continued sum of fours. In this form the multiplication is equivalent to the sum of five numbers, each 4.

In a similar way, there is a method of expressing a product of like numbers in a simpler form. For example,

$$4 \cdot 4 \cdot 4$$

is written in the form

$$4^3.$$

Here the second number, 3, is called an *exponent*, and it indicates that the number to be assigned to 4^3 is the same as that assigned to $4 \cdot 4 \cdot 4$. The exponent 3 indicates a continued product of 3 factors, each factor being 4. The number 4 is the first number and is called the *base*. The exponent, or second number, is always written after the base and at a superior (or higher) position. The number $64 = 4 \cdot 4 \cdot 4$ which is assigned to 4^3 is called the *third power* of four. Thus we have

$$\underset{\text{base}}{\overset{\downarrow}{4}}\,{}^{\overset{3}{\searrow}}_{\text{exponent}} \quad = \quad \underset{\text{power}}{\overset{\downarrow}{64}}$$

and say, "the third power of 4 is 64."

Generally:

DEFINITION: *If a is any cardinal number considered as a base, and b is any cardinal number, not zero, then we define the* bth power of a,

$$a^b,$$

by the following:

$$a^1 = a \qquad (b = 1)$$
$$a^b = \underbrace{a \cdot a \cdot a \cdot \;\cdots\; \cdot a}_{b \text{ factors}} \qquad (b > 1)$$

The operation is called raising a to the bth power.

Thus, $2^3 = 2 \cdot 2 \cdot 2$; $4^1 = 4$; $5^4 = 5 \cdot 5 \cdot 5 \cdot 5$; $3^2 = 3 \cdot 3$; etc.

If we examine the above definition, we note that raising to a power is a binary operation. The given numbers (a, b) are an ordered pair (base, exponent) to which is assigned the number $\underbrace{a \cdot a \cdot a \cdot \;\cdots\; \cdot a}$ to b factors.

The bth power of a equals c.

$$\underbrace{\underbrace{(a, b)}_{\text{Ordered pair}} \longrightarrow \underbrace{c}_{\text{Power}}}_{a^b = c}$$

Thus, the third power of 2 equals 8. What is the second power of 3?

The operation of raising to a power is sometimes called *involution.* Because of the analogy of a^2 and a^3 to the area and volume, respectively, of a square and cube of side a units, these two powers are frequently called the *square* and the *cube* of a, respectively.

In the above definition, 0 was ruled out as an exponent. For convenience it is frequently desirable to define a^0. If we start with the number 1, multiply it by a to get a second term, then the result by a to get a third term, and so on, we get the following sequence of terms:

$$\{1,\ 1 \cdot a,\ 1 \cdot a \cdot a,\ 1 \cdot a \cdot a \cdot a,\ 1 \cdot a \cdot a \cdot a \cdot a,\ \ldots,\ 1 \cdot \underbrace{a \cdot a \cdot a \cdot \cdots \cdot a}_{b \text{ factors}}\}$$

which can be written as

$$\{1,\ a^1,\ a^2,\ a^3,\ a^4,\ \ldots,\ a^b\}$$

All of the terms are powers of a except the first. To keep the *pattern* in terms of a, it would seem plausible to write a^0 in place of 1. This we agree to do.

DEFINITION: *If a is any cardinal number,*

$$a^0 = 1 \quad \textit{for} \quad a \neq 0.$$

Thus,

$$1^0 = 1; \qquad 5^0 = 1;$$
$$10^0 = 1; \quad 100^0 = 1;$$

and so on.

With this definition, involution is an internal law of composition for the cardinal numbers, except for one expression, namely,

$$0^0.$$

Can we assign a value to this power? According to the product law 0^b with $b \neq 0$ always gives 0. According to the definition of a zero exponent 0^0 should be 1, since a^0 is 1 for every a except $a = 0$. In higher mathematics (analysis) the expression 0^0 takes on different values in different expressions. However, we shall use the following:

DEFINITION: *For the cardinal number zero,*

$$0^0 = 1.$$

Now we shall get consistent results, and further, and more desirable, with the above definitions involution is always possible; that is, *involution is an internal law of composition.* Thus,

$$0^0 = 1; \quad 0^1 = 0; \quad 0^8 = 0;$$
$$3^0 = 1; \quad 5^0 = 1;$$
$$b^0 = 1, b \text{ any cardinal.}$$

It is easy to prove that raising to a power is not commutative. For example, $2^3 = 8$, but $3^2 = 9$, and therefore $2^3 \neq 3^2$. Further, involution is not associative. Consider the expression

$$2^{3^4}.$$

Until we give further information, this expression is meaningless. We shall define it to mean

$$(2^3)^4.$$

Then its value is $8^4 = 8 \cdot 8 \cdot 8 \cdot 8 = 4096$. Let us now find the value of

$$2^{(3^4)} \text{ or } 2^{81}.$$

This value is $2 \cdot 2 \cdot 2 \cdot \cdots \cdot 2$ to 81 factors, or approximately two million billion billion. Thus $(2^3)^4 \neq 2^{(3^4)}$ and involution is not associative.

It is easy to see that there is no identity element; i.e., there is no number x, such that $a^x = x^a = a$ for every a. Check this for the values of 0 and 1 for x.

As noted above, involution, or raising to a power, is an internal law of composition, and so the set of cardinal numbers is closed to the operation of raising to a power. This can be shown by a table of powers, part of which is reproduced here:

Involution Table

(b across the top; a down the side)

a^b	0	1	2	3	$\cdots$	b	$\cdots$
0	1	0	0	0	$\cdots$	0	$\cdots$
1	1	1	1	1	$\cdots$	1	$\cdots$
2	1	2	4	8	$\cdots$	2^b	$\cdots$
3	1	3	9	27	$\cdots$	3^b	$\cdots$
4	1	4	16	64	$\cdots$	4^b	$\cdots$
$\vdots$	$\vdots$	$\vdots$	$\vdots$	$\vdots$		$\vdots$	
a	1	a	a^2	a^3	$\cdots$	a^b	$\cdots$
$\vdots$	$\vdots$	$\vdots$	$\vdots$	$\vdots$		$\vdots$	

4.2 PRODUCTS AND POWERS OF POWERS WITH THE SAME BASE

Consider the expression

$$2^3 \cdot 2^5,$$

which is the product of two powers with the *same base.* Expanding each power into a product, we obtain

$$(2 \cdot 2 \cdot 2) \cdot (2 \cdot 2 \cdot 2 \cdot 2 \cdot 2),$$

which is the same as 2^8. Thus,

$$2^3 \cdot 2^5 = 2^8.$$

Generally, for any base, we note that

$$a^3 \cdot a^5 = (a \cdot a \cdot a) \cdot (a \cdot a \cdot a \cdot a \cdot a) = a^8.$$

For any exponents p and q, neither equal to zero, we have

$$a^p \cdot a^q = \underbrace{\underbrace{(a \cdot a \cdot \;\cdots\; \cdot a)}_{p \text{ factors}} \cdot \underbrace{(a \cdot a \cdot a \cdot \;\cdots\; \cdot a)}_{q \text{ factors}}}_{(p+q) \text{ factors}} = a^{p+q}.$$

If either p or q is zero, we have

$$a^0 \cdot a^q = 1 \cdot a^q = a^{0+q} \qquad \text{or} \qquad a^p \cdot a^0 = a^p \cdot 1 = a^{p+0}.$$

Hence we have the following *principle of multiplying powers with the same base:*

> *In the domain of cardinal numbers, for all exponents, the* product *of powers with the same base is*
>
> $$a^p \cdot a^q = a^{p+q}.$$

Thus, $3^2 \cdot 3^4 = 3^{2+4} = 3^6; \quad 5^0 \cdot 5^6 = 5^{0+6} = 5^6;$

$0^0 \cdot 0^6 = 0^{6+0} = 0$, also $0^0 \cdot 0^6 = 1 \cdot 0^6 = 0.$

Next we consider raising a power to a power. We have defined

$$a^{b^c} \quad \text{to mean} \quad (a^b)^c.$$

Is there a way of expressing this as a single power? To find the answer, we first consider a particular example $(2^3)^4$. By definition we have

$$(2^3)^4 = 2^3 \cdot 2^3 \cdot 2^3 \cdot 2^3.$$

By the principle of multiplying powers with the same base, we have

$$(2^3)^4 = 2^{3+3+3+3}.$$

But $3 + 3 + 3 + 3 = 3 \cdot 4$. Hence

$$(2^3)^4 = 2^{3 \cdot 4}.$$

(Note that $2^{(3^4)}$ is not the same as $(2^3)^4$.) Generally:

In the domain of cardinal numbers, if a power is raised to a power, the result is a power of the base with exponent equal to the product of the two exponents:

$$(a^b)^c = \underbrace{a^b \cdot a^b \cdot \cdots \cdot a^b}_{c \text{ factors}} = a^{\overbrace{b+b+\cdots+b}^{c \text{ addends}}} = a^{b \cdot c}$$

or

$$(a^b)^c = a^{b \cdot c}.$$

Thus,

$$(3^2)^3 = 3^{2 \cdot 3} = 3^6;$$
$$(3^0)^4 = 3^{0 \cdot 4} = 3^0 = 1; \quad (3^4)^0 = 3^{4 \cdot 0} = 3^0 = 1;$$
$$(0^0)^3 = 0^{0 \cdot 3} = 0^0 = 1, \text{ also } (0^0)^3 = 1^3 = 1.$$

4.3 POWERS OF PRODUCTS

We now consider raising a product to a power; for example, $(2 \cdot 3)^4$. By definition we have

$$(2 \cdot 3)^4 = (2 \cdot 3) \cdot (2 \cdot 3) \cdot (2 \cdot 3) \cdot (2 \cdot 3).$$

Using the commutative and associative laws of multiplication, we find that the right-hand member becomes

$$(2 \cdot 2 \cdot 2 \cdot 2) \cdot (3 \cdot 3 \cdot 3 \cdot 3),$$

and so

$$(2 \cdot 3)^4 = 2^4 \cdot 3^4.$$

Generally:

For the cardinal numbers,

$$(a \cdot b)^c = \underbrace{(a \cdot b) \cdot (a \cdot b) \cdot \cdots \cdot (a \cdot b)}_{c \text{ factors}}$$

$$= \underbrace{(a \cdot a \cdot \cdots \cdot a)}_{c \text{ factors}} \cdot \underbrace{(b \cdot b \cdot \cdots \cdot b)}_{c \text{ factors}}$$

or

$$(a \cdot b)^c = a^c b^c.$$

This formula expresses the fact that *involution is distributed over multiplication* in a manner similar to the distributivity of multiplication over addition. Thus,

$$(3 \cdot 5)^4 = 3^4 \cdot 5^4 = 81 \cdot 625; \quad (3 \cdot 10)^6 = 3^6 \cdot 10^6 = 729 \cdot 10^6.$$

It is easy to verify that

$$(2 + 3)^2 \neq 2^2 + 3^2$$

since $5^2 = 25$ and $2^2 + 3^2 = 4 + 9$, or 13, and so *involution is not distributed over addition.* The expression $(2 + 3)^2$ is called "the square of a binomial" and is found either by adding and squaring the result,

$$5^2 = 25,$$

or by expanding (omitting the multiplication dot between factors in parentheses)

$$(2 + 3)(2 + 3)$$

as follows. Using distributivity of multiplication over addition, we have

$$\begin{aligned} (2 + 3)^2 &= (2 + 3)(2 + 3) \\ &= (2 + 3)2 + (2 + 3)3 \\ &= (2 \cdot 2 + 3 \cdot 2) + (2 \cdot 3 + 3 \cdot 3) \\ &= 2^2 + 2(2 \cdot 3) + 3^2 \\ &= 4 + 12 + 9 = 25. \end{aligned}$$

4.4 EXERCISES

1. Find the cardinal number equal to each of the following:

   (a) 3^4 (b) 5^3 (c) 0^8 (d) 0^0 (e) 4^0
   (f) 3^1 (g) 4^2 (h) 2^4 (i) 2^{10} (j) 7^5

2. Simplify each of the following:

   (a) $x \cdot x \cdot x$ (b) $x \cdot x \cdot y \cdot y \cdot y \cdot z$ (c) $0 \cdot 0 \cdot 0 \cdot 0 \cdot 0$
   (d) $1 \cdot 1 \cdot 1 \cdot 1$ (e) $a \cdot b \cdot a \cdot b \cdot a \cdot b \cdot a \cdot b$

3. Starting with 1, multiply it by 3, then the result by 3, etc.; write each result in order as a power of 3. Where would 3^0 fall in this sequence? Define 3^0.

4. Do the same as in Exercise 3, multiplying by 0. Where would 0^0 fall in this sequence? Define 0^0. Distinguish 0^0 from 0^1.

5. For 2^{2^2} compare $2^{(2^2)}$ with $(2^2)^2$. Explain your answer.

6. For 3^{3^3} compare $3^{(3^3)}$ with $(3^3)^3$. Explain your answer.

7. Using the results of Exercises 5 and 6, tell why raising a power to a power is not associative. Why was it associative in Exercise 5?

8. Simplify each of the following:

   (a) $2^3 \cdot 2^5$ (b) $3^2 \cdot 3^0$ (c) $5^4 \cdot 5^1$
   (d) $a^2 \cdot a^3$ (e) $0^0 \cdot 0^4$ (f) $2^2 \cdot 2^3 \cdot 2^4$

9. Simplify each of the following:

(a) $(2^3)^4$ (b) $(3^2)^3$ (c) $(5^2)^0$ (d) $(5^0)^4$
(e) $(8^2)^0$ (f) $(4^3)^2$ (g) $(2 \cdot 3)^4$ (h) $(3 \cdot 2 \cdot 5)^2$
(i) $(2 \cdot 8 \cdot 10)^2$ (j) $10^4 \cdot 10^2$ (k) $(10 \cdot 10)^6$

10. Evaluate:

(a) $(3 + 5)^2$ (b) $(3 + 5)(2 + 5)$ by expanding
(c) $(1 + 2)^3$ (d) $(1 + 2)(1 + 4 + 4)$ by expanding

11. (a) Explain why there is no identity element for the operation of involution (raising to a power).
(b) Distinguish between $a \cdot b^n$ and $(a \cdot b)^n$ and between $a + b \cdot c$ and $(a + b) \cdot c$.

12. A *unary operation* is a mapping which assigns a number to one given number. Thus "adding 5" is a unary operation as shown by the following table

$$\begin{array}{cccccc} 0 & 1 & 2 & 3 & \ldots & n \\ 5 & 6 & 7 & 8 & \ldots & n+5 \end{array} \qquad \underbrace{x \to x + 5}_{\text{operation of adding 5}}$$

Show that for numbers 5 or greater, "subtracting 5" is a unary operation.

13. For the cardinal numbers, show that "multiplying by 3" is a unary operation; i.e., to any number one can assign 3 times that number.

14. Show that "squaring a number" is a unary operation, which is indicated by $x \to x^2$.

15. Show that "cubing a number" is a unary operation.

16. Generalize Exercises 14 and 15 to the case of any constant exponent.

17. If $n < p$ and $a \geq 2$, show that

$$a^n < a^p.$$

Hint: If $n < p$, then $p = n + k$, $k > 0$. Now expand each product.

18. If $n > p$ and $a \geq 2$, show that

$$a^n > a^p.$$

19. If $n = p$ and $a \geq 2$, show that

$$a^n = a^p.$$

20. Show by the indirect method that for $a \geq 2$

(a) if $a^n < a^p$, then $n < p$;
(b) if $a^n > a^p$, then $n > p$;
(c) if $a^n = a^p$, then $n = p$.

21. Consider the relations in Exercises 17 to 20 when $a = 1$ and when $a = 0$.

22. Generalize Exercises 17 to 21 in one statement.

A sentence which relates numbers is often called an *arithmetical sentence* or a *mathematical sentence*. Examples of such sentences are $2 + 3 = 5$; $8 - 2 = 6$; 4 is the square of 2 or $4 = 2^2$; $5 < 7$; $8 + 2 > 7$; $3 < 3$ *or* $3 = 3$, which is frequently written as $3 \leq 3$, and is true because by the inclusive use of *or*, $3 = 3$ is true. All the above sentences are readily recognized as *true* sentences.

We could also write *false* sentences, for example, $2 + 3 = 7$; $8 - 2 = 5$; 2 is the square of 4 or $2 = 4^2$; $5 > 7$; $8 + 2 < 7$; $3 \geq 4$, where $3 > 4$ and $3 = 4$ are both false. Whenever a mathematical sentence contains only symbols for numbers which are related by such symbols as $=$, $<$, $>$, $\neq$, $\leq$, $\geq$, etc., it can immediately be tested as to its truth or falsity. Such sentences are called *statements.*

DEFINITION: *A* statement *is a mathematical sentence that is true or is false.*

Note that in this definition the *or* is exclusive; that is, a statement can be called *only one* of the two: true, false. In this book we shall be mostly concerned with true statements.

There are other kinds of sentences in mathematics. One of these contains a variable, denoted by such a symbol as x, y, or z. In such arithmetical sentences, the variable can be replaced by any symbol for the numbers under consideration. Thus far in this book the only numbers considered are the cardinal numbers,

$$C = \{0, 1, 2, 3, \ldots, 10, \ldots, n, \ldots\},$$

and for the present this set will be the *domain of the variable* (section 1.2). Examples of sentences containing a variable are

$$x + 2 = 7;\ x - 8 = 3;\ 3x = 27;\ \sqrt{x} = 3;\ y < 5;$$
$$y + 2 > 6;\ 3 + z \leq 10;\ \text{and so on.}$$

As these sentences appear, *they are neither true nor false.* For until x is replaced by the symbol for a number, you cannot tell anything about the truth or falsity of the sentence. They are called *open sentences.*

DEFINITION: *An* open sentence *is a mathematical sentence containing one or more variables, and is neither true nor false.*

An open sentence with the equality sign is called an *equation.* An open sentence with an inequality sign is sometimes called an *inequation* or more frequently an *inequality.*

We shall now learn how to *solve* open sentences, that is, to find those numbers which when substituted for the variables (or more precisely when their numerals are substituted for the variables) yield true statements. The set of numbers which yield true statements is called the *solution set,* or frequently merely the *solution.*

EXAMPLE 1. If in $x + 2 = 7$, x is replaced by 5, we obtain $5 + 2 = 7$, which is true. Hence 5 is a solution to the open sentence, or $\{5\}$ is the solution set, since no other replacement would give a true statement.

EXAMPLE 2. In $x - 8 = 3$, if x is replaced by 10, we obtain $10 - 8 = 3$, which is false. Hence 10 is not a solution. But if x is replaced by 11, we obtain $11 - 8 = 3$, and $\{11\}$ is the solution set.

EXAMPLE 3. In $3x = 27$, if x is replaced by 9 we obtain the true statement $3 \cdot 9 = 27$, and so $\{9\}$ is the solution set.

EXAMPLE 4. In $y < 5$, we can replace y by 0, 1, 2, 3, or 4 and always have a true statement. The solution set is $\{0, 1, 2, 3, 4\}$.

EXAMPLE 5. For $y + 2 > 6$ the solution set is all the cardinal numbers greater than 4, that is $\{5, 6, 7, 8, \ldots, n, \ldots\}$.

Not all open sentences have solutions. For example,

$$x = x + 1$$

has no replacement for x that yields a true statement, for if it did, a cardinal number would be equal to its successor, which is false. Again

$$3 + x = 1$$

has no solution, for if any cardinal number is added to 3, the sum is 3 or more and could not possibly be equal to 1. Also

$$3x = 17$$

has *no solution in the cardinal numbers*, for $3 \cdot 5 = 15$ and $3 \cdot 6 = 18$ and there is no cardinal number greater than 5 but less than 6.

Let us consider the open sentence

$$b + x = a, \qquad \text{(I)}$$

where b and a are *any given* cardinal numbers and the domain of x is the set of cardinal numbers. We ask, "Under what conditions can this sentence have a solution?"

First we note that *a must be at least as great as b or greater*, since the least value x can have is 0 and $b + 0 = b$. Further, b plus a number not zero always yields a sum greater than b. Thus, if $a < b$, sentence (I) has no solution. The solution set is the empty set $\{\ \}$.

If $a = b$, we can write $a = b + 0$, and the sentence (I) becomes

$$b + x = b + 0.$$

By the cancellation law of addition this becomes

$x = 0$. The solution set is $\{0\}$.

(Note that this is *not* the empty set.)

If $a > b$, then $a = b + d$, where d is a cardinal number other than zero. Then the sentence (I) becomes

$$b + x = b + d,$$

and by the cancellation law

$x = d$. The solution set is $\{d\}$.

Using these results, we can give a new definition of subtraction.

Let (a, b) be a given ordered pair of cardinal numbers. Then there is a cardinal number d which is the solution to the sentence

$$b + x = a$$

if and only if $a \geq b$.

4.6 EXERCISES

1. Tell which of the following are statements and which are open sentences:

   (a) $3 + 4 = 9$ (b) $2 \cdot 7 = 14$ (c) $3 \cdot 7 = 28$
   (d) $3 \cdot x = 27$ (e) $4 < 3$ (f) $3 + x > 10$
   (g) $3 + x < 2$ (h) $5 \cdot 7 < 6 \cdot 4$ (i) $3 + 2 < 3 \cdot 2$
   (j) $x + y = 3$

2. For the statements in Exercise 1, tell which are true and which are false.
3. Using numerals and the symbols $=, <, >, \leq, \neq$, write five statements that are true and five that are false.
4. Using numerals, one variable, and the symbols of Exercise 3, write five open sentences, and give the solution set to each sentence.

Find the solution set to each of the following open sentences:

5. $x + 3 = 8$ 6. $5 + x = 2$ 7. $x + 3 < 8$
8. $x + 3 \leq 8$ 9. $x + 4 \neq 4$ 10. $2 + x > 5$
11. $2 + x \not> 5$ 12. $5 + x = 6 + x$ 13. $5 + x = 25$
14. $3x = 24$ 15. $3x < 24$ 16. $3x > 24$
17. $3x = 17$ 18. $3x < 17$ 19. $3x > 17$
20. Show that $a + b = x$ always has a solution. What is the solution called? (Here a and b are any two given cardinal numbers.)
21. Show that $ab = x$ always has a solution. What is the solution called?
22. Consider $ax = b$. Is a solution always possible?
23. For $a < b$, define "subtraction," $a - b$, as having the value "0 and a deficit," e.g., $2 - 5 = 0$, deficit 3. Is the set of cardinals closed to this operation?

Just as subtraction was redefined in section 4.5 in relation to addition (the solutions to $b + x = a$ for every ordered pair of cardinals (a, b) with $a \geq b$), we can define a new operation called *division* in relation to multiplication. We use the cardinal numbers as our domain.

Consider the open sentence

$$bx = a \tag{II}$$

formed from a given ordered pair (a, b) and the variable x, and ask, "Under what conditions does the sentence (II) have a unique solution?"

First, we note that if both $b = 0$ and $a = 0$, x could be any cardinal number. For then sentence (II) becomes

$$0 \cdot x = 0,$$

and replacing x by any cardinal number gives a true statement. The solution set is the set of all cardinal numbers, and the solution is not unique.

Next we note that b *cannot be* 0 if $a \neq 0$. For if b is 0 and a is not 0, we get a false statement for every replacement of x, because $0 \cdot x$ is always 0, and $0 = a$ is false. The solution set is the empty set.

If $b \neq 0$ and $a = b$, then since $b = b \cdot 1$, we can write the sentence (II) as

$$b \cdot x = b \cdot 1,$$

and by the cancellation law of multiplication we obtain

$$x = 1. \text{ The solution set is } \{1\}.$$

If $b \neq 0$ and $a = 0$, then we can write $a = b \cdot 0$ and (II) becomes

$$b \cdot x = b \cdot 0,$$

and by the cancellation law

$$x = 0. \text{ The solution set is } \{0\}.$$

If $b \neq 0$ and a is a multiple of b, that is, if a is any one of the numbers in the set

$$\{b \cdot 0, b \cdot 1, b \cdot 2, b \cdot 3, \ldots, b \cdot q, \ldots\},$$

then sentence (II) can be written as

$$b \cdot x = b \cdot q,$$

and since $b \neq 0$, by the cancellation law we obtain

$$x = q. \text{ The unique solution is } \{q\}.$$

If $b \neq 0$ and a is not a multiple of b, then the sentence has no solution.

We can summarize the foregoing discussion as follows:

> *Let (a, b) be a given ordered pair of cardinal numbers with $b \neq 0$. Then there is a unique cardinal number q which is the solution to the sentence*
>
> $bx = a$
>
> *if and only if a is a multiple of b.*

We can now use the above results to define a new operation on the set of cardinal numbers which is called *exact division.*

For a given ordered pair of numbers (a, b), $b \neq 0$, if there exists a number q, such that $b \cdot q = a$, then q is called the *exact quotient*, or the number arising by *dividing a exactly by b.* Thus

Operation of exact division

$$\underbrace{\underset{\text{Ordered pair}}{(a, b)} \longrightarrow \underset{\text{Quotient}}{q}}_{a \div b = q \Leftrightarrow b \cdot q = a}$$

The numbers a and b are called, respectively, *dividend* and *divisor.*

Note that *the set of cardinal numbers is open to exact division.* Only if the dividend is a multiple of the divisor, do we obtain an exact quotient. In a division table, many cells are left unoccupied as shown below:

Exact Division Table

$b \neq 0$

÷	1	2	3	4	5	6	...
0	0	0	0	0	0	0	...
1	1						...
2	2	1					...
3	3		1				...
4	4	2		1			...
5	5				1		...
6	6	3	2			1	...
⋮	⋮	⋮	⋮	⋮	⋮	⋮	

(a labels the rows)

Exact division is not commutative and not associative, and it has no identity element. The proof of this statement is left as an exercise. (See section 4.10, Exercise 23.)

DIVISION WITH A REMAINDER

In school you learned how to find the answer for a division problem and to write it as a quotient with a remainder. To review this process, consider the sentence

$$3x = 17.$$

Since 17 is not a multiple of 3, there is no exact quotient for $17 \div 3$. However, if we write out the multiples of 3 in an ordered set,

$$\{3 \cdot 0, 3 \cdot 1, 3 \cdot 2, 3 \cdot 3, 3 \cdot 4, 3 \cdot 5, 3 \cdot 6, \ldots\},$$

we find that 17 falls between two *successive* multiples, namely $3 \cdot 5$ and $3 \cdot 6$; that is, $3 \cdot 5 < 17$ and $17 < 3 \cdot 6$. We write this as

$$3 \cdot 5 < 17 < 3 \cdot 6.$$

Then $3 \cdot 5$ is the greatest multiple of 3 that is less than 17, and $3 \cdot 6$ is the least multiple of 3 that is greater than 17. We say that $17 \div 3$ has the *total quotient* 5. Numbers less than 5, for example 4, 3, 2, 1, 0, are also quotients, called *partial quotients.* They are *partial* because they do not yield the *greatest* multiple of 3 less than 17.

To generalize the foregoing example, let N and d be a given dividend and divisor. Then we can write the multiples of d as the following set:

$$\{d \cdot 0, d \cdot 1, d \cdot 2, \ldots, d \cdot q, \overset{N}{\updownarrow} d \cdot (q + 1), \ldots\}$$

If one of these numbers, for example $d \cdot q$, is equal to N, the division is exact and q is an exact quotient. If none of these numbers is N, then N must fall between two consecutive multiples. Let the greatest multiple less than N be $d \cdot q$. Then q is the total quotient arising from dividing N by d. Numbers less than q are partial quotients.

Now consider the two inequalities

$$dq \leq N \quad \text{and} \quad N < d(q + 1) \quad (\text{or } N < dq + d).$$

Note that dq can equal N if the quotient is exact, but N is always less than the next higher multiple of d, which is $d(q + 1)$. If we subtract dq from each member of each of the inequalities (recall section 3.8), we obtain:

$$dq - dq \leq N - dq \qquad N - dq < (dq + d) - dq$$

$$\text{or} \qquad\qquad \text{or}$$

$$0 \leq N - dq \qquad N - dq < d$$

The quantity $N - dq$ is called the *remainder*, r. The first inequality says that *the remainder is equal to or greater than zero.* The second inequality says that *the remainder is less than the divisor.* Thus in $17 \div 3$, we have

$$3 \cdot 5 < 17 < 3 \cdot 6,$$

and hence

$$0 < 17 - 3 \cdot 5 < 3 \cdot 6 - 3 \cdot 5 \quad \text{or} \quad 2 < 3;$$

i.e., the remainder 2 is less than the divisor 3.

If $N < d$, then

$$d \cdot 0 < N < d \cdot 1,$$

and $q = 0$ and $r = N$.

We can now define a new binary operation, called *division with a remainder.* This type of division is always possible if the divisor is not zero. However, to each ordered pair (N, d), $d \neq 0$, we now associate an ordered pair (q, r) of elements called the *total quotient* and the *remainder*, respectively. This can be illustrated diagrammatically as follows:

Operation of division with remainder

$$\underbrace{\underbrace{(N, d)}_{\text{(Dividend, Divisor)}} \quad \underbrace{(q, r)}_{\text{(Total quotient, Remainder)}}}_{N \div d \Leftrightarrow (N = d \cdot q + r, \quad 0 \leq r < d)}$$

If $r = 0$, the total quotient is an exact quotient, and exact division is simply division with a remainder of zero. The following table shows that *the set of cardinal numbers is closed to division with a remainder with zero not used as the divisor:*

Division Table with Remainders

$d \neq 0$

	÷	1	2	3	4	5	6	...
	0	(0, 0)	(0, 0)	(0, 0)	(0, 0)	(0, 0)	(0, 0)	...
	1	(1, 0)	(0, 1)	(0, 1)	(0, 1)	(0, 1)	(0, 1)	...
	2	(2, 0)	(1, 0)	(0, 2)	(0, 2)	(0, 2)	(0, 2)	...
	3	(3, 0)	(1, 1)	(1, 0)	(0, 3)	(0, 3)	(0, 3)	...
N	4	(4, 0)	(2, 0)	(1, 1)	(1, 0)	(0, 4)	(0, 4)	...
	5	(5, 0)	(2, 1)	(1, 2)	(1, 1)	(1, 0)	(0, 5)	...
	6	(6, 0)	(3, 0)	(2, 0)	(1, 2)	(1, 1)	(1, 0)	...
	⋮	⋮	⋮	⋮	⋮	⋮	⋮	

The student should compare this table with the one for exact division and then extend both up to and including $10 \div 10$. (See section 4.10, Exercise 7.)

4.9 PROPERTIES OF DIVISION

Consider the division of two powers having the same base,

$$a^m \div a^n,$$

for example, $3^5 \div 3^2$. Surely 3^5 is a multiple of 3, and hence we ask whether it is a multiple of 3^2. Now by the multiplication of powers with the same base, we have $3^5 = 3^3 \cdot 3^2$ and hence 3^5 is a multiple of 3^2, and we can write

$$3^5 \div 3^2 = 3^3 \Leftrightarrow 3^5 = 3^3 \cdot 3^2.$$

On the other hand, $3^2 \div 3^5$ has no solution because 3^2 is not a multiple of 3^5. Explain why. The greatest value the divisor can be in this case is 3^2 because $3^2 = 1 \cdot 3^2 = 3^0 \cdot 3^2$, and we have

$$3^2 \div 3^2 = 3^0 \Leftrightarrow 3^2 = 3^2 \cdot 1.$$

In general, if $m > n$, we can write m in the form

$$(m - n) + n.$$

[Let $d = m - n$; then $m = d + n = (m - n) + n$.]

Thus $a^m = a^{(m-n)+n}$, but by the multiplication law of powers with the same base this becomes

$$a^m = a^{m-n} \cdot a^n.$$

Thus a^m is a multiple of a^n. The multiple is a^{m-n}, which is the exact quotient of $a^m \div a^n$. Stated formally we have

If $m \geq n$, then $a^m \div a^n$ is an exact quotient expressed by the formula

$$a^m \div a^n = a^{m-n}.$$

Thus,

$4^8 \div 4^3 = 4^{5+3} \div 4^3 = 4^5 \cdot 4^3 \div 4^3$. Hence $4^8 \div 4^3 = 4^{8-3} = 4^5$.
$4^8 \div 4^0 = 4^{8+0} \div 4^0 = 4^8 \cdot 4^0 \div 4^0$. Hence $4^8 \div 4^0 = 4^{8-0} = 4^8$.

$4^3 \div 4^5$ is not possible because $3 < 5$, and hence 4^3 cannot be a multiple of 4^5.

Next we note that in exact division,

$$N \div d = q \Leftrightarrow N = q \cdot d.$$

Multiplying each side of the last sentence by a number $k \neq 0$ (section 3.8), we have

$$N \cdot k = q \cdot d \cdot k$$

or

$$(Nk) = q(dk). \qquad \text{(By the associative principle)}$$

But this latter sentence says

$$(N \cdot k) \div (d \cdot k) = q,$$

which is the same quotient as $N \div d$. We have established the property that

In an exact division, if the divisor and dividend are multiplied by the same number, not zero, the quotient is unchanged.

Also, consider $N \div d$ where

$$N = d \cdot q + r, \quad 0 < r < d.$$

Now multiplying each side of the sentence by k, we have

$$N \cdot k = (d \cdot q + r)k \quad \text{or} \quad Nk = d \cdot q \cdot k + rk.$$

The last sentence can be written in the form

$$N \cdot k = (d \cdot k)q + rk,$$

which implies that if $(N \cdot k)$ is divided by $(d \cdot k)$ the quotient is q and the remainder is rk. We have established another property that

In a division with a remainder, if the divisor and dividend are each multiplied by the same number $k \neq 0$, the quotient is unchanged, but the remainder is a multiple of k.

Thus, $24 \div 6 = 4$ and $(8 \cdot 24) \div (8 \cdot 6) = 4$; the quotient is unchanged. Also,

$$20 \div 7 \Rightarrow q = 2, \quad r = 6, \text{ and}$$

$$(20 \cdot 6) \div (7 \cdot 6) \Rightarrow q = 2, \quad r = 36.$$

From the table of division with a remainder, it is easy to discover the following properties:

As the dividend N increases and the divisor d remains the same, the quotient remains the same or increases. As the dividend N remains the same and the divisor increases, the quotient remains the same or decreases.

4.10 EXERCISES

1. Which of the following divisions have exact quotients?

   (a) $6 \div 2$ (b) $0 \div 4$ (c) $5 \div 3$ (d) $27 \div 27$ (e) $8 \div 6$
   (f) $2 \div 4$ (g) $36 \div 4$ (h) $36 \div 9$ (i) $9 \div 36$ (j) $0 \div 0$

2. State a division problem for which the exact quotient is:

   (a) 1 (b) 0 (c) 2 (d) nonexistent
   (e) 5 (f) 21

3. Compare subtraction with division in respect to

   (a) the equation used to define the operation.
   (b) 0 in subtraction and 1 in division.
   (c) the conditions for an exact answer.
   (d) two subtractions having the same difference and two divisions having the same quotient.
   (e) increasing the minuend with the subtrahend constant, and increasing the dividend with the divisor constant.
   (f) $2 - 3$ and $2 \div 3$ as (1) exact operations, (2) answer with a deficit or a remainder.

4. In an exact division $a \div b = q$. If a remains fixed, what is the largest number that can be added to b without changing the total quotient? Give a numerical example.

5. In an exact division $a \div b = q$. If b remains fixed, what is the largest number that can be added to a without changing the total quotient? Give a numerical example.

6. If $a \div d = q$ and $b \div d = q'$, show that $a + b$ is exactly divisible by d.

7. Make a table for total division with a remainder from $0 \div 1$ to $10 \div 10$.

   (a) In this table show how the extension can be made without carrying out the divisions.
   (b) For any given divisor (say 5) how do the remainders vary as the dividend increases? How does the quotient vary as the dividend increases?
   (c) Call the diagonal from $0 \div 1$ to $9 \div 10$ the *central diagonal*, and tell how the values in the cells in the parallel diagonals above this diagonal are related. How are the values in the diagonal cells below this diagonal related? Explain why the values are constructed in this manner.

8. $17 = 3 \cdot 0 + 17$
   $17 = 3 \cdot 1 + 14$
   $17 = 3 \cdot 2 + 11$
   $17 = 3 \cdot 3 + 8$
   $17 = 3 \cdot 4 + 5$
   $17 = 3 \cdot 5 + 2$

   All the statements shown at the left state a fact about 17 and multiples of 3. Which numbers are partial quotients? What are the respective remainders? State a theorem about the remainder for a partial quotient.

9. In Exercise 8, we could also write $17 = 3 \cdot 6 - 1$. Is 1 a remainder as defined in this textbook?

10. The example at the right shows a division problem from an elementary school textbook. Write the two partial quotients with their remainders. Explain how the final answer was obtained, namely $435 = 8 \cdot 54 + 3 \Rightarrow$ quotient 54, remainder 3.

$$\begin{array}{r} \left.\begin{array}{r} 4 \\ 50 \end{array}\right\} 54 \\ 8\overline{)435} \\ \underline{400} \\ 35 \\ \underline{32} \\ 3 \end{array}$$

Solve the following, where possible.

11. $2^5 \div 2^4$ 12. $8^3 \div 8^3$ 13. $5^{100} \div 5^{10}$ 14. $5^{15} \div 5^5$

15. $2^3 \div 2^5$ 16. $12^0 \div 12^0$ 17. $0^5 \div 0^0$ 18. $0^0 \div 0^5$

19. $28 \div 4$ (exactly) 20. $28 \div 4$ (total quotient and remainder)

21. $267 \div 43$ 22. $15^{15} \div (3 \cdot 5)^{14}$

23. Prove that exact division is not commutative and not associative, and that it has no identity element.

4.11 REFERENCE QUESTIONS

1. In this chapter, powers of whole numbers were defined. Is there any power of 6 whose decimal numeral does not end with "6"? For an answer to this and similar questions, see

   Smith, Shelby D. "A Discussion of Powers of Whole Numbers," *The Mathematics Teacher*, LV: 535–537; 1962.

2. How is the total quotient identified when a division algorithm such as that in problem 10 of the last problem set is used? For a fuller discussion of this "subtractive" approach to division, see

   Capps, Lelon R. "Making Division Meaningful and Logical," *The Arithmetic Teacher*, 9: 198–202; 1962.

   See also

   Hilaire, Paul A. "Let's Take a Look at Division," *The Arithmetic Teacher*, 8: 220–225; 1961.

3. As presented in this chapter, what is the distinction between a *statement* and an *open sentence?* For another discussion of this topic (with accompanying problems), see

   National Council of Teachers of Mathematics. *Topics in Mathematics for Elementary School Teachers* (29th yearbook). Washington, D.C.: NCTM, 1964. Pp. 335–344.

5 SYSTEMS OF NUMERATION AND COMPUTATION ALGORISMS

IN THE STUDY OF CARDINAL NUMBERS, *a new number name was invented for the successor of each given number. Thus the successor of four was named five, and its successor, in turn, named six, and so on. It is evident that if we were to continue this process, it would soon become an excessive burden on the memory to remember all these names.*

Yet we desire to be able to state the number of a set of objects, no matter how large, by using a number name. For this purpose, we need a system in which a few number names can be used efficiently to name the size of any collection of objects. Such systems are called systems of numeration, *and the symbolic representation of the names is called a* system of notation. *We shall use the two non-italicized phrases as equivalent in this book.*

5.1 DIGIT, NUMERAL, NUMBER

In ordinary writing it is necessary to use *words* to name the thing, action, or property in which we are interested. To create these words there is a fundamental set of symbols (called *letters*) which is an *alphabet*. The letters of the alphabet are arranged in certain ways to form *words* which name an *idea*. This is a part of a *language system*.

Similarly, in talking about arithmetic we must have a fundamental set of symbols which can be arranged in certain ways to form a name of a number. This part of arithmetic is called a *system of numeration*. Constructing such a system is analogous to the process of *counting* the elements of a set.

In any system of numeration the set of symbols is called the *fundamental set*. Any element of the fundamental set is called a *digit*. The systematic arrangement of the digits is called a *numeral*. The concept named by the numeral is called a *number*.

LANGUAGE		NUMERATION
Alphabet	$\leftrightarrow$	Fundamental Set
Letter	$\leftrightarrow$	Digit
Word	$\leftrightarrow$	Numeral
Idea	$\leftrightarrow$	Number

Different systems make use of different symbols and different procedures for arranging the symbols. Thus in the Roman system of numeration (or notation) XVI means "ten plus five plus one," and we refer to this as an *additive system*. The system also has a *subtractive* principle, for XIV means "ten plus five minus one." On the other hand, in the Hindu-Arabic system of numeration the numeral 324 means $3 \cdot 100 + 2 \cdot 10 + 4 \cdot 1$. This is a *multiplicative-additive-place system* because it involves the addition of products, in which the place of the digit in the numeral determines the multiplier. For example, 3 is multiplied by 100; 2 by 10, and 4 by 1. In this chapter we shall study the structure of multiplicative-additive-place systems.

To initiate such a system, we must select a set of ordered cardinal numbers, beginning with zero, each represented by a unique name or a unique symbol. This set of symbols is the fundamental set of digits for the system, and the number of elements in this set is called the *base* of the system. For example, in the decimal system, we have the fundamental set of digits

$$\{0, 1, 2, 3, 4, 5, 6, 7, 8, 9\},$$

and the base is called "ten." For the quinary system we have the fundamental set of digits

$$\{0, 1, 2, 3, 4\},$$

and the base is called "five." The binary system of numeration uses the smallest fundamental set of digits, which is

$$\{0, 1\},$$

and the base is called "two." If we use a duodecimal system, the fundamental set of digits is

$$\{0, 1, 2, 3, 4, 5, 6, 7, 8, 9, t, e\}$$

where t is the unique symbol or digit for the successor of 9, and e is the successor of t; the base is called "twelve." We could also use the ordinary names ten, and eleven, but we cannot use the decimal numerals for ten or eleven.

In summary, the base of a system of numeration is the number of the set of cardinal numbers less than the base. This set is the fundamental set. Each element of the set is a digit and is represented by a single symbol. Thus a digit is the name or symbol of a cardinal number less than the base of the system.

Our problem now becomes: Given a base and the set of digits, how can we express a number of any size in terms of the base, the digits, addition, and multiplication? We shall solve this problem first for the base ten, then generally for any base x, where $x \geq 2$.

The base of this system is ten, written "10," and the digits are the elements of the set

$$\{0, 1, 2, 3, 4, 5, 6, 7, 8, 9\}.$$

Now suppose that a collection of any size is given and we desire to give it a name. If the collection has a number less than the base, it can be named by one of the digits. If the collection has more than ten elements, we proceed as follows: Partition the collection into subsets, each of size 10, until the number of elements remaining is less than 10. This is equivalent to dividing the given number N by 10 to obtain a quotient q_1 and a remainder u_0, where u_0 is a digit. We write

$$N = q_1 \cdot 10 + u_0, \quad u_0 < 10, \tag{A}$$

where, of course, we do not as yet know the name (size) of N or of q_1. (We are trying to find a name for N, and q_1 is the unknown number of subsets, each of size ten.)

Now we attempt to count the number of subsets of size ten. If q_1 is less than ten, then it can be represented by a digit, say u_1, and

$$N = u_1 \cdot 10 + u_0$$

and our number is named. For example if $u_0 = 7$, $u_1 = 6$, our number is $6 \cdot 10 + 7$ or "six · ten plus seven" or simply "sixty-seven."

But suppose that q_1 is greater than 10. We then partition the collection of sets of size ten into new subsets of ten (that is, into subsets with number $10 \cdot 10$, or 10^2) until there are less than ten of the size ten sets remaining. This is equivalent to dividing q_1 by 10, obtaining a quotient q_2 and a remainder u_1 and we write

$$q_1 = q_2 \cdot 10 + u_1, \quad u_1 < 10. \tag{B}$$

For example, if $q_1 = 3 \cdot 10 + 6$, then substituting in formula (A) we have:

$$N = (3 \cdot 10 + 6) \cdot 10 + 7 \qquad \text{(using } u_0 = 7 \text{ from previous example)}$$

$$= 3 \cdot 10^2 + 6 \cdot 10 + 7, \quad \text{or three hundred sixty-seven}$$

If, however, q_2 is greater than 10, we apply the same process to q_2 as we did for q_1 and obtain

$$q_2 = q_3 \cdot 10 + u_2, \quad u_2 < 10. \tag{C}$$

We continue this partitioning, or the corresponding division, until sooner or later we obtain

$$q_{n-1} = q_n \cdot 10 + u_{n-1}, \quad u_{n-1} < 10. \tag{K}$$

But $q_n = 0 \cdot 10 + u_n$, that is,

$$q_n = u_n. \tag{L}$$

In this case q_n is a digit and the process terminates.

We summarize as follows:

1. Divide N by 10 to obtain $N = q_1 \cdot 10 + u_0, \quad u_0 < 10.$ (A)
2. Divide q_1 by 10 to obtain $q_1 = q_2 \cdot 10 + u_1, \quad u_1 < 10.$ (B)
3. Divide q_2 by 10 to obtain $q_2 = q_3 \cdot 10 + u_2, \quad u_2 < 10.$ (C)
4. Continue this way until for some quotient, q_{n-1}

$$q_{n-1} = q_n \cdot 10 + u_{n-1}, \quad u_{n-1} < 10, \tag{K}$$

but

$$q_n = u_n, \quad u_n < 10. \tag{L}$$

Now substitute (B) in (A) and obtain

$$N = (q_2 \cdot 10 + u_1)10 + u_0 = q_2 \cdot 10^2 + u_1 \cdot 10 + u_0. \tag{A$_1$}$$

Substitute (C) in (A_1) and obtain

$$\begin{aligned} N &= (q_3 \cdot 10 + u_2)10^2 + u_1 \cdot 10 + u_0 \\ &= q_3 \cdot 10^3 + u_2 \cdot 10^2 + u_1 \cdot 10 + u_0. \end{aligned} \tag{A$_2$}$$

Continuing this substitution until u_n is substituted for q_n, we obtain

$$N = u_n \cdot 10^n + u_{n-1} \cdot 10^{n-1} + \cdots + u_2 \cdot 10^2 + u_1 \cdot 10 + u_0$$

where all the $u_0, u_1, \ldots, u_n$ are digits. Since $10^1 = 10$ and $10^0 = 1$, we can also write this as

$$\begin{aligned} N = u_n \cdot 10^n &+ u_{n-1} \cdot 10^{n-1} \\ &+ \cdots + u_2 \cdot 10^2 + u_1 \cdot 10^1 + u_0 \cdot 10^0. \end{aligned} \tag{I}$$

We have thus succeeded in representing the number N in the decimal system of notation.

EXAMPLE 1. Let $u_0 = 3$, $u_1 = 0$, $u_2 = 8$, $u_3 = 7$, and $u_4, u_5, \ldots$ all zero. Then the numeral is

$$7 \cdot 10^3 + 8 \cdot 10^2 + 0 \cdot 10 + 3 \cdot 1,$$

or

$$7 \cdot 10^3 + 8 \cdot 10^2 + 0 \cdot 10^1 + 3 \cdot 10^0.$$

EXAMPLE 2. Suppose that:

$$\begin{aligned} N &= q_1 \cdot 10 + 6 \\ q_1 &= q_2 \cdot 10 + 7 \\ q_2 &= q_3 \cdot 10 + 8 \\ q_3 &= q_4 \cdot 10 + 0 \\ q_4 &= 5 \end{aligned}$$

Find the numeral for the number N.

Solution:

$$\begin{aligned} N &= q_1 \cdot 10 + 6 \\ &= (q_2 \cdot 10 + 7)10 + 6 = q_2 \cdot 10^2 + 7 \cdot 10^1 + 6 \cdot 10^0 \\ &= (q_3 \cdot 10 + 8)10^2 + 7 \cdot 10^1 + 6 \cdot 10^0 \\ &= q_3 \cdot 10^3 + 8 \cdot 10^2 + 7 + 10^1 + 6 \cdot 10^0 \\ &= (q_4 \cdot 10 + 0)10^3 + 8 \cdot 10^2 + 7 \cdot 10^1 + 6 \cdot 10^0 \\ &= q_4 \cdot 10^4 + 0 \cdot 10^3 + 8 \cdot 10^2 + 7 \cdot 10^1 + 6 \cdot 10^0 \\ &= 5 \cdot 10^4 + 0 \cdot 10^3 + 8 \cdot 10^2 + 7 \cdot 10^1 + 6 \cdot 10^0. \end{aligned}$$

It is evident from the way in which it was constructed that there is only one decimal form for the representation of a given number. For in each succeeding division by 10, there can be only one total quotient and a unique remainder. Hence the $u_0, u_1, u_2, \ldots, u_{n-1}, u_n$ are unique for any given number. However, the same number can be given a different representation by using a base other than ten, as we shall see in the next section.

Thus for each number we have a decimal numeral expressed as a sum of products of a digit multiplied by a power of the base 10.

$$\begin{aligned} N = u_n \cdot 10^n + u_{n-1} \cdot 10^{n-1} \\ + \cdots + u_2 \cdot 10^2 + u_1 \cdot 10^1 + u_0 \cdot 10^0 \end{aligned} \qquad \text{(I)}$$

where $u_0, u_1, \ldots$ are all digits. This expression for N is called a *numerical polynomial* of degree n to the base 10, and the *coefficient*, u_i,† of each *term* is less than 10. Of course some of the coefficients may be 0, but u_n is not zero if the number is represented by a polynomial of the nth degree.

Instead of writing all the powers of ten, and the addition signs, we can write the digits in the order they occur from left to right as

$$u_n, u_{n-1}, \ldots, u_2, u_1, u_0.$$

We can tell by the subscript, or by the place each digit occupies in the sequence, the power of ten by which it is multiplied. This enables us to write a very abbreviated form of the name of a number. We drop the commas, and merely write

$$N = \overline{u_n u_{n-1} \ldots u_2 u_1 u_0} \qquad \text{(I}_\text{a}\text{)}$$

where the bar (or vinculum) indicates that (1) each u_i is a digit to be multiplied by 10^i and (2) the resulting products are to be added (not multiplied). Thus the bar indicates that this expression does not represent a product, and the dots "..." merely indicate any missing places. If we use specific digits instead of the variables u_i, we drop the bar. Thus

$$N = 2604 = 2 \cdot 10^3 + 6 \cdot 10^2 + 0 \cdot 10^1 + 4 \cdot 10^0.$$

This abbreviated notation is called the *digital place notation* for a number, because the place of each digit is fixed, and hence its multiplying power of 10 is determined.

In reading a number, we use a language that does not always conform to the way the symbolic representation was developed. For example, after the base 10 is reached, the next number is one ten *and* one, or dropping the "and," one ten one, or abbreviating ten to ty (tee), we could say: "one-ty one," written $11 = 1 \cdot 10^1 + 1 \cdot 10^0$. However, we say "eleven" in ordinary language, and for 12 we say "twelve" instead of "one-ty two." Similarly, all teen numbers are spoken

† u_i is a way of referring to any one of the digits $u_0, u_1, \ldots u_n$; $0 \le i \le n$.

in reverse order. For example 16 is $1 \cdot 10^1 + 6 \cdot 10^0$ or one-ty six, but we say "six-teen" or really "6 and ten." These language conventions are not mathematically structured, but they are a part of our everyday communication language.

Instead of saying 10-squared for the third place from the right, we coin a new word and call it *hundred.* Similarly, for 10^3 we use the word *thousand.* The next place to the left is 10^4 which can be written $10^1 \cdot 10^3$ (tell why) and we read it *ten thousand.* Similarly 10^5 is read as $10^2 \cdot 10^3$ or *hundred thousand.* Finally 10^6 is given a new name, *million.* From here on the pattern is repeated.

$10^7 = 10^1 \cdot 10^6 =$ *ten million;* $\qquad 10^8 = 10^2 \cdot 10^6 =$ *hundred million;*

$10^9 =$ *billion;* $\qquad 10^{12} =$ *trillion;*

$10^{15} =$ *quadrillion;* $\qquad 10^{18} =$ *quintillion;* etc.

When numbers are expressed in digital place notation, they can be compared as to size, that is, ordered. Two cases arise, the one in which the numerals have the same number of places, and that in which the number of places is different.

(a) *If two numerals have a different number of places, the numeral with the greater number of places represents the greater number.*

Thus 684 > 73; 24657 > 9999; and so on. The proof of this is left as an exercise.

(b) *If two numerals have the same number of places, the numeral in which the first digit going from left to right exceeds the corresponding digit of the other numeral represents the greater number.*

Thus 684 > 468 because 6 > 4; 68321 > 68213 because, while the first two numerals left to right agree, the first digits to disagree are in the hundredth place and 3 > 2. The proof is left as an exercise.

5.4 EXERCISES

1. Give a definition of (a) cardinal number, (b) digit, (c) numeral.
2. Distinguish a number system from a system of numeration.
3. Show how counting and a system of numeration are related.
4. What is the fundamental set of cardinals for the base seven? The base 3? the base 20?
5. How many elements are in the fundamental set of a given base n?
6. What is the greatest cardinal number of the fundamental set for the base ten? the base five?

7. Write the following numerals in digital place notation:

   (a) $3 \cdot 10^4 + 8 \cdot 10^3 + 0 \cdot 10^2 + 0 \cdot 10^1 + 2 \cdot 10^0$

   (b) $4 \cdot 10^5 + 5 \cdot 10^4 + 2 \cdot 10^3 + 3 \cdot 10^2 + 0 \cdot 10^1 + 1 \cdot 10^0$

   (c) $u_4 \cdot 10^4 + u_3 \cdot 10^3 + u_2 \cdot 10^2 + u_1 \cdot 10^1 + u_0 \cdot 10^0, \ u_i < 10$

8. Write the following numerals in polynomial form:

   (a) 3685 (b) 20004 (c) 684,127

   (d) $100 \cdot 271 + 28$ (e) $1000 \cdot 486 + 22$

9. There are four trays. The first consists of 10 small pockets, each capable of holding only one ball. The second tray consists of ten cells, each capable of holding the full contents of tray one. The third tray consists of ten sections, each capable of holding the full contents of tray two, and the fourth tray holds ten deep boxes, each capable of holding the full contents of tray three. Tell how to use these trays to develop a place-multiplicative-additive system of notation, indicating in algebraic and numerical symbolism the result of each step in the development.

10. Prove: If two numerals have an unequal number of places, the numeral with the greater number of places represents the greater cardinal number.

11. Show that if all the coefficients of a numerical polynomial to base 10 are 9, and the polynomial is of degree n, the number represented is smaller than that given by $1 \cdot 10^{n+1}$.

12. What are the coefficients of the terms of the polynomial which represents each of the following:

   (a) one thousand (b) one million (c) one hundred million

13. Prove: If two numerals have the same number of places, the numeral in which the first digit going from left to right exceeds the corresponding digit of the other numeral represents the greater number

14. When do two numerals represent the same number? Prove your answer.

15. How many cardinal numbers are represented by numerals having (a) one digit, (b) two digits, (c) three digits. Generalize the results of (a), (b), and (c) for n digits.

16. In writing the numerals 0 to 100, how many times do you write "9"?

17. In numbering the pages in a book having 300 pages, how many times is the symbol "0" used? Paging begins with 1.

18. In a book of 200 pages, how many different digits are used to number all the pages?

19. If children are asked to write the numerals, beginning with 0 and ending with 100, how many digits must they write?

Sometimes bases other than 10 are used. Some electronic computers use base 2, some a combination of the bases two and ten. A society of many years' standing, called the Duodecimal Society, is advocating the use of base twelve. We shall now develop a system to any base, which we shall call x. By substituting for x any cardinal number, and having unique symbols, or digits, for each number less than x, we then have a special system of numeration. As you study the following development, from time to time replace x with a special base, for example seven, or five, or eight.

Let x be the base of a system of numeration. Then the fundamental set of digits is $\{0, 1, 2, 3, \ldots, d\}$, where $d + 1 = x$. Now let the number of a given set be N. We partition the set into subsets of size x.

(1) If the set with number N is less than the set of digits, the number is represented by the last digit used in counting, say u_0.

(2) If the set being counted is equivalent to the set of fundamental digits, the number is x and is represented by 10, that is, the base. (Think of the symbol "10" not as "ten," but as "one base.")

(3) If the set is greater than x, then by continued partition we find some *total* quotient q_1 of the number of sets of size x, and a remainder u_0, which is the number of elements in the remainder set. The symbol u_0 is one of the digits; q_1 is unknown. Briefly

$$N = q_1 \cdot x + u_0, \quad u_0 < x. \tag{A}$$

Now consider q_1, the number of sets of size x (the base). We repeat steps (1), (2), and (3) with these sets of size x as new elements. Then if $q_1 > x$ we have

$$q_1 = q_2 \cdot x + u_1, \quad u_1 < x, \tag{B}$$

where q_2 is unknown. The size of the sets, the number of which is q_2, is $x \cdot x$, or x^2.

We continue with the q_2 sets by repeating steps (1), (2), and (3), and find

$$q_2 = q_3 \cdot x + u_2, \quad u_2 < x. \tag{C}$$

Continuing this way until the last partitioning gives us a set whose elements number less than x, we obtain

$$q_{n-1} = q_n \cdot x + u_{n-1}, \quad u_{n-1} < x, \tag{K}$$

but

$$q_n = 0 \cdot x + u_n, \quad \text{or} \quad q_n = u_n, \quad u_n < x. \tag{L}$$

In this way we obtain a series of numbers

$$N, q_1, q_2, \ldots, q_{n-1}, q_n$$

all of which are decreasing in value until q_n is less than x.

We also get an ordered set of remainders

$$u_0, u_1, u_2, \ldots, u_{n-1}, u_n$$

all of which are digits in the base x. Our problem is to represent N in terms of the remainders u_i, the base x, and use only multiplication and addition.

Notice that the preceding development parallels that for the base ten in section 5.2. We now substitute (B) for q_1 in (A), then substitute (C) for q_2 in the result, and so on, until we substitute u_n for q_n. We can also proceed as follows: Write down the equations (A), (B), (C), ..., (K), (L) and multiply each side of them, respectively, by $x^0 = 1, x^1, x^2, x^3, \ldots, x^{n-1}, x^n$.

$$\left.\begin{aligned} N &= q_1 \cdot x + u_0 \\ q_1 &= q_2 \cdot x + u_1 \\ q_2 &= q_3 \cdot x + u_2 \\ &\cdots\cdots\cdots \\ q_{n-1} &= q_n \cdot x + u_{n-1} \\ q_n &= u_n \end{aligned}\right\} \Longrightarrow \left\{\begin{aligned} N &= q_1 \cdot x^1 + u_0 \\ q_1 \cdot x^1 &= q_2 \cdot x^2 + u_1 \cdot x^1 \\ q_2 \cdot x^2 &= q_3 \cdot x^3 + u_2 \cdot x^2 \\ &\cdots\cdots\cdots \\ q_{n-1} \cdot x^{n-1} &= q_n \cdot x^n + u_{n-1} \cdot x^{n-1} \\ q_n \cdot x^n &= u_n \cdot x^n \end{aligned}\right.$$

Adding each side of the equalities in the right-hand column, we obtain

$$\begin{aligned} N + (q_1 \cdot x^1 + q_2 \cdot x^2 + \cdots + q_{n-1} \cdot x^{n-1} + q_n \cdot x^n) \\ = (q_1 \cdot x^1 + q_2 \cdot x^2 + \cdots + q_{n-1} \cdot x^{n-1} + q_n \cdot x^n) \\ + u_0 + u_1 \cdot x^1 + \cdots + u_{n-1} \cdot x^{n-1} + u_n \cdot x^n. \end{aligned}$$

By the cancellation law, each of the expressions in parentheses can be dropped and

$$N = u_n \cdot x^n + u_{n-1} \cdot x^{n-1} + \cdots + u_2 \cdot x^2 + u_1 \cdot x^1 + u_0 \cdot x^0, \qquad \text{(II)}$$

where the order of the terms in u_i has been reversed by the Generalized Associative Principle of addition.

The expression (II) is called a *numerical polynomial* of degree n in the base x. The u_i are called *coefficients*, and each of these is a digit in the base x, and hence for every u_i, $u_i < x$. The expression for N is a numeral and represents the number.

The place values, from *right to left* are

$$x^0, x^1, x^2, x^3, \ldots, x^{n-1}, x^n.$$

If we agree that the place which a coefficient holds determines the place value which is the multiplier of the coefficient, we can write the numeral in digital place notation as

$$\overline{u_n u_{n-1} \ldots u_2 u_1 u_0}_{(\text{base } x)}, \qquad (\text{II}_\text{a})$$

where the bar indicates that the expression below it is *not a product* but an abbreviated way of writing the right member of (II).

Notice that (II_a) above and (I_a) of section 5.3, have exactly the same form. The expression (I_a), however, was limited to the decimal base; that is, the u_i can be replaced by any of the digits 0 to, and including, 9. In the expression (II_a) we cannot tell what values the u_i can take until we are told the exact value of the base x. If x is seven, then the u_i can take any of the values $\{0, 1, 2, 3, 4, 5, 6\}$. If the base x is fourteen, we use the set $\{0, 1, 2, 3, 4, 5, 6, 7, 8, 9, t, e, d, b\}$ where t, e, d, and b are unique symbols for ten, eleven, twelve, and thirteen.

The base of any system is always written 10; that is, $u_1 = 1$, $u_0 = 0$ or $\overline{u_1u_0} = 10$. This is because the multiplier of the second place from the right is the base of the system. Then the other powers of the base, or multipliers of the 3rd, 4th, 5th, ... places from the right, are

$$x \cdot x = 10 \cdot 10 = 100; \qquad x \cdot x \cdot x = 10^3 = 1000; \qquad \ldots;$$
$$x^n = 10^n = \underbrace{100\ldots0}_{n \text{ zeros}}.$$

These numerals do not represent powers of *ten* but powers of the *base*. Only in the decimal system do they represent powers of ten. In the base seven, 10^2 = seven squared, 10^3 = seven cubed, etc.

As a specific example, let us examine the case when x is six. We shall assume the decimal system of naming numbers is known. Here the fundamental set of digits is

$$\{0, 1, 2, 3, 4, 5\}.$$

The base is six, written $10_{(\text{six})}$. (Only for the base ten do we omit the subscript name signifying the base.) The numerical polynomial is of the form

$$u_n \cdot 10^n + u_{n-1} \cdot 10^{n-1} + \cdots + u_2 \cdot 10^2 + u_1 \cdot 10^1 + u_0 \cdot 10^0{}_{(\text{six})}, \qquad u_i < 10_{(\text{six})}.$$

The digital place representation is

$$\overline{u_nu_{n-1}\ldots u_2u_1u_0}_{(\text{six})}, \quad u_i < 10_{(\text{six})}.$$

The names of the places must be decided upon. We call u_0 the units digit. It is multiplied by $10^0{}_{(\text{six})}$ or one. The sixes digit is u_1. It is multiplied by $10^1{}_{(\text{six})}$ and we say "u_1 six." The u_2 is the six-squared digit. It is multiplied by $10^2{}_{(\text{six})}$ and we say "u_2 six-squared."† Similarly, we can call u_3 the "six-cubed" digit, etc. Thus we would read $4523_{(\text{six})}$ as 4 six-cubed 5 six-squared 2 six 3. Writing the numerals of cardinal numbers in the base six system would proceed as follows:

0	10	20	...	50	100	110	...	550	1000
1	11	21	...	51	101	111	...	551	1001
2	12	22	...	52	102	112	...	552	.
3	13	23	...	53	103	113	...	553	.
4	14	24	...	54	104	114	...	554	.
5	15	25	...	55	105	115	...	555	.

EXAMPLE 3. Construct, and illustrate the use of, a binary place system.

Solution: The fundamental set of digits is $\{0, 1\}$; the base is $10_{(\text{two})}$, or two. The place values, from right to left, are $10^0{}_{(\text{two})}$ or

† Similarly, in the base ten we could have said "ten-squared" instead of coining a new word "hundred."

units; $10^1{}_{(\text{two})}$ or two; $10^2{}_{(\text{two})}$ which we call "four"; $10^3{}_{(\text{two})}$ which we call "eight"; etc. Thus we use the decimal names to name the place values, as well as to indicate the power of each place. The numerical polynomial is

$$u_n \cdot 10^n + u_{n-1} \cdot 10^{n-1} + \cdots + u_2 \cdot 10^2 + u_1 \cdot 10^1 + u_0 \cdot 10^0{}_{(\text{two})}$$

where the u_i are either 0 or 1. As an illustration

$$1 \cdot 10^5 + 0 \cdot 10^4 + 0 \cdot 10^3 + 1 \cdot 10^2 + 1 \cdot 10^1 + 1 \cdot 10^0{}_{(\text{two})}$$

is in digital place notation

100111

and is read thirty-two four two one. In decimal notation the number is 39.

5.6 CHANGE OF BASE

At times it is desirable to transform a numeral from one base to another base. It is also desirable to operate on numerals in a given base. Since we have already learned, in the elementary school, all the fundamental addition and multiplication facts, as well as the computational processes for the four fundamental operations *in the decimal system of numeration*, it will not be necessary to learn new tables for the new bases. It will be sufficient to be able to transform a numeral in base ten to one representing the same number in any other base and vice versa.

By substituting the given base in expression (II) in section 5.5, we can transform a numeral given in that base to the corresponding numeral in base ten. Let us be given a numeral

$$\overline{u_n u_{n-1} \ldots u_2 u_1 u_0}_{(\text{base } x)}.$$

Each digit can be written in the decimal notation. If $u_i <$ ten, it is already in decimal notation, and if $u_i \geq$ ten, the base is greater than ten, and the symbol for u_i can be changed to the decimal numeral. The base x can be written in decimal notation, e.g., $10_{(\text{eleven})}$ would be written 11. Then carrying out the implied operations, namely

$$u_n \cdot 10^n{}_{(\text{base } x)} + u_{n-1} \cdot 10^{n-1}{}_{(\text{base } x)} + \cdots + u_1 \cdot 10^1{}_{(\text{base } x)} + u_0 \cdot 10^0{}_{(\text{base } x)},$$

we obtain the decimal numeral.

EXAMPLE 4. Change $24165_{(\text{seven})}$ to a decimal numeral.

Solution: Write $10^1{}_{(\text{seven})}$ as 7, and generally $10^n{}_{(\text{seven})}$ as 7^n. Then $24165_{(\text{seven})} = 2 \cdot 7^4 + 4 \cdot 7^3 + 1 \cdot 7^2 + 6 \cdot 7 + 5$ or 6270.

EXAMPLE 5. Change $2te05_{(\text{twelve})}$ to a decimal numeral.

Solution: For $10^n{}_{(\text{twelve})}$ write 12^n; for t write 10; for e write 11, and we have

$$2te05_{(\text{twelve})} = 2 \cdot 12^4 + 10 \cdot 12^3 + 11 \cdot 12^2 + 0 \cdot 12^1 + 5 \cdot 12^0 \quad \text{or} \quad 60{,}341.$$

The steps used to arrive at expression (II) in section 5.5 can be developed in any base. Thus this systematic procedure, or general *algorism*, can be used to change a numeral in base ten to any other base. We merely divide the decimal number by the desired base and note the remainder. This is the units digit. We then divide the quotient by the desired base and note the remainder. This is the first-power digit. We continue this until the final quotient obtained is less than the base. This is the u_n digit.

EXAMPLE 6. Change 41,835 to a numeral in base eight.

Solution: The algorism illustrated below indicates that we divide successively by eight and the remainders are respectively 3, 5, 5, 1, 2, 1:

Quotients	Remainders
41835	
5229	(3)
653	(5)
81	(5)
10	(1)
1	(2)
0	(1)

Hence the numeral in base eight is $121553_{(\text{eight})}$. The reader should further justify this by writing

$$41835 = 5229 \cdot 8 + 3$$
$$5229 = 653 \cdot 8 + 5; \quad \text{etc., to } 1 = 0 \cdot 8 + 1$$

and using successive substitutions to arrive at $121553_{(\text{eight})}$.

To change a numeral from one base to another base, neither of these the base ten, it is only necessary to convert the first base to the decimal system and then convert the result to the second base.

EXAMPLE 7. Change $26543_{(\text{seven})}$ to base twelve.

Solution: $26543_{(\text{seven})} = 2 \cdot 7^4 + 6 \cdot 7^3 + 5 \cdot 7^2 + 4 \cdot 7^1 + 3 \cdot 7^0 = 7136$

$7136 = 594 \cdot 12 + (8)$; $594 = 49 \cdot 12 + (6)$;
$49 = 4 \cdot 12 + (1)$; $4 = 0 \cdot 12 + (4)$

Then $7136 = 4168_{(\text{twelve})}$.

So, $26543_{(\text{seven})} = 4168_{(\text{twelve})}$.

5.7 EXERCISES

1. (a) When does "10" mean "ten"?
   (b) When does "10" represent a cardinal other than ten?
2. Distinguish $234_{(\text{seven})}$ from 234. Is $234_{(\text{seven})}$ an odd number or an even number?
3. Write a numerical polynomial in one variable x, of degree five, having digital coefficients.
   (a) Which coefficient is not zero?
   (b) If x is six what is the fundamental set of digits?
   (c) Represent $241503_{(\text{six})}$ in polynomial form with base six and with base ten.
4. (a) What is $10^4{}_{(\text{seven})}$ in decimal notation?
   (b) What is 10^4 in base seven representation?
5. Write the entire set of ordered numerals, from one digit to 4 digits for the base 3. Create a system for reading the numerals in base 3.
6. (a) If starting with a *gill*, two gills equal one *cup*, two cups equal one *pint*, two pints equal one *quart*, two quarts equal a *can*, and two cans equal a *gallon*, show how these italicized words can be used to name place values in a binary system.
   (b) With the given words what is the largest possible number that can be represented?
   (c) What is the decimal equivalent of this numeral?
7. Change 24687 to
   (a) base five. (b) base twelve. (c) base eight.
8. Change $6432_{(\text{twelve})}$ to
   (a) base ten. (b) base eight. (c) base six.
9. (a) Using t for ten, $\bar{9}$ for 11, $\bar{8}$ for 12, $\bar{7}$ for 13, etc. to $\bar{1}$ for 19, tell how to construct a place system of numeration to the base twenty.
   (b) Change $29t_{(\text{twenty})}$ to the base ten.
   (c) Change 28467 to the base twenty.
10. In algebra we learn that

$$x^4 + x^2 + 1 = (x^2 + x + 1)(x^2 - x + 1).$$

    Using this result, prove that in any base, the number 10101 is divisible by 111. Verify your result for the bases two, five, eight, ten, and twelve.
11. If weights of $2^0, 2^1, 2^2, 2^3, 2^4, \ldots, 2^n$ ounces, one of each type, are available, show that any number of ounces can be formed up to and including $(2^{n+1} - 1)$ ounces.
12. If weights of $3^0, 3^1, 3^2, 3^3, 3^4, \ldots, 3^n$ ounces, two of each type, are available, show that any number of ounces can be found up to $(3^{n+1} - 1)$ ounces.
13. Frame a problem similar to Exercises 11 and 12 for weights $5^0, 5^1, 5^2, \ldots, 5^n$ and prove it.

In the study of the fundamental binary operations on cardinal numbers we constructed tables showing the results in the decimal system of numeration for the numbers 0 to 10. These tables are frequently referred to as the fundamental facts for the operation. The use of (a) these facts, along with (b) the properties of a decimal system of numeration and the use of (c) the commutative, associative, and distributive principles of addition and multiplication enable us to perform the binary operation on numbers of any size. The generalization of the processes will enable us to carry out the algorisms in a system of numeration of any base.

In the following discussion, the development of the algorisms may be justified by the five principles of number, even though we may not always write out each step of the development or its justification. Thus if we have

$$(8 \cdot 10^3 + \cdots) + (4 \cdot 10^3 + \cdots),$$

by the general associative law we can rearrange these terms to obtain

$$(8 \cdot 10^3 + 4 \cdot 10^3) + (\cdots),$$

and by the distributive law the first expression becomes $(8 + 4) \cdot 10^3$, which is $(10 + 2) \cdot 10^3$, which again is $10 \cdot 10^3 + 2 \cdot 10^3$ or $1 \cdot 10^4 + 2 \cdot 10^3$. (Give the reasons for the last three transformations.) As the reader studies the algorisms, he should make himself aware of the use of these laws, the use of the properties of numeration, and the fundamental facts.

Addition:

The following examples illustrate the addition algorism:

EXAMPLE 8. Illustrate the step by step procedure in the algorism for $56 + 79$.

Solution: $56 + 79 = (5 \cdot 10 + 6) + (7 \cdot 10 + 9)$
Principle of Numeration

$= (5 \cdot 10 + 7 \cdot 10) + (6 + 9)$
Commutative and Associative Laws

$= (5 + 7) \cdot 10 + 15$
Distributive Law

$= 12 \cdot 10 + 15$
Basic Facts

$= (10 + 2) \cdot 10 + 1 \cdot 10 + 5$
Principle of Numeration

$= (10 \cdot 10 + 2 \cdot 10) + (1 \cdot 10 + 5)$
Distributive Law

$= 1 \cdot 10^2 + (2 + 1) \cdot 10 + 5$
Associative Law; Distributive Law

$= 1 \cdot 10^2 + 3 \cdot 10 + 5$ Basic Facts

$= 135$ Principle of Numeration

EXAMPLE 9. Find the sum of 268 and 3574.

Solution:

$$268 = 2 \cdot 10^2 + 6 \cdot 10^1 + 8 \cdot 10^0$$
$$3574 = 3 \cdot 10^3 + 5 \cdot 10^2 + 7 \cdot 10^1 + 4 \cdot 10^0$$

Adding like powers, we have

$$268 + 3574 = 3 \cdot 10^3 + (2 + 5) \cdot 10^2 + (6 + 7) \cdot 10^1 + (8 + 4) \cdot 10^0.$$

Now $6 + 7 = 10 + 3$. Then

$$(6 + 7) \cdot 10^1 = (10 + 3) \cdot 10^1 = 10^2 + 3 \cdot 10^1.$$

Also $8 + 4 = 10 + 2$; thus

$$(8 + 4) \cdot 10^0 = (10 + 2) \cdot 10^0 = 10^1 + 2 \cdot 10^0.$$

Substituting these values and combining the coefficients of like powers of the base we have

$$268 + 3574 = 3 \cdot 10^3 + (2 + 5 + 1) \cdot 10^2 + (3 + 1) \cdot 10^1 + 2 \cdot 10^0 = 3842.$$

In practice we proceed mentally as follows:

$8 + 4 = 1 \cdot 10 + 2$.

This is 2 units and another 10. Then,

$6 + 7 + ① = 10 + 4$.

This is 4 tens and another 10^2.

$2 + 5 + ① = 8$. This is 8 hundreds. The sum is 3 thousand, 8 hundred, forty, two.

```
  ① ①
3 5 7 4
  2 6 8
-------
3 8 4 2
```

If another base than ten is used, we calculate the same way, doing the fundamental additions in the decimal system and then converting to the given base.

EXAMPLE 10. Add $3625_{(\text{seven})}$, $5634_{(\text{seven})}$, $2443_{(\text{seven})}$.

Solution: $3 + 4 + 5 = 12$ or 1 seven and 5. We combine (carry) the seven to the sevens column. $4 + 3 + 2 + ① = 10$ or 1 seven and 3. We have 3 sevens and 1 seven-squared to be combined with the column next to the left. $4 + 6 + 6 + ① = 17$ or 2 sevens and 3. We have 3 seven-squared, and 2 seven-cubed to be combined with the next column to the left. $2 + 5 + 3 + ② = 12$ or 1 seven and 5. We have 5 seven-cubed and 1 seven-fourthed.

```
    ② ① ①
  3 6 2 5
  5 6 3 4
  2 4 4 3
---------
1 5 3 3 5
```

Subtraction:

In one algorism for subtraction it is necessary to have each digit in the minuend equal to or greater than the corresponding place digit in the subtrahend. To do this, it is frequently necessary to reverse the exchange procedure of addition and exchange one of a given power of the base for 10 of the next lower power: That is, we use $10^3 = 10 \cdot 10^2$, or $10^5 = 10 \cdot 10^4$, and so on. The following example illustrates this procedure.

EXAMPLE 11. Find $3804 - 675$.

Solution: Since $4 < 5$ in the units place, it is necessary to increase the 4 by transforming one higher power to 10 of the next lower power.

Since there are no powers of ten in the given minuend, we proceed to the 10^2 column, where the digit is 8. We write $8 \cdot 10^2$ as $7 \cdot 10^2 + 1 \cdot 10^2$ and then write $1 \cdot 10^2$ as $10 \cdot 10$, which in turn is changed to $9 \cdot 10^1 + 1 \cdot 10^1$ or $9 \cdot 10^1 + 10 \cdot 10^0$.

Hence $8 \cdot 10^2$ becomes $7 \cdot 10^2 + 9 \cdot 10^1 + 10 \cdot 10^0$.

The minuend is now

$$3 \cdot 10^3 + 7 \cdot 10^2 + 9 \cdot 10^1 + 14 \cdot 10^0.$$

The subtrahend is

$$6 \cdot 10^2 + 7 \cdot 10^1 + 5 \cdot 10^0.$$

Since each coefficient in the minuend is greater than the corresponding coefficient in the subtrahend we can subtract. The difference is

$$3 \cdot 10^3 + 1 \cdot 10^2 + 2 \cdot 10^1 + 9 \cdot 10^0$$

or 3129.

We can use this same process for any base.

EXAMPLE 12. Find $2645_{(\text{seven})} - 1566_{(\text{seven})}$.

Solution: All in base seven where "10" denotes seven, the work is done as follows:

	10^3	10^2	10^1	10^0
$2645_{(\text{seven})}$	2	5	13	$15_{(\text{seven})}$
$1566_{(\text{seven})}$	1	5	6	$6_{(\text{seven})}$
	1	0	4	$6_{(\text{seven})}$

Exchange a seven for seven units and add to the 5 units to give a seven plus 5 units, written 15. Exchange a seven-squared for 7 sevens, to add to the 3 sevens, to give seven + 3 sevens, written 13. Now every coefficient in the minuend is equal to or greater than the corresponding coefficient in the subtrahend and the algorism is accomplished so that we can subtract. The difference is $1046_{(\text{seven})}$.

Another commonly used algorism for subtraction (the so-called Austrian method of subtracting numbers) is one that makes use of the following theorem:

THEOREM: *If the minuend and subtrahend are each increased by the same number, the difference is unchanged. In symbols,*

$$(a + n) - (b + n) = a - b.$$

Proof: By the definition of subtraction

$$(a + n) - (b + n) = x \Rightarrow a + n = x + (b + n). \quad (1)$$

By the associative law, applied to the right-hand member we have

$$a + n = (x + b) + n. \quad (2)$$

Then by the cancellation law (n from each side)

$$a = x + b. \quad (3)$$

By the definition of subtraction

$$a = x + b \Rightarrow a - b = x. \quad (4)$$

From (1) and (4) by substitution for x we have

$$(a + n) - (b + n) = a - b.$$

Thus, if a power of the base, for example 10^1, is added to the subtrahend, the equal value $10 \cdot 10^0$ is added to the minuend. For example, $85 - 59$ becomes $(85 + 10) - (59 + 10)$ or $(80 + 15) - (60 + 9)$ which is $(20 + 6)$, that is:

$$\begin{array}{r} 85 \\ -59 \\ \hline \end{array} \Rightarrow \begin{array}{r} (80 + 15) \\ -(60 + \ 9) \\ \hline (20 + \ 6) \end{array}$$

Similarly:

$$\begin{array}{r} 2645_{(\text{seven})} \\ -1566_{(\text{seven})} \\ \hline \end{array} \quad \text{becomes} \quad \begin{array}{r|r|r|r} 2 & 6 & 4 & 15_{(\text{seven})} \\ -1 & 5 & 10 & 6_{(\text{seven})} \\ \hline \end{array}$$

Then we add 10^2 to the subtrahend and the equal value $10 \cdot 10^1$ to the minuend and the problem becomes

$$\begin{array}{r|r|r|r} 2 & 6 & 14 & 15_{(\text{seven})} \\ -1 & 6 & 10 & 6_{(\text{seven})} \\ \hline 1 & 0 & 4 & 6_{(\text{seven})} \end{array}$$

and now each coefficient of the minuend is equal to or greater than the corresponding coefficient of the subtrahend and we can subtract, power by power.

Multiplication:

In multiplying a base by a base, we have $10 \cdot 10 = 10^2$ or 100. Similarly, $10^2 \cdot 10 = 10^3 = 1000$; $10^2 \cdot 10^2 = 10000$, etc. Thus we note:

> *If two powers of the base are multiplied, the resulting power can be expressed by a numeral consisting of the digit 1, followed by as many zeros as the sum of the exponents of the powers.*

Now consider the product $426 \cdot 3$. We write

$$(4 \cdot 10^2 + 2 \cdot 10^1 + 6 \cdot 10^0) \cdot 3 = (10 + 2) \cdot 10^2 + 6 \cdot 10^1 + (10 + 8) \cdot 10^0$$

or simplifying, $1 \cdot 10^3 + 2 \cdot 10^2 + 7 \cdot 10^1 + 8 \cdot 10^0$, that is 1278. If we change the problem to $426_{(\text{seven})} \cdot 3_{(\text{seven})}$ the same procedure is followed. The work is done mentally as follows:

$$\begin{array}{r} 4\,2\,6_{(\text{seven})} \\ 3_{(\text{seven})} \\ \hline 1\,6\,1\,4_{(\text{seven})} \end{array}$$

$3 \cdot 6$ is 2 sevens and 4; write 4 in the units column and mentally retain the 2 sevens.
$3 \cdot 2$ is 6 sevens plus the 2 (from the first product) is 1 seven-squared and 1 seven. Write 1 in the sevens column and carry 1 seven-squared mentally.
$3 \cdot 4 = 1$ seven-cubed and 5 seven-squared. Add the one carried (mentally) to give 6 seven-squared. The result is

$$1 \cdot 10^3 + 6 \cdot 10^2 + 1 \cdot 10^1 + 4 \cdot 10^0{}_{(\text{seven})}.$$

To multiply $426_{(\text{seven})}$ by $30_{(\text{seven})}$ is the same as to multiply

$$[426 \cdot 3] \cdot 10_{(\text{seven})}, \quad \text{since } 30 = 3 \cdot 10.$$

The multiplication in brackets has already been performed and to multiply this by 10 is to change the place value of each digit to the next higher power, that is to move each digit of the bracket product one place to the left, and insert a zero in the now empty units place. Since, in base seven

$$426 \cdot 3 = 1614, \text{ in the same base } 426 \cdot 30 = 16140.$$

Similarly, multiplying by 10^2, or 100, transfers each digit two places to the left; by 1000, or 10^3, three places to the left, and so on.

Thus, if we have a problem $426 \cdot 345$, we partition the problem into three partial products and add these products to get the total product. This is illustrated in the following work for base seven.

$$
\begin{array}{r}
4\,2\,6 \\
5 \\
\hline
3\,1\,0\,2 \\
10^0 \\
\hline
3\,1\,0\,2
\end{array}
\qquad
\begin{array}{r}
4\,2\,6 \\
4 \\
\hline
2\,3\,4\,3 \\
10 \\
\hline
2\,3\,4\,3\,0
\end{array}
\qquad
\begin{array}{r}
4\,2\,6 \\
3 \\
\hline
1\,6\,1\,4 \\
10^2 \\
\hline
1\,6\,1\,4\,0\,0
\end{array}
\qquad
\begin{array}{r}
4\,2\,6 \\
3\,4\,5 \\
\hline
3\,1\,0\,2 \\
2\,3\,4\,3\,\underline{0} \\
1\,6\,1\,4\,\underline{0}\,\underline{0} \\
\hline
2\,2\,1\,2\,3\,2_{\text{(seven)}}
\end{array}
$$

The underlined zeros may be omitted.

Division:

Division can be achieved by the reverse of the multiplication algorism. Consider the decimal example $64158 \div 26$. We notice that $26 \cdot 10$, $26 \cdot 100$, and $26 \cdot 1000$ are all less than the dividend, but $26 \cdot 10^4$ is greater than 64,158. Hence the highest power of the base in the quotient is 10^3.

64,158	
52,000	$2 \cdot 10^3 \cdot 26$
12,158	
10,400	$4 \cdot 10^2 \cdot 26$
1,758	
1,560	$6 \cdot 10^1 \cdot 26$
198	
182	$7 \cdot 10^0 \cdot 26$
16	

Next we note that

$$
\begin{aligned}
26 \cdot 1(10^3) &= 26{,}000; \\
26 \cdot 2(10^3) &= 52{,}000; \\
\text{and}\quad 26 \cdot 3(10^3) &= 78{,}000,
\end{aligned}
$$

which is greater than the dividend. Hence the coefficient of the highest power is 2. We subtract 52,000 from 64,158 and consider the remainder 12,158.

To determine the coefficient of 10^2 in the quotient we note that

$$26 \cdot 4(10^2) < 12{,}158 < 26 \cdot 5(10^2)$$

and hence the coefficient of 10^2 is 4. We subtract 10,400 from 12,158, and consider the remainder 1758. For the coefficient of 10^1, in the quotient, we note that $26 \cdot 6(10^1) < 1758 < 26 \cdot 7(10^1)$ and hence the coefficient is 6. Finally, the coefficient of 10^0 is 7 since $7 \cdot 26 < 198 < 8 \cdot 26$. Hence

$$64{,}158 = (2 \cdot 10^3 + 4 \cdot 10^2 + 6 \cdot 10^1 + 7 \cdot 10^0)26 + 16.$$

The total quotient is 2467 with a remainder of 16.

It is customary to arrange this computation in some such way as this:

$$
\begin{array}{r@{\,}r}
 & 2467 \\
\cline{2-2}
26 \big) & 64158 \\
 & 52\underline{000} \\
\cline{2-2}
 & 121\underline{58} \\
 & 104\underline{00} \\
\cline{2-2}
 & 175\underline{8} \\
 & 156\underline{0} \\
\cline{2-2}
 & 198 \\
 & 182 \\
\cline{2-2}
 & 16
\end{array}
$$

The underlined digits may be omitted.

The same process can be applied to numerals in any base.

EXAMPLE 13. Find $221{,}232_{(\text{seven})} \div 345_{(\text{seven})}$.

Solution: The work is done mentally. We assume all work is in the base seven. Note that

$345 \cdot 10^2 < 221{,}232 < 345 \cdot 10^3.$

So the highest power is 10^2. By trial

$4 \cdot 345 = 2046$, while
$5 \cdot 345 = 2424$,

$$\begin{array}{|r|l}
221{,}232 & \\
\underline{204{,}600} & 4 \cdot 10^2 \cdot 345 \\
13{,}332 & \\
\underline{10{,}230} & 2 \cdot 10 \cdot 345 \\
3{,}102 & \\
\underline{3{,}102} & 6 \cdot 10^0 \cdot 345 \\
0 &
\end{array}$$

so 4 is the coefficient of the power 10^2. To find the coefficient of the power 10, we note $2 \cdot 345 = 1023$ while $3 \cdot 345 = 1401$. Thus, 2 is the coefficient. Finally, the coefficient of 10^0 is 6 because $6 \cdot 345 = 3102$. The quotient is $426_{(\text{seven})}$. Check by multiplying 345 by 426 to obtain the dividend.

Note that the theory of the algorisms can be developed generally for any base by the extensive use of algebraic numerical polynomials of the form

$$u_n x^n + u_{n-1} x^{n-1} + \cdots + u_2 x^2 + u_1 x^1 + u_0 x^0, \qquad \text{(II)}$$

where initially all coefficients u_i are digits in a given base. Then this polynomial can be transformed by regrouping. For example, since

$$u_2 x^2 + u_1 x = (u_2 - 1)x^2 + (x + u_1)x \qquad \text{(III)}$$

we may substitute the right member in place of the left member in the given polynomial. All the numerical examples of the four operations can be generalized by substituting the algebraic polynomials and the transformation of the coefficients of formulas II and III.

5.9 EXERCISES

1. Explain each of the following algorisms:

(a) $\begin{array}{r} 52 \\ \underline{-28} \end{array} \Rightarrow \begin{array}{r} (50 + 12) \\ \underline{-(30 + \ 8)} \end{array}$

(b) $\begin{array}{r} 52 \\ \underline{-28} \end{array} \Rightarrow \begin{array}{r} (52 + 72) \\ \underline{-(28 + 72)} \end{array} \Rightarrow (52 + 72) - 100$

(c) $\begin{array}{r} 52 \\ \underline{-28} \end{array} \Rightarrow \begin{array}{r} (40 + 12) \\ \underline{-(20 + \ 8)} \end{array}$

(d) $\begin{array}{r} 52 \\ \underline{-28} \end{array} \Rightarrow \begin{array}{r} (52 + \ 8) \\ \underline{-(28 + \ 8)} \end{array} \Rightarrow \begin{array}{r} 60 \\ \underline{-36} \end{array}$

Carry out the following computations:

2. $2413_{\text{(five)}} + 3424_{\text{(five)}}$

3. $18764_{\text{(nine)}} - 7821_{\text{(nine)}}$

4. $467_{\text{(eight)}} \times 5_{\text{(eight)}}$

5. $24642_{\text{(seven)}} \div 315_{\text{(seven)}}$

6. $213_{\text{(four)}}$
$321_{\text{(four)}}$
$312_{\text{(four)}}$
$+231_{\text{(four)}}$

7. $245_{\text{(six)}} \times 34_{\text{(six)}}$

8. $3te14_{\text{(twelve)}}$
$t2e35_{\text{(twelve)}}$
$+56789_{\text{(twelve)}}$

9. $42t1_{\text{(eleven)}} \times 9t_{\text{(eleven)}}$

10. $62{,}357_{\text{(eight)}} \div 245_{\text{(eight)}}$

11. Which of the following are odd numbers, and which are even numbers?
    (a) $303_{\text{(seven)}}$ (b) $6_{\text{(seven)}}$ (c) $222_{\text{(three)}}$
    (d) $10101_{\text{(seven)}}$ (e) $10101_{\text{(six)}}$ (f) $24te_{\text{(twelve)}}$

12. (a) Construct an addition table and a multiplication table for the base "five," using "10" to represent five.
    (b) Using the tables of part (a), find $a + b$, $a - b$, $a \cdot b$, and $a \div b$ if $a = 43144_{\text{(five)}}$ and $b = 123_{\text{(five)}}$.

13. (a) Express $2x^3 + 5x^2 + 6x^1 + 5x^0{}_{(\text{base } x)}$ as a digital place numeral.
    (b) What can you say about the value of x?
    (c) If x is eight, find the equivalent decimal numeral.

14. (a) If $x =$ ten, show how to obtain the sum of
    $3x^3 + 5x^2 + 4x^1 + 6x^0{}_{(\text{base } x)}$
    and $5x^3 + 5x^2 + 5x^1 + 5x^0{}_{(\text{base } x)}$.
    (b) Simplify the result of part (a) if $x = 10_{\text{(seven)}}$.

15. Given two numerals to base x,
    (1) $a_3x^3 + a_2x^2 + a_1x^1 + a_0x^0{}_{(\text{base } x)}$, $a_i < x$,
    (2) $b_3x^3 + b_2x^2 + b_1x^1 + b_0x^0{}_{(\text{base } x)}$, $b_i < x$,

    where $b_3 < a_3$, but $b_2 > a_2$, $b_1 > a_1$, and $b_0 > a_0$.

    Rewrite polynomial (1) so that every new coefficient of each power will be greater than the coefficient of the corresponding power of polynomial (2).

5.10 REFERENCE QUESTIONS

1. What is meant by a multiplicative-additive-place system of numeration? For a brief discussion of various numeration systems, see

   Willerding, Margaret F. "Other Number Systems—Aids to Understanding Mathematics," *The Arithmetic Teacher*, 8: 350–356; 1961.

   For a fuller discussion of historical systems of numeration, see

   Eves, Howard. *An Introduction to the History of Mathematics.* New York: Holt, Rinehart, and Winston, 1953. Pp. 7–27.

2. What number serves as the base of the decimal system of numeration? Could *negative ten* (Chapter 14) also serve as a base number? See

   Twaddle, Richard D. "A Look at the Base Negative Ten," *The Mathematics Teacher*, LVI: 88–90; 1963.

3. In this chapter, the role of properties both of operations and of the decimal system of numeration in the arithmetic algorithms was discussed. For a related discussion, see

   Lowry, William C. "Structure and the Algorisms of Arithmetic," *The Arithmetic Teacher*, 12: 146–150; 1965.

6 NONMETRIC GEOMETRY

IN THIS CHAPTER, *we consider some aspects of* nonmetric geometry. *The adjective "nonmetric" refers to properties of geometric figures which are independent of "size" or measurement. Thus, in this chapter we shall not be concerned with such measurement concepts as length, area, volume, etc.; it is nevertheless true that many nonmetric concepts are basic to an understanding of measurement. In the development of the chapter, we shall see that the set concepts and language developed in Chapter 1 are also applicable to discussion of geometric figures as sets of points.*

6.1 POINTS

It is not uncommon to hear directions such as "Go three miles beyond the point at which Route 3 meets Route 46," in which the word *point* is used to denote a location. Such a use of the word "point" is applicable to a location anywhere in space; consider, for instance, a reference to the "point" at which a particular satellite reentered the atmosphere. Thus, the intuitive connotation of the word "point" is one of *location,* or *position,* in space. Care must be taken that "point" be used to denote *exact location* rather than what might be called a region; while one might speak of the intersection of two city streets as a point, he would not refer to an entire neighborhood as a point.

The intuitive notion of point as an exact location is given further substance by the many references to "sharp point" in everyday conversation. If a sharpened pencil is held stationary, the sharp point of the pencil is an exact location in space; and similarly for the point of a pin, the point of a knife, or a corner of a metal file cabinet.

The pencil, the pin, the knife, and the file cabinet corner afford *physical representations* of what we want to call a "point." In order to represent a point on this sheet of paper, a "dot" is drawn on the paper. Care must be taken that the dot is made as small as practicable. Thus, in Figure 6–1, two dots are shown; the

FIGURE 6–1

one on the left is a poor representation of a point, while the one on the right much more nearly represents, say, the point of a pin. However, in order to make a point on a line stand out clearly, it is permissible to use a somewhat larger dot, as has been done in the figures in this book. In any event, the dot is not the point; it is only a physical representation of the point.

A point is usually named (for reference purposes) by means of a capital letter. In Figure 6–2, two points—point A and point B—are represented. In this case,

• B

• A

FIGURE 6–2

A and B are *distinct* points; that is, "A" and "B" do not refer to the same point. To say, for example, "$R = S$," is to say that R and S are simply names for the same point.

It is important to be aware of the fact that our discussion of points has been entirely at a level that can only be called intuitive. We have noted, by appeal to physical objects, that a point may be thought of as denoting exact position in space; and while this is a description of something a point may be thought of as doing, it is in no sense a definition. We shall, in fact, formulate no definition for the word "point." As words are introduced in the vocabulary development for any field of study, they are defined in terms of the words that have preceded them. Obviously, however, there must be a beginning; the first word cannot be defined in terms of preceding words since there are none. Such a word is said to be an *undefined*, or *primitive term*. There may in fact be a number of undefined terms in any field of study, and this is the case in any formal development of geometry. At this time, then, we take note of the fact that however clear the intuitive notion of point may be, in a formal study of geometry, "point" is an undefined term.

6.2 SETS OF POINTS

One may speak of a set of points, just as he may speak of a set of numbers or a set of people or a set of any kind of elements whatsoever. For example, the three points represented in Figure 6–3 may be designated as set S, as follows:

$$S = \{A, B, C\}$$

These three points are distinct, and set S contains exactly three elements; it is therefore a finite set of points.

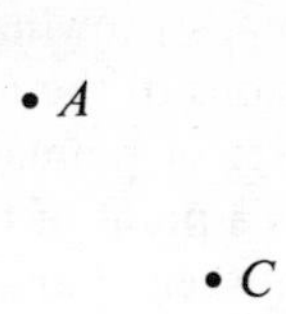

• B

• A

• C

FIGURE 6–3

As noted in the preceding section, any location in space—on, off, or within the earth—may be denoted by a point. And in fact mathematical space is the *set of all points.* Thus, space is an infinite set of points; it is impossible, even theoretically, to count all points in space.

It is not with the totality of points, or space, that we shall be primarily concerned, however. Rather, certain subsets of space will be singled out for attention. Such subsets are commonly called by the generic term "geometric figures," and each of them is dependent upon the basic notions of "point" and "set of points."

6.3 SEGMENTS

Consider two points, such as *A* and *B* in Figure 6–4, and a *path* between them. Any such path, one of which is illustrated in the figure, is a set of points. To

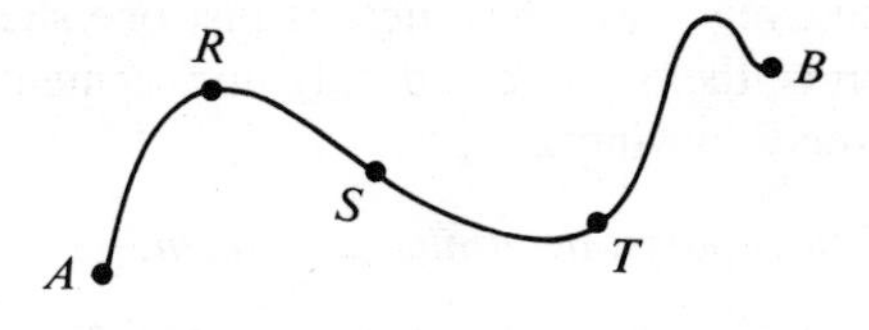

FIGURE 6–4

emphasize this, three different points—*R*, *S*, and *T*—have been indicated on the path in the figure. If one were to speak of the most *direct* path between *A* and *B*, he would surely not mean the path traced in Figure 6–4, but rather one like that shown in Figure 6–5—a path that might be traced by means of a straight-

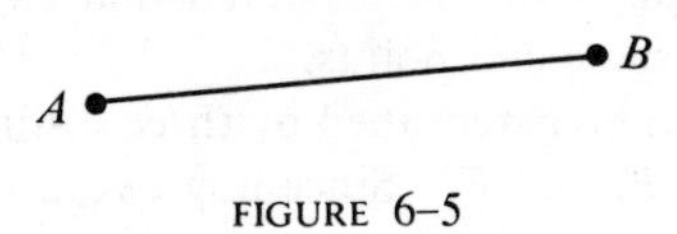

FIGURE 6–5

edge, such as a ruler. Such a path—the most direct—between two points is called a *line segment*, or more briefly, a *segment*.

Physical representations of segments are commonplace, even within the confines of a classroom. As one traces his finger along the edge of a cubical block, he is tracing out a segment. An edge of a rectangular sheet of paper, the intersection of two classroom walls, and maps showing airline routes between cities are other examples of physical expressions of the notion of segment.

Is a segment a finite or an infinite set of points? Consider again a segment between two points A and B. There is a point of the segment "between" A and B; call it C_1. There is then a point between A and C_1; call it C_2. Again, there is a point between A and C_2; call it C_3. Such points are represented in Figure 6–6,

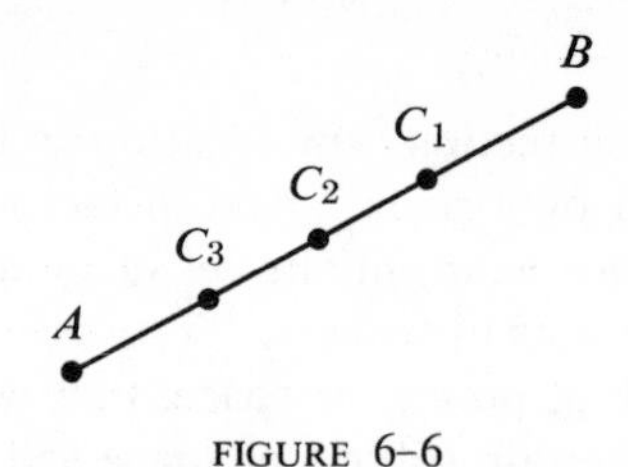

FIGURE 6–6

and it seems clear that the process can be continued indefinitely. Thus, this process is one way of illustrating that the number of points contained in a segment is endless; that is, a segment is an infinite set of points.

Although the number of points contained in a segment is infinite, the segment has two *end points.* If A and B are two distinct points, then the segment joining them has the points A and B as end points, and the segment is denoted by the symbol "$\overline{AB}$." In the same way, the symbol "$\overline{XY}$" refers to the segment joining a point X and a point Y.

Given two points A and B, for how many segments are these points end points? It seems intuitively clear that there is just one such segment. That is, given two distinct points, there is one and only one segment joining them, a fact usually expressed in the following way:

Two distinct points determine a segment.

Here the word "determine" means that the geometric figure is selected from all others in space and is unique. While we accept the preceding italicized statement as valid in our study of space, we have made no pretense of "proving" it; such a statement is called an *axiom.*

Of course, in naming a segment, it makes no difference which end point is recorded first. Thus, "$\overline{AB}$" and "$\overline{BA}$" refer to the same segment, the one joining points A and B; that is, $\overline{AB} = \overline{BA}$ since "$\overline{AB}$" and "$\overline{BA}$" name the same set of points. In this connection, it should be noted that two segments are equal if and only if they have the same end points.

How many segments can be determined by three distinct points as represented in Figure 6–7—points D, E, and F? Since any two distinct points determine a

• F

D •

$\dot{E}$

FIGURE 6–7

segment, we seek every possible pair of points from among the three. We have the pair D and E, the pair D and F, and the pair E and F. Hence, there are three pairs of distinct points; and there are therefore three segments determined by the three distinct points, as indicated in Figure 6–8. An interesting pattern

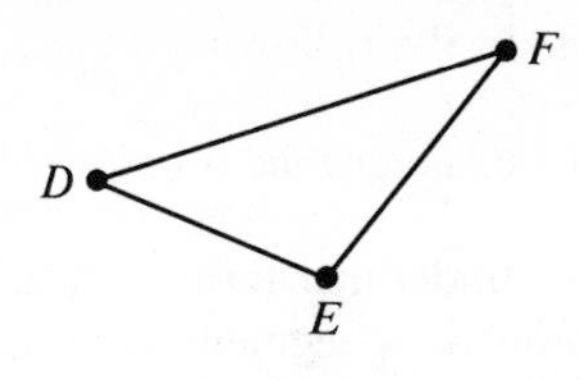

FIGURE 6–8

emerges if one determines the number of segments determined by 2, 3, 4, 5, etc., distinct points. Investigation of this pattern is left for the exercises.

6.4 LINES

It has been established that two distinct points determine a segment. Physically, one may think of a rubber band stretched between two points in space. The band may then be stretched further, thus "extending" the physical segment. A succession of such stretchings is shown in Figure 6–9. Each segment repre-

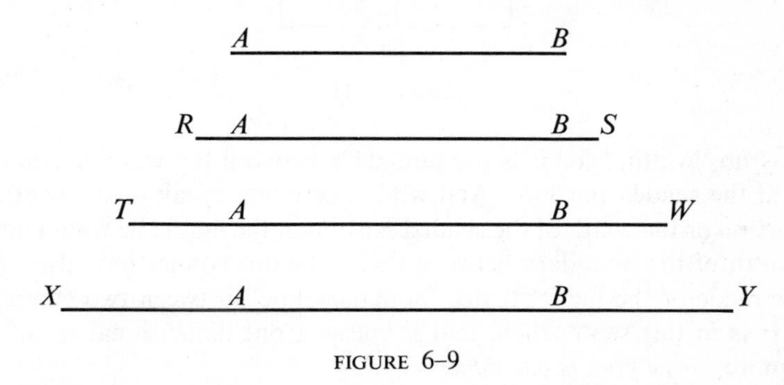

FIGURE 6–9

sents a stretching of the segment immediately above it. Physically, this process must end at the time the rubber band breaks. Theoretically, however, we are not so restricted. We can imagine this "stretching" process continuing without end, and this gives rise to the mathematical notion of *line*. Given two distinct points A and B, the line containing A and B has no end points, but continues indefinitely in each direction, as suggested by the arrowheads in the representation of Figure 6–10. For reference purposes, this line is denoted by the symbol "$\overleftrightarrow{AB}$." (Contrast this with the symbol "$\overline{AB}$.") Hence, a segment and a line are

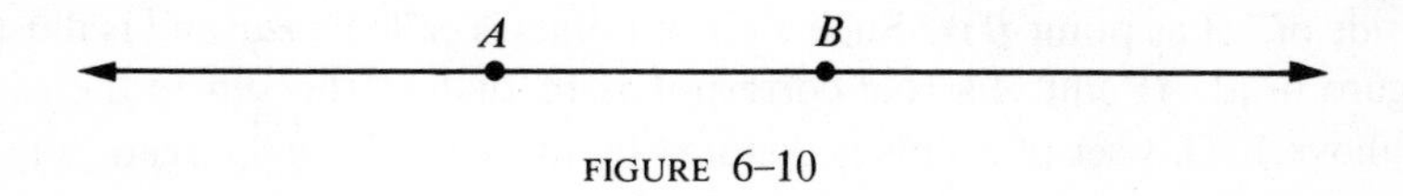

FIGURE 6–10

different kinds of sets. A segment has two end points, while a line has no end points. Observe, incidentally, that segment $\overline{AB}$ is contained entirely in line $\overleftrightarrow{AB}$; thus $\overline{AB} \subset \overleftrightarrow{AB}$.

We mentioned earlier that two points determine a segment. Similarly, it seems clear that there is one and only one line containing two distinct points. Again, the statement is usually made in the following way:

Two distinct points determine a line.

"Line," like "point," is an undefined term. Observe that we have discussed a line as the endless extension of a segment, and segment in turn was simply described (not defined) as the "most direct" path between two points. (Because a line continues forever in each direction, physical representations of a line are not available. For this reason, it is probably easier to introduce the concept of segment first, as was done in this chapter.)

Since two points determine a line, a third point may or may not lie on the same line. Points that lie on one line are said to be *collinear* points.

A line is a *one-dimensional* figure. To appreciate the impact of this statement, let us consider a subset of a line, segment $\overline{AB}$ in Figure 6–11. $\overline{AB}$ has a "length,"

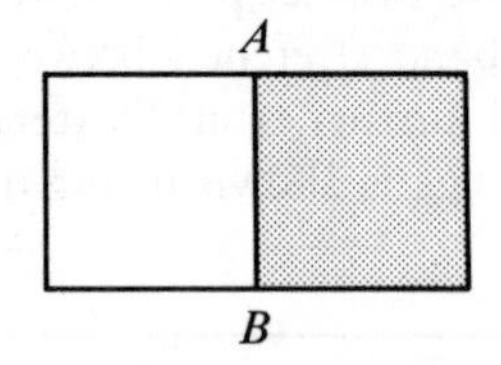

FIGURE 6–11

but it has no "width," for it is the boundary between the white portion of the figure and the shaded portion. And while one might speak of the width of the white portion or the width of the shaded portion of the figure, he would not speak of the width of the boundary between them. In this connection, also, mention might be made of the fact that the "boundary line" between two states has no width. It is in this sense, then, that a line is a one-dimensional set of points. Furthermore, *every path is one-dimensional.*

6.5 RAYS

The word "ray" finds its way into the language in a variety of ways. As one example, a light ray is considered to emanate from the sun (as a starting point) and to continue endlessly in one direction (disregarding the possibility that it may be reflected or refracted by some substance). It is in roughly this sense that the word is used in geometry also. Given two distinct points A and B, consider the set of points including A together with all points of $\overleftrightarrow{AB}$ which are "on the same side of" A as point B is. Such a set of points is called a *ray* and is illustrated in Figure 6–12. (Point A's role corresponds to that of the sun in the example cited above.) This set of points is denoted by the symbol "$\overrightarrow{AB}$," read "ray AB."

A B

FIGURE 6–12

Point A may be considered as an end point of the above ray; furthermore, it is the only end point of the ray. In naming a ray, the end point is always recorded first, regardless of how the points may be oriented in space. Thus, "$\overrightarrow{RS}$" is a name for the ray illustrated in Figure 6–13. Other names for this ray are "$\overrightarrow{RT}$"

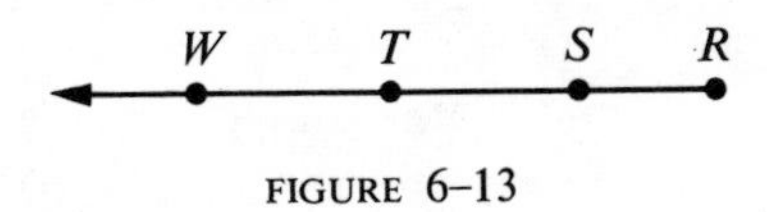

FIGURE 6–13

and "$\overrightarrow{RW}$." While the end point must be recorded first, any other point of the ray may serve as the second component for the name. It is correct to write "$\overrightarrow{RS} = \overrightarrow{RT} = \overrightarrow{RW}$" since all of these symbols name the same set of points.

6.6 EXERCISES

1. What is meant by the phrase "geometric figure"?
2. What is the significance of the word "determine" in the statement "Two distinct points determine a line"?
3. Refer to the figure below in deciding whether each of the following statements is true or false:

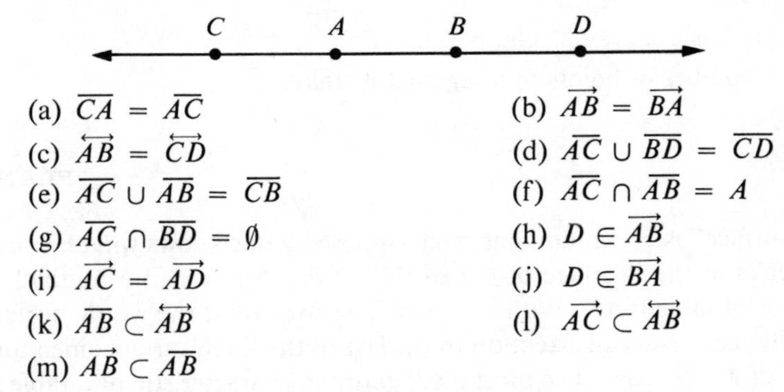

(a) $\overline{CA} = \overline{AC}$
(b) $\overrightarrow{AB} = \overrightarrow{BA}$
(c) $\overleftrightarrow{AB} = \overleftrightarrow{CD}$
(d) $\overline{AC} \cup \overline{BD} = \overline{CD}$
(e) $\overline{AC} \cup \overline{AB} = \overline{CB}$
(f) $\overline{AC} \cap \overline{AB} = A$
(g) $\overline{AC} \cap \overline{BD} = \emptyset$
(h) $D \in \overrightarrow{AB}$
(i) $\overrightarrow{AC} = \overrightarrow{AD}$
(j) $D \in \overrightarrow{BA}$
(k) $\overline{AB} \subset \overleftrightarrow{AB}$
(l) $\overrightarrow{AC} \subset \overleftrightarrow{AB}$
(m) $\overrightarrow{AB} \subset \overline{AB}$

4. Complete the following statements concerning the figure below:

R S T W X

(a) $\overline{RS} \cup \overline{ST} =$
(b) $\overline{RS} \cap \overline{ST} =$
(c) $\overrightarrow{TR} \cup \overrightarrow{TX} =$
(d) $\overrightarrow{TR} \cap \overrightarrow{TX} =$
(e) $\overline{RT} \cap \overline{SW} =$
(f) $\overline{RT} \cap \overline{WX} =$
(g) $\overrightarrow{TX} \cap \overrightarrow{TW} =$
(h) $\overrightarrow{TX} \cup \overrightarrow{TW} =$
(i) $\overline{TX} \cap \overline{TW} =$

5. In section 6.3 of the text, it was observed that 2 distinct points determine 1 segment, and 3 distinct noncollinear points determine 3 segments. Continue this investigation by completing the following table, where n is any whole number greater than 1:

Number of Distinct Noncollinear Points	Number of Segments Determined
2	1
3	3
4	?
5	?
6	?
n	?

6. If 3 points are collinear, is it still true that they determine exactly three segments? Explain.
7. Indicate whether each of the following statements is true or false:
   (a) For any two points X and Y, $\overline{XY} = \overline{YX}$.
   (b) For any two points X and Y, $\overleftrightarrow{XY} = \overleftrightarrow{YX}$.
   (c) For any two points X and Y, $\overrightarrow{XY} = \overrightarrow{YX}$.
   (d) If $\overline{AB} = \overline{AC}$, then $B = C$.
   (e) A segment is a subset of a line.
   (f) A line is a subset of space.
   (g) Two distinct points determine a ray.
   (h) If $\overrightarrow{AB} = \overrightarrow{AC}$, then $B = C$.
   (i) A ray has exactly one end point.
   (j) The number of points in a segment is finite.

6.7 PLANES

The word "surface" is a common one, and supposedly one knows what he means when he speaks of the "surface of the earth" or the "surface of a football" or the "surface of a table top." Without quarreling over what the word "surface" might actually mean, we call attention to the last of the three surfaces mentioned above—that of a table top. The most distinguishing characteristic of a table top is that it is "flat," and such a flat surface is a physical representation of a set of points known in geometry as a *plane*. Actually, a table top is a representation of only a part of a plane; for while the table top is bounded, a plane extends indefinitely. (Perhaps some idea of this can be obtained by imagining pancake batter being poured onto a flat surface but continuing to flow outward without end.)

How may a plane be represented? A rectangular piece might be cut from a sheet of cardboard (preferably, a very thin sheet); this cardboard, being relatively "flat," represents a part of a plane. Such a representation is illustrated in Figure 6–14, where it is assumed one's line of sight is perpendicular to the sur-

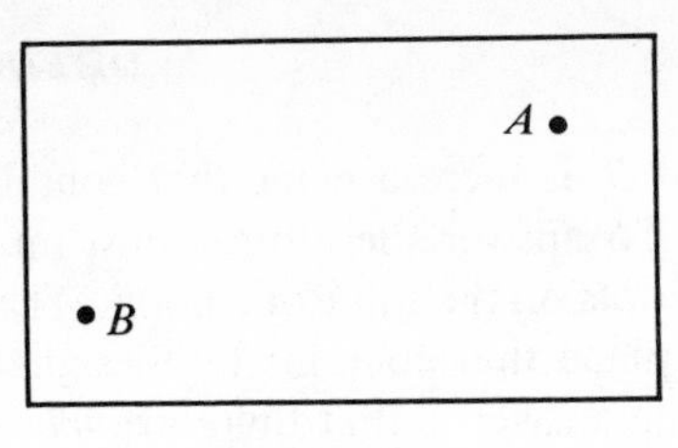

FIGURE 6–14

face of the cardboard. Thus, points A and B are at roughly the same distance from the observer's eyes. If the rectangular piece of cardboard is tilted in space (the top going back) its representation is more accurately drawn as a parallelogram. This is illustrated in Figure 6–15, where point A is now farther away than

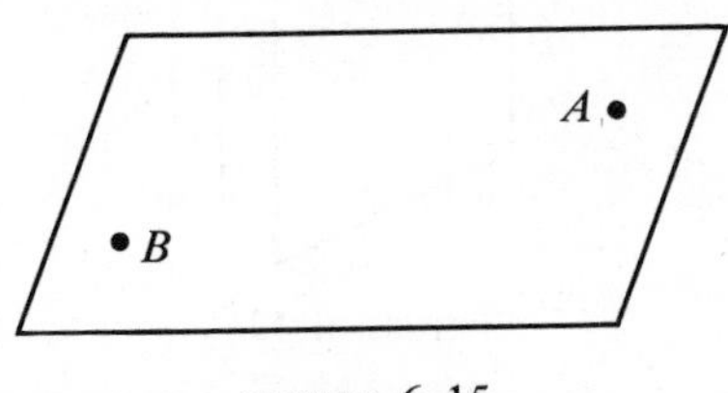

FIGURE 6–15

point B. It is in this way that a plane (again, more accurately, a part of a plane) is usually represented.

6.8 LINES IN A PLANE

Suppose R and S are two distinct points in a plane E. We have seen previously that these two points determine a line $\overleftrightarrow{RS}$. How is the line $\overleftrightarrow{RS}$ related to the plane E? Physically, if one marks two dots on a sheet of cardboard and then stretches a string tautly between the two dots, the stretched string will "cling to" the cardboard. This physical phenomenon illustrates what is meant by the following statement about points, lines, and planes:

> *If two points lie in a given plane, then the line determined by the two points is contained in the plane.*

The statement is illustrated in Figure 6–16. Since any one line in a plane contains an infinite number of points, it seems clear that a plane too is an infinite set of points.

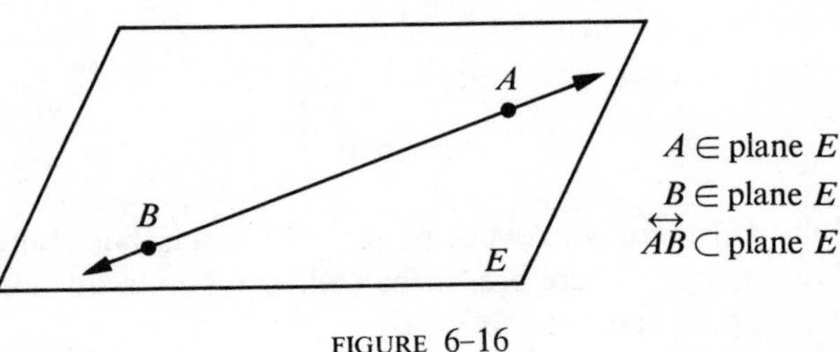

$A \in$ plane E
$B \in$ plane E
$\overleftrightarrow{AB} \subset$ plane E

FIGURE 6–16

Given two points, A and B, is there a plane that contains the points? Is there more than one plane? To answer these questions, imagine that A and B are represented physically as dots on the spine of a book. Then each page of the book represents (a part of) a plane that contains the designated points as illustrated in Figure 6–17. Thus, the answer is that there are *many* planes containing two distinct points; that is, two distinct points do not determine a plane.

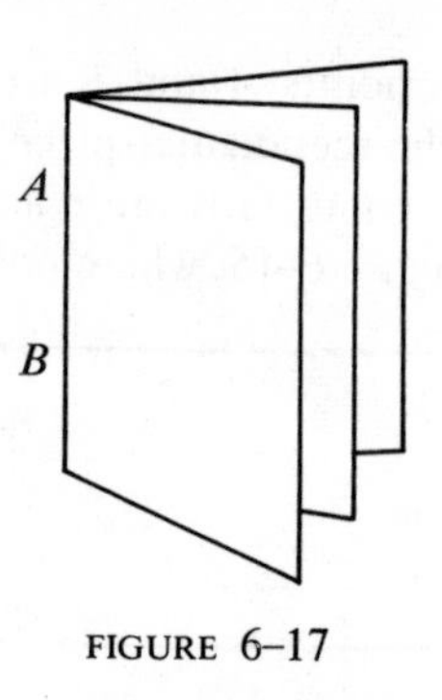

FIGURE 6–17

Next consider three distinct noncollinear points, A, B, and C, that is, points which do not all lie on the same line; three such points are represented in Figure 6–18. Physically, it is easy to see that this sheet of paper is the only repre-

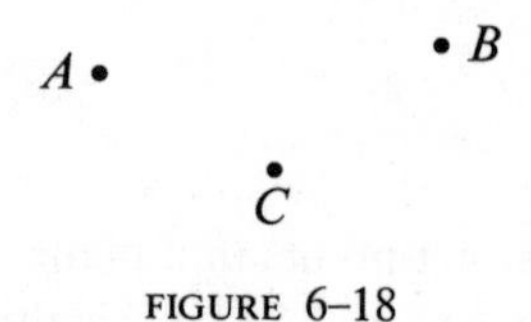

FIGURE 6–18

sentation of a plane that contains all of the above points. If one of the dots—say C—is pulled out from the sheet, there will still be only one plane containing A, B, and C. Or choose any three "corners" of a room; again it is apparent that only one plane contains the three points. Hence, three points, not all on one line, determine a plane.

Why has it been so carefully specified that the three points must not all lie on one line? If they were to lie on one line, we would again be in the "book

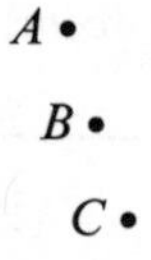

A •

B •

C •

FIGURE 6–19

spine" situation, and there would not be just one plane, but many planes containing the three points. Therefore, three collinear points do not determine a plane, but the following statement is valid:

Three noncollinear points determine a plane.

Consider a line $\overleftrightarrow{AB}$, and also a point C contained in the line, as in Figure 6–20. Such a point C is said to *separate* the line into two *half lines*. ("Half" here is not being used in the same sense that it is used in the fraction $\frac{1}{2}$.) One of the half lines contains all points of the line "on one side" of C; the other half line

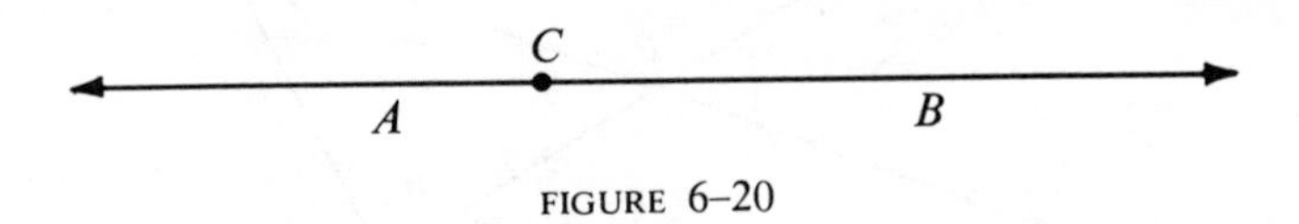

FIGURE 6–20

contains all points of the line on the "other side" of C. The point C itself does not belong to either half line. Thus, three sets are involved in the separation of a line—two half lines and the separating point. The union of these three sets is the line itself. That is,

$$\text{half line } AC \cup \{C\} \cup \text{half line } CB = \overleftrightarrow{AB}.$$

Furthermore, the sets are disjoint; and so we have a partitioning of the line. It should be emphasized that there is nothing special about the point C except that it is an element of $\overleftrightarrow{AB}$; any other point on the line might have been selected. That is, any point of a line separates the line into two half lines.

[Note that there is a fine distinction between the notions of half line and ray. The ray $\overrightarrow{CB}$ contains the point C, while the half line CB does not contain this point. This distinction is not always made, for a ray is sometimes taken to be what we have called a half line here. At the elementary level, however, it seems advisable to make such a distinction.]

Just as a point separates a line, so a line separates a plane. If $\overleftrightarrow{AB} \in$ plane E, then $\overleftrightarrow{AB}$ determines two *half planes* of plane E (Fig. 6–21). One half plane contains all points of E on one side of $\overleftrightarrow{AB}$; the other contains all points of E on the other side of $\overleftrightarrow{AB}$. $\overleftrightarrow{AB}$ itself belongs to neither half plane, but is called the *edge* of each half plane. The union of the two half planes and their common edge is the plane itself. Any line of a plane partitions the plane into three subsets—two half planes and the line itself.

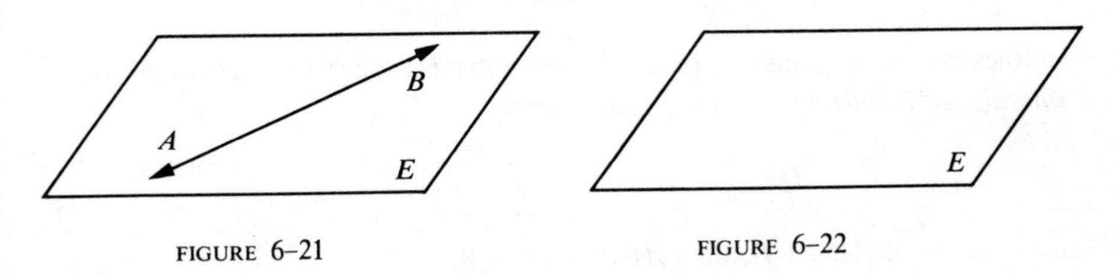

FIGURE 6–21 FIGURE 6–22

Continuing with the concept of separation of a set of points, a plane separates space into two *half spaces*. In Figure 6–22, one can imagine one half space "above" the plane E, and another half space "below" the plane. The union of the plane and the two half spaces that it determines is space itself. Any plane separates space into two half spaces.

Suppose $\overleftrightarrow{AB}$ and $\overleftrightarrow{CD}$ are two lines in a plane. If the lines intersect, their intersection is a single point. If this point of intersection is called P, as illustrated in

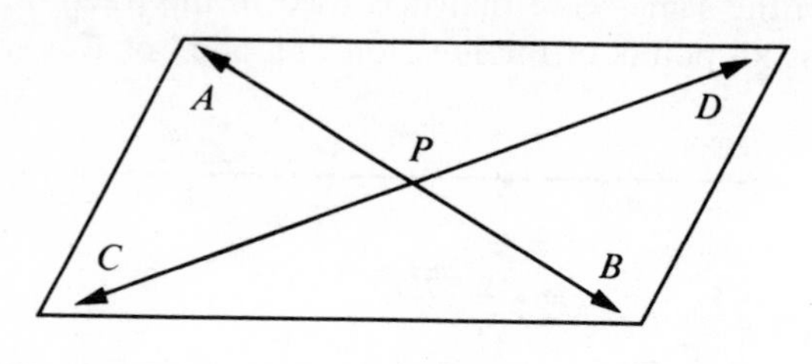

FIGURE 6–23

Figure 6–23, we may write

$$\overleftrightarrow{AB} \cap \overleftrightarrow{CD} = \{P\}.$$

It is impossible for two distinct lines to intersect in two different points. This follows from the fact that two points determine a line, something we have already agreed upon. And if two distinct lines intersected in two different points, then those points would not determine a line. We summarize this by stating:

If two distinct lines intersect, their intersection is a point.

Why was the word "if" used in the above statement? Is it possible that two lines may not intersect? The answer to this latter question is an affirmative one, and such a situation may arise in two ways. First, as illustrated in Figure 6–24,

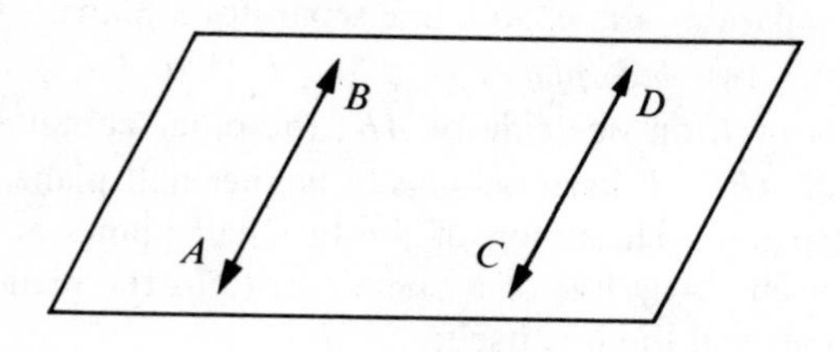

FIGURE 6–24

two lines may lie in the same plane and not intersect; such lines are then said to be *parallel*. If $\overleftrightarrow{AB}$ and $\overleftrightarrow{CD}$ are parallel, we write

$$\overleftrightarrow{AB} \parallel \overleftrightarrow{CD}.$$

Thus, if $\overleftrightarrow{AB} \parallel \overleftrightarrow{CD}$, then $\overleftrightarrow{AB} \cap \overleftrightarrow{CD} = \emptyset$.

Secondly, it is possible that two lines may be nonintersecting and yet not be parallel lines; such lines are called *skew* lines. In Figure 6–25, imagine $\overleftrightarrow{AB}$ as

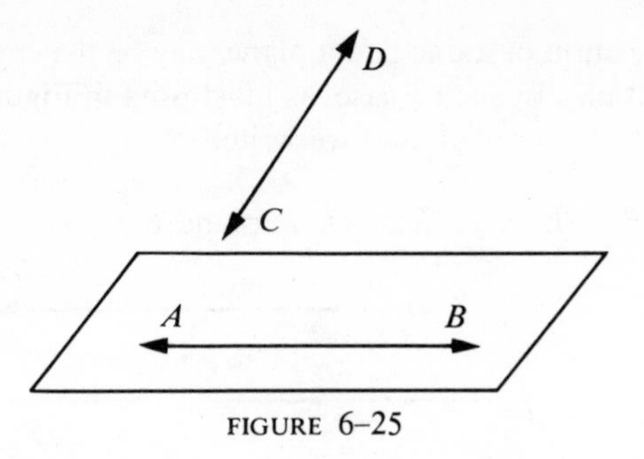

FIGURE 6–25

the line determined by a pencil lying on a desk, and $\overleftrightarrow{CD}$ as a line determined by a pencil held in the air above the desk, and not parallel to the pencil on the desk. The lines so determined do not intersect. However, because they are not in the same plane, they are not parallel; for, by definition, parallel lines lie in the same plane.

If a line and a plane intersect, what kind of geometric figure is the intersection? Imagine a sheet of cardboard being "punctured" by a sharp rod, as suggested in Figure 6–26. This physical analogy makes it clear that the intersection of a

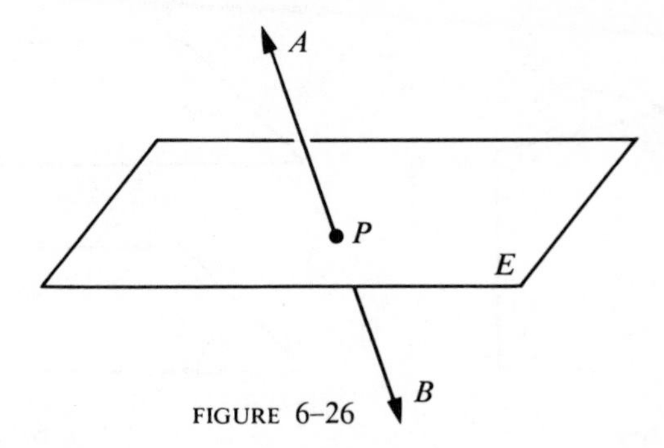

FIGURE 6–26

line and a plane might be a point. In this case,

$$\text{plane } E \cap \overleftrightarrow{AB} = \{P\}.$$

Of course, the line might be contained entirely in the plane. Then the intersection of the line and the plane would be the line itself. (This is, after all, the set of points common to the line and the plane.) In this case,

$$\text{plane } E \cap \overleftrightarrow{AB} = \overleftrightarrow{AB},$$

as illustrated in Figure 6–27.

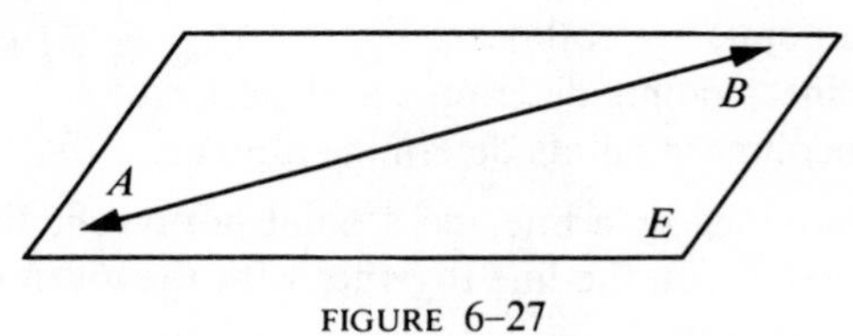

FIGURE 6–27

Lastly, the intersection of a line and a plane may be the empty set; that is, they may not intersect at all. In such a case, as illustrated in Figure 6–28, the line and the plane are said to be parallel, and we write:

$$\text{If } \overleftrightarrow{AB} \parallel \text{plane } E, \text{ then } \overleftrightarrow{AB} \cap \text{plane } E = \emptyset.$$

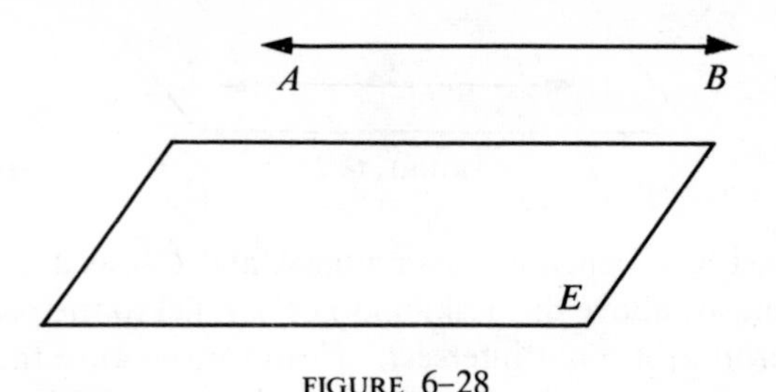

FIGURE 6–28

Consider next the intersection of two planes. The pages of a book, the intersecting walls of a classroom, and the edge of a box, among other physical representations, suggest that if two planes intersect, the intersection is a line, as illustrated in Figure 6–29. In Figure 6–30, two parallel planes are illustrated.

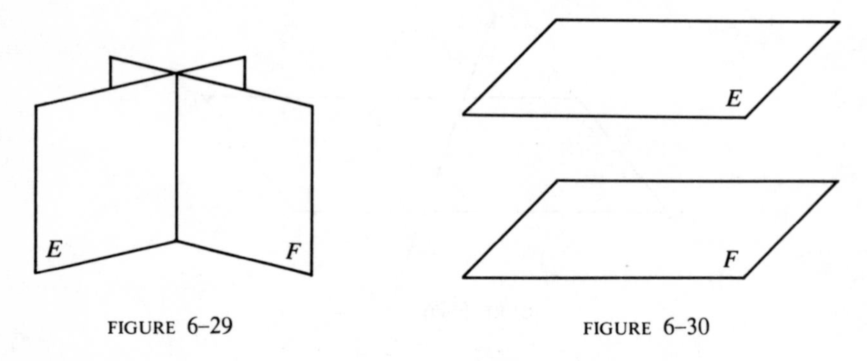

FIGURE 6–29

FIGURE 6–30

These planes do not intersect, and we have the following statement:

$$\text{If plane } E \parallel \text{plane } F, \text{ then plane } E \cap \text{plane } F = \emptyset.$$

6.12 EXERCISES

1. Indicate whether each of the following statements is true or false:
   (a) Any two points are collinear.
   (b) Any three points are collinear.
   (c) Three collinear points determine a plane.
   (d) Three noncollinear points determine a plane.
2. Is a plane determined by a line and a point not on the line? (Hint: Consider two points on the line together with the given point.)
3. Do two intersecting lines determine a plane?

4. Indicate whether each of the following statements is true or false:
   (a) A point separates a plane.
   (b) A point separates a line.
   (c) A ray separates a plane.
   (d) A segment separates a plane.
   (e) A line separates a plane.
   (f) A line separates space.
   (g) A plane separates space.
   (h) $A \in \overrightarrow{AB}$.
   (i) $A \in$ half line AB.

5. (a) Do the lines represented below intersect? Explain.

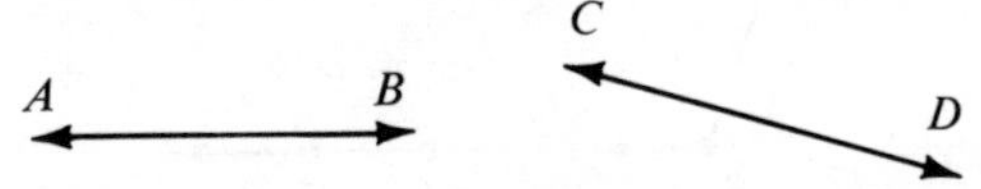

   (b) Do the segments represented below intersect? Explain.

6. Complete the following statements:
   (a) If $A \in$ plane E and $B \in$ plane E, then $\overleftrightarrow{AB} \cap$ plane $E =$ ________.
   (b) If A, B, and C are noncollinear points, then $\overleftrightarrow{AB} \cap \overleftrightarrow{BC} =$ ________.
   (c) If A, B, and C are collinear points, then $\overleftrightarrow{AB} \cap \overleftrightarrow{BC} =$ ________.
   (d) If $A \in$ plane E, $B \notin$ plane E, then $\overleftrightarrow{AB} \cap$ plane $E =$ ________.
   (e) If $\overleftrightarrow{AB} \parallel \overleftrightarrow{CD}$, then $\overleftrightarrow{AB} \cap \overleftrightarrow{CD} =$ ________.

6.13 ANGLES

A ray has been defined as a particular kind of set of points. Each ray, it will be recalled, has precisely one end point; and it is possible for two or more rays to have a common end point. Consider two such rays, indicated in Figure 6–31.

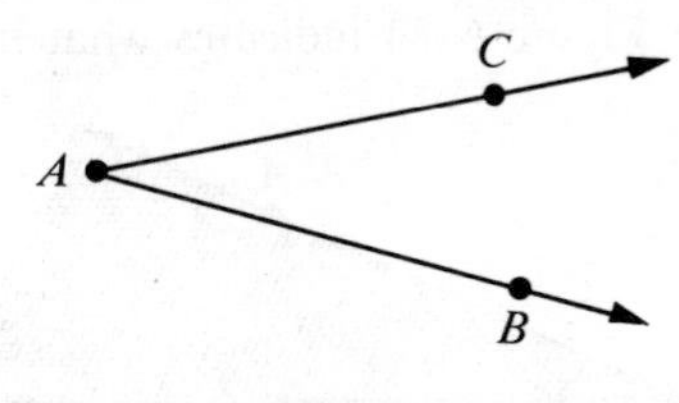

FIGURE 6–31

Point A is the end point of $\overrightarrow{AC}$ and also the end point of $\overrightarrow{AB}$. The union of these two rays is a set of points called an *angle*. Thus we make the following definition:

DEFINITION: *An* angle *is the union of two rays having a common end point.*

The common end point is called the *vertex* of the angle; the vertex is an element of each of the two rays forming the angle. The angle in Figure 6–31 is designated "angle BAC" or "angle CAB," often abbreviated as "$\angle BAC$" and "$\angle CAB$." Note that the angle has been named by three capital letters; the name of the vertex is in the center, and it is flanked by the names of two points of the angle, one on each ray.

The meaning of the word "union" must be carefully recalled in considering the definition of an angle. Thus, in Figure 6–32, the points X, Y, Z are all ele-

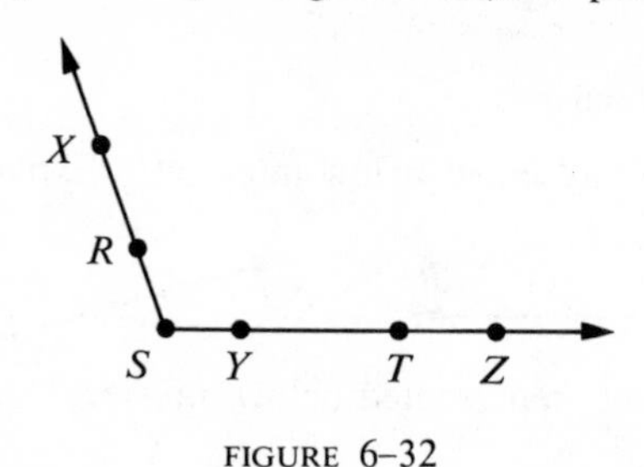

FIGURE 6–32

ments of the angle RST since the union of two rays contains any point that belongs to either ray (or to both of them, as in the case of the vertex).

Figure 6–32 also serves to emphasize that an angle may be named in many ways. Thus, the following are all names for the angle shown: $\angle RST$, $\angle TSR$, $\angle XSY$, $\angle YSX$, $\angle RSZ$, etc. It is correct to say then, for example, $\angle RST = \angle XSY$, since these are names for the same angle.

It may be the case that the two rays with a common end point are parts of the same line, as shown in Figure 6–33. In such a case, the rays are called *oppo-*

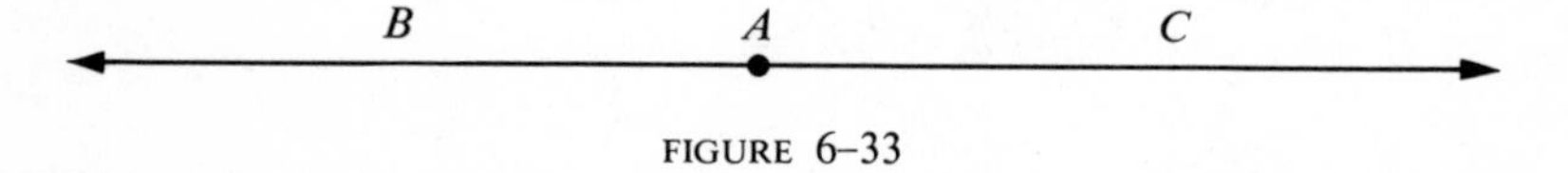

FIGURE 6–33

site rays; their union is the line itself. Technically, however, this set of points satisfies the definition of angle, and such an angle plays an important role in advanced mathematics. An angle which is the union of two opposite rays is called a *straight angle.*

The shaded portion of Figure 6–34 indicates what intuition would dictate to

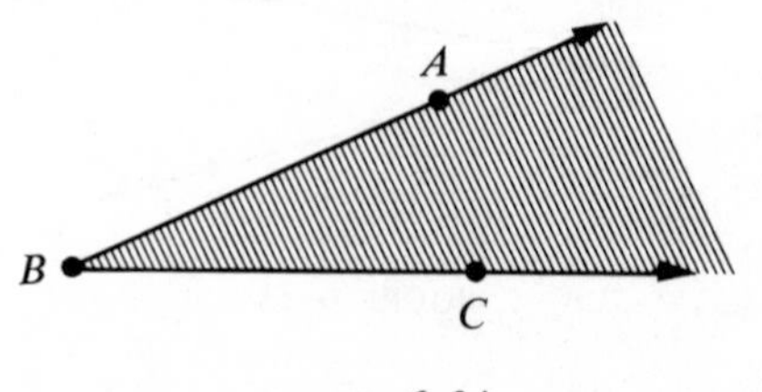

FIGURE 6–34

be the "interior" of $\angle ABC$. This notion of "interior of an angle" offers an excellent opportunity to use some of the notions developed earlier to formulate a precise definition which is consistent with our intuition. Consider the line $\overleftrightarrow{AB}$ determined by the ray $\overrightarrow{BA}$; this line, $\overleftrightarrow{AB}$, separates the plane into two half planes.

In Figure 6–35, the half plane determined by $\overleftrightarrow{AB}$ and containing C has been shaded. Similarly, the line $\overleftrightarrow{BC}$ (not the ray) separates the plane into two half

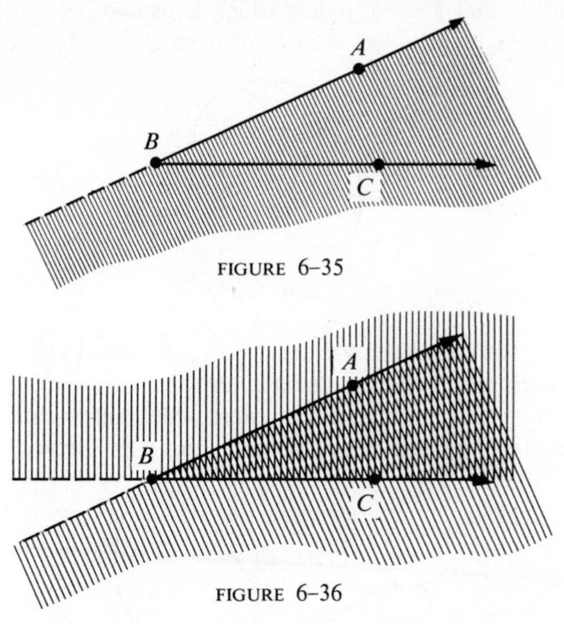

FIGURE 6–35

FIGURE 6–36

planes. In Figure 6–36, the half plane determined by $\overleftrightarrow{BC}$ and containing point A has been shaded, this shading being superimposed over the previous shading. This enables us to see that the interior of the angle is the intersection of the two half planes specified above. Thus, the interior of $\angle ABC$ is defined as follows:

DEFINITION: *Given $\angle ABC$, the* interior *of $\angle ABC$ is the intersection of two half planes, the half plane determined by $\overleftrightarrow{AB}$ and containing C, and the half plane determined by $\overleftrightarrow{BC}$ and containing A.*

A point that is not in the interior of an angle, and is not a part of the angle itself, is said to be in the *exterior* of the angle. Thus, an angle determines three subsets of the plane: the angle itself, the interior of the angle, and the exterior. The union of these three subsets is the entire plane. In Figure 6–37, point S is

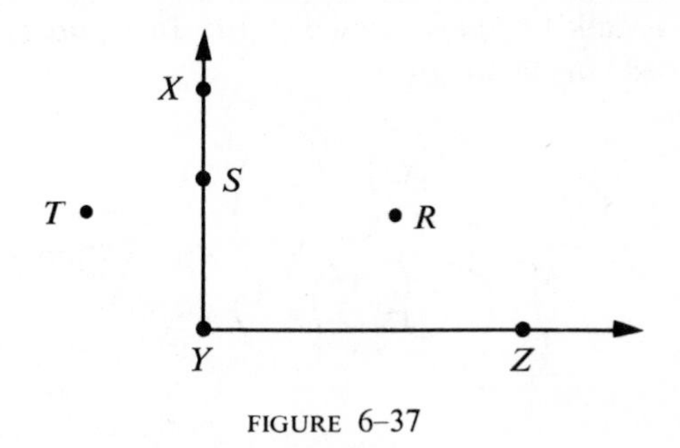

FIGURE 6–37

a part of $\angle XYZ$, point R is in the interior of $\angle XYZ$, and point T is in the exterior of $\angle XYZ$.

It was stated earlier that a set of points which joins two points may be called a *path.* In Figure 6–38, a path from A to B (or from B to A) has been represented.

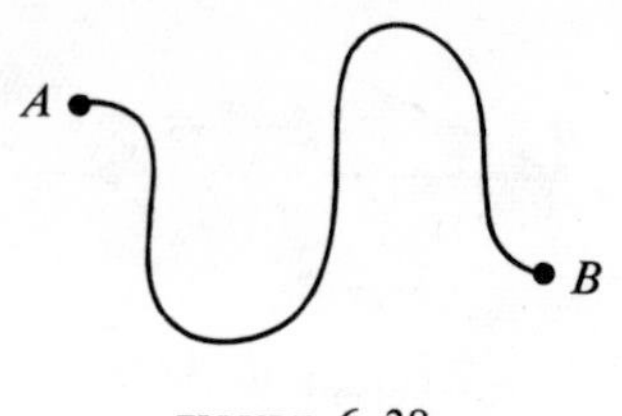

FIGURE 6–38

It was in this way that a segment was developed as a special kind of path between two points. A path may also be called a *curve.*

In Figure 6–39, a path or curve is illustrated which differs in a significant way from those considered earlier. For this path does not have two end points; it

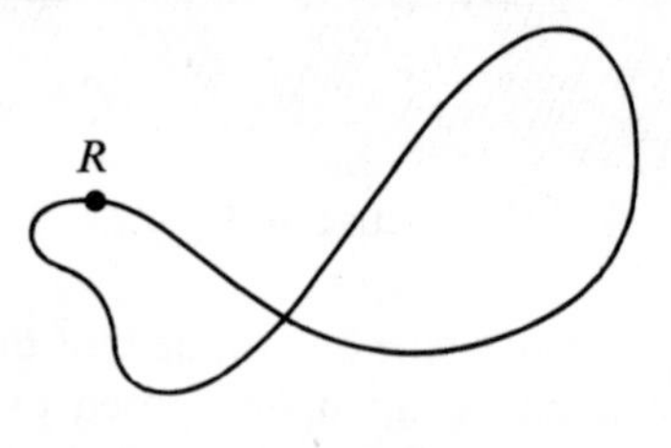

FIGURE 6–39

has, in fact, no end points at all. Note that one may start at a point on the path—say R—and "trace" along the path, eventually arriving again at point R. Such a path, which may be conceived of as starting and ending at the same point, is called a *closed path* or *closed curve.* The familiar "figure eight" is then a frequently seen representation of a closed path or curve.

A circle is also a closed curve, but it possesses a property not possessed by a figure such as a figure eight. This property may be expressed by saying that the circle (unlike the figure eight) does not "cross itself" at any point; that is, the path may be traced without touching any point more than once. A closed curve with this property is called a *simple closed curve.* In Figure 6–40, three illustrations of simple closed curves are given.

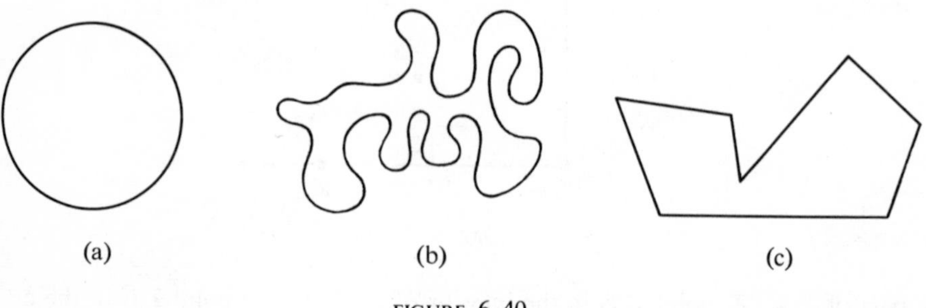

FIGURE 6-40

Figure 6–40(c) is worth special notice. It may be described as the union of seven segments. A simple closed curve which is the union of a finite number of segments is called a *polygon.* Observe that every polygon is a simple closed curve, but not every simple closed curve is a polygon. Also it is not enough to say that a polygon is the union of a finite number of segments. For example, Figure 6–41

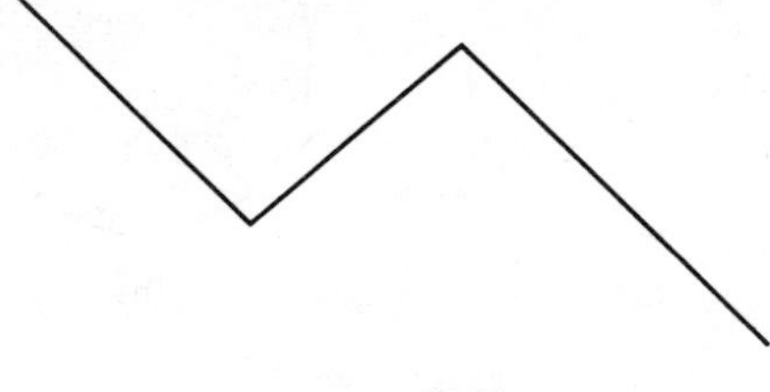

FIGURE 6–41

shows a path which is the union of three segments. However, it is not a polygon because it is not a simple closed curve. Such a path is called *polygonal.*

6.15 REGIONS

We have previously considered what is meant by the interior of an angle, and now we consider the notion of interior of a simple closed curve. A simple closed curve partitions the plane into three subsets—the curve itself, the interior of the curve, and the exterior of the curve. In Figure 6–42, point F is a part of the curve, point H is in the interior, and point G is in the exterior.

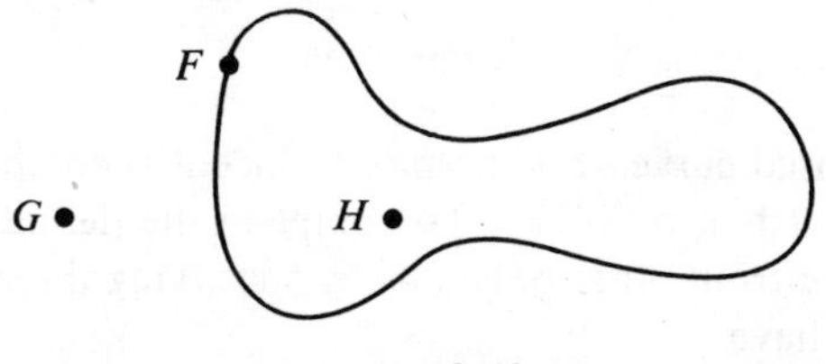

FIGURE 6–42

Often (for example, in studying area) one needs to consider a simple closed curve together with its interior—that is, the union of a simple closed curve and its interior. Such a set of points is called a *region.* In Figure 6–43 is shown the

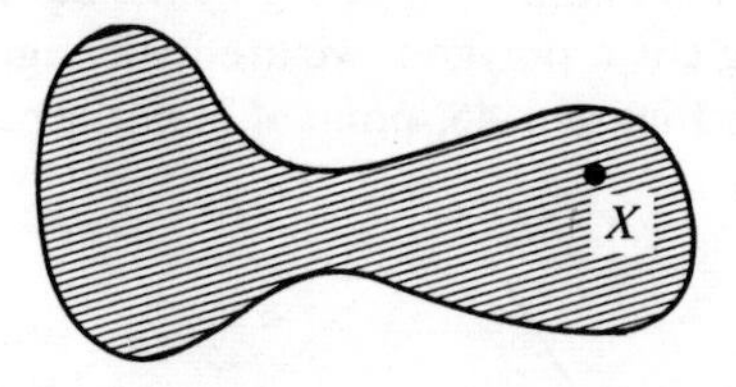

FIGURE 6–43

region corresponding to the simple closed curve of Figure 6–42. Thus, while a point such as X is an element of the region, it is not an element of the simple closed curve. Figure 6–44(a) shows a circle, which is a simple closed curve. Figure 6–44(b) shows a circular region, the union of the circle and its interior, which is frequently referred to as a *disc*.

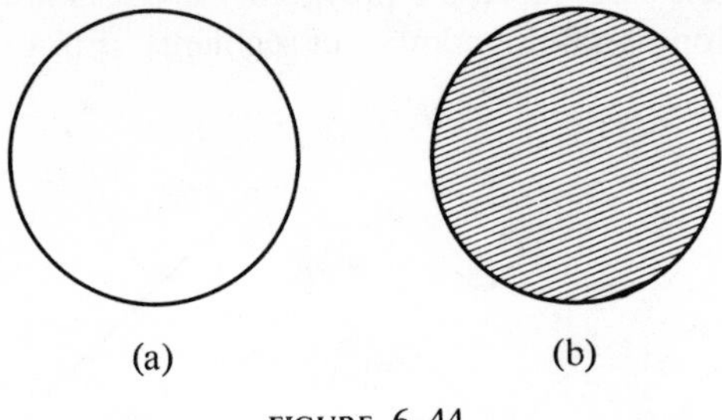

FIGURE 6–44

6.16 POLYGONS AND POLYGONAL REGIONS

Figure 6–45 shows the familiar figure of a triangle. While recognition of a triangle is immediate, it is not so easy to state a precise definition of a triangle. Considering the definitions of preceding sections, however, we note that a tri-

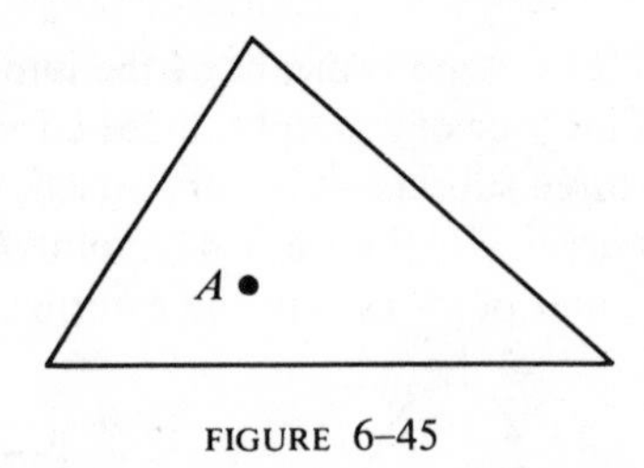

FIGURE 6–45

angle is a simple closed curve. Furthermore, since it is composed entirely of the union of segments, it is a polygon. To complete the definition, then, we must distinguish a triangle from other polygons by specifying the number of segments involved. Thus we have:

DEFINITION: *A* triangle *is a polygon which is the union of three segments.*

At first glance, the preceding definition might seem redundant. However, it would be incorrect to say simply that a triangle is the "union of three segments." (Sketch a figure which is the union of three segments, but which is not a triangle.)

In stating that a triangle is a polygon, we are really agreeing that a triangle is a "line figure." Thus, in Figure 6–45, point A is not a part of the triangle; it is

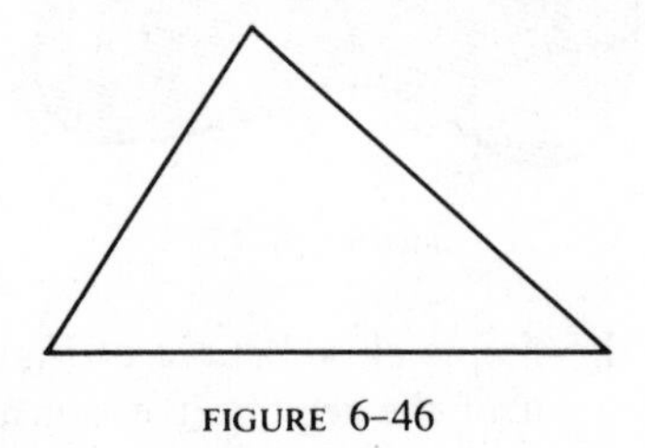

FIGURE 6–46

instead a part of the interior of the triangle. With this in mind, physical representations of triangles should be carefully chosen. The familiar triangle used as a musical instrument is one good representation; three straws strung together properly is another. On the other hand, cutting a triangular shape from a sheet of cardboard is less desirable as a physical representation of a triangle since it emphasizes the triangle together with its interior, or the triangular region. Stated formally, a triangular region may be defined as follows:

DEFINITION: *A* triangular region *is the union of a triangle and the interior of the triangle.*

Figure 6–47(a) shows a triangle, while Figure 6–47(b) shows a triangular region.

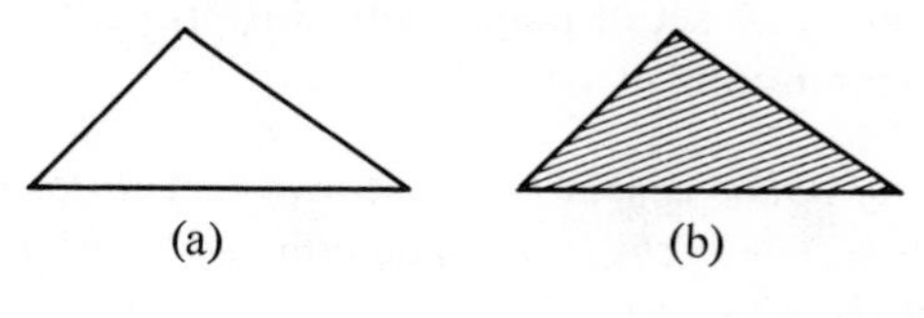

FIGURE 6–47

As in the case of the triangle, one may speak, for example, of a rectangular region as well as of a rectangle, and of a square region as well as a square. In general, the union of any polygon and its interior is a *polygonal region.*

6.17 CONVEX SETS

We have seen that certain sets of points are designated by the term "region." Thus, the shading in Figure 6–48 indicates that a region, not just a simple closed

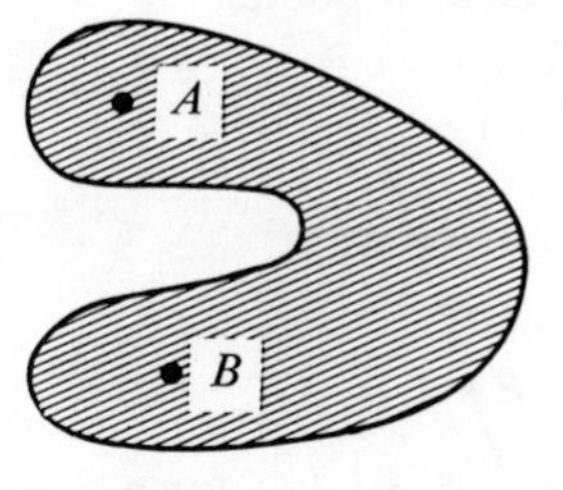

FIGURE 6–48

curve, is to be considered. Specifically, the points A and B are elements of this region. Being distinct points, they determine a segment, $\overline{AB}$. If one were to draw a representation of this segment $\overline{AB}$, it is visually apparent that some points of the segment would lie *outside* the region. That is, $\overline{AB}$ is not a subset of the region.

On the other hand, there are regions in which it is impossible to single out two points such that part of the segment joining them lies outside the region. That is, for any two points in such a region, the segment determined by the points is a subset of the region. Examples of such regions are commonplace. Consider the circular region and the triangular region shown in Figure 6–49. It is easy to see that the segment joining each pair of points of either of these regions

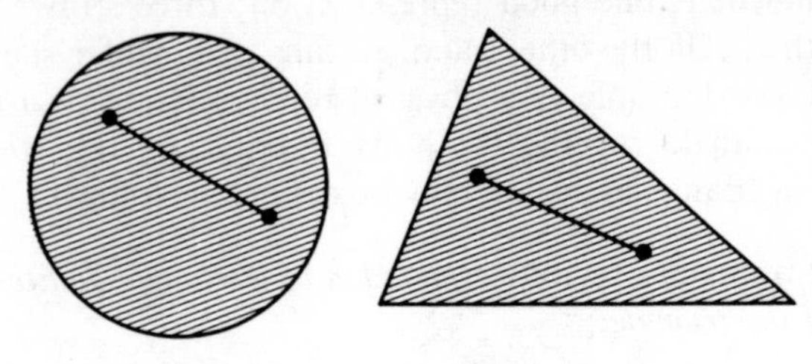

FIGURE 6–49

is a subset of the region. A set of points with this property is said to be *convex*, and the following definition is made:

DEFINITION: *A set of points is said to be a* convex set *if, for every pair of points in the set, the segment determined by the points is a subset of the given set.*

There are sets of points other than regions which are convex. For example, a line is a convex set since the segment joining any two points of the line is a subset of the line. Segments and rays are also convex sets. On the other hand, while the interior of an angle is convex, the angle itself is not convex. (Why?) Other examples of convex sets may be found in the exercises.

6.18 EXERCISES

1. (a) Give as many different names as possible for the angle shown below, using the indicated points.

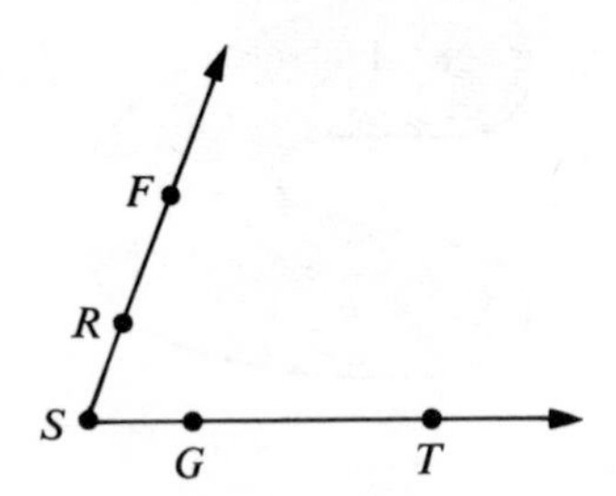

   (b) In the angle above, what is the point S called?
   (c) Give a precise definition of the interior of $\angle RST$.
2. Criticize the following "definition":
   An angle is the union of two rays.
3. Determine whether each of the following statements is true or false:
   (a) Every closed curve is a simple closed curve.
   (b) Every simple closed curve is a closed curve.

(c) Every polygon is a closed curve.
(d) Every polygon is a simple closed curve.
(e) Every simple closed curve is a polygon.
(f) A circle is a polygon.
(g) A circle is a simple closed curve.
(h) A triangle is a polygon.
(i) A triangle is a simple closed curve.
(j) The union of any three segments is a triangle.
(k) A polygon composed of three segments is a triangle.

4. (a) Draw a closed curve which is not a simple closed curve.
(b) Draw a simple closed curve which is not a polygon.
(c) Draw a simple closed curve which is a polygon.
(d) Draw a region which is convex.
(e) Draw a region which is not convex.
(f) Draw a polygon composed of four segments and such that its polygonal region is convex.
(g) Draw a polygon composed of four segments and such that its polygonal region is not convex.

5. Decide whether each of the following sets is convex or not convex:

(a) triangle
(b) triangular region
(c) angle
(d) interior of an angle
(e) exterior of an angle
(f) ray
(g) half line
(h) half plane
(i) half space
(j) line
(k) segment
(l) circle
(m) circular region
(n) simple closed curve
(o) polygon
(p) polygonal region

6. (a) Draw two convex regions whose union is also convex.
(b) Draw two convex regions whose union is not convex.

7. (a) Is a plane convex? Explain.
(b) Is the union of two half planes convex? Explain.

8. Is the intersection of two convex sets necessarily convex? Explain.

6.19 REFERENCE QUESTIONS

1. Does every simple closed curve have an interior and an exterior? For a discussion of the significance of the answer to this question, see

Kasner, Edward and Newman, James. *Mathematics and the Imagination.* New York: Simon and Schuster, 1940. Pp. 265–298.

2. What is a simple closed surface? For the answer, see

Rutland, Leon and Hosier, Max. "Some Basic Geometric Ideas for the Elementary Teacher," *The Arithmetic Teacher*, 8: 357–362; 1961.

7 MODULAR ARITHMETIC

IN EARLIER CHAPTERS, *we have discussed the set of whole numbers (or cardinal numbers) and their important properties. In this chapter, we shall develop a special kind of arithmetic of whole numbers, called* modular arithmetic. *Because this chapter deals exclusively with the whole numbers, the word "number" should, throughout the chapter, be interpreted to mean "whole number." We begin our study with a brief review of division.*

7.1 REMAINDERS; EQUAL REMAINDERS

It will be recalled that when a is divided by b (section 4.8), we have

$$a = bq + r, \quad 0 \leq r < b.$$

Thus, if the number 39 is divided by the number 5, one obtains a quotient of 7 and a remainder of 4; that is, $39 = 5 \cdot 7 + 4$. In this chapter, we shall be especially concerned with the remainder in division. Therefore, it is emphasized again that the remainder is to be less than the divisor. For instance, in dividing by 5, the remainder must be a member of the following set of numbers:

$$\{0, 1, 2, 3, 4\}$$

Thus, division by 5 gives rise to precisely five possible remainders.

EXAMPLE 1. If the number 7 is used as divisor, what are the possible remainders?

Solution: Here it must be the case that $0 \leq r < 7$. Therefore, the set of possible remainders is $\{0, 1, 2, 3, 4, 5, 6\}$. We note that there are seven of them.

EXAMPLE 2. If the number n is used as divisor, what are the possible remainders?

Solution: $\{0, 1, 2, \ldots, n - 1\}$.

We noted above that dividing 39 by 5 yields a remainder of 4. Also, 14 divided by 5 gives a remainder of 4. We say then that the numbers 14 and 39 yield *equal remainders* when divided by 5, and this is a phrase we shall refer to often in sections to follow. Of course, there are many other numbers which yield remainder 4 when divided by 5 (e.g., 4, 9, 34).

7.2 MULTIPLES

What is meant by a multiple of a number? We say, for example, that 12 is a multiple of 3 since $12 = 3 \cdot 4$. A number n is a multiple of 3 if there is a whole number k such that $n = 3 \cdot k$. We may then indicate the set of multiples of 3 as follows:

$$\{3 \cdot 0,\ 3 \cdot 1,\ 3 \cdot 2,\ 3 \cdot 3,\ \ldots,\ 3 \cdot k,\ \ldots\}$$

Of course, multiples of any whole number n may be defined in a way analogous to that in which multiples of 3 were defined above. Let n be a whole number; then the set of multiples of n is as follows:

$$\{n \cdot 0,\ n \cdot 1,\ n \cdot 2,\ \ldots,\ n \cdot k,\ \ldots\}$$

EXAMPLE 3. What numbers are multiples of 7?

Solution: $0, 7, 14, 21, 28, \ldots, 7k, \ldots$

EXAMPLE 4. Is 147 a multiple of 7?

Solution: $147 = 7 \cdot 21$. Therefore, 147 is of the form $7k$, with k a whole number. So 147 is a multiple of 7.

EXAMPLE 5. Is 38 a multiple of 5?

Solution: There is no whole number k such that $38 = 5k$. Hence, 38 is not a multiple of 5.

On the basis of the above examples, we may formulate the following definition:

DEFINITION: *A whole number a is a* multiple of *a whole number b if there is a whole number k such that* $a = b \cdot k$.

Suppose that two numbers, a and a', yield equal remainders when divided by the same number b. Thus, with

$$a = bq + r, \quad 0 \leq r < b, \tag{1}$$

$$a' = bq' + r', \quad 0 \leq r' < b, \tag{2}$$

we also have

$$r = r'. \tag{3}$$

From equalities (1), (2), and (3) above we shall deduce a significant conclusion. From (1) we have

$$r = a - bq. \tag{4}$$

And from (2) we have

$$r' = a' - bq'. \tag{5}$$

Then, since $r = r'$, we may write:

$$a - bq = a' - bq' \tag{6}$$

$$a - a' = bq - bq' \tag{7}$$

$$a - a' = b(q - q') \tag{8}$$

Note that the distributive property was used to form equality (8) from equality (7). Look carefully at (8). The left member of this equality represents the difference between a and a' (we assume here $a \geq a'$). The right member represents a multiple of the number b since it is the product of b and the whole number $q - q'$. Therefore, we may place the following verbal interpretation upon equality (8): The difference between a and a' is a multiple of b. Recalling the assumption we made at the outset, we have proved the following:

If two numbers a and a' yield equal remainders when divided by the same number b, then the difference between a and a' is a multiple of b.

As a specific instance of this theorem, consider again the numbers 39 and 14. As noted earlier, these numbers yield equal remainders when divided by 5. The above theorem then guarantees that the difference between them is a multiple of 5. This is easily seen to be the case since

$$39 - 14 = 25 = 5 \cdot 5.$$

We can also argue "in the opposite direction" by supposing that two numbers a and a' differ by a multiple of b and by then concluding that a and a' yield equal remainders when divided by b. The proof is outlined below:

We are assuming that a and a' ($a \geq a'$) differ by a multiple of b. So we can write

$$a - a' = bk. \tag{9}$$

Now both a and a' can be divided by b, giving rise to the following:

$$a = bq + r, \quad 0 \leq r < b \tag{10}$$

$$a' = bq' + r', \quad 0 \leq r' < b \tag{11}$$

Note that r is the remainder when a is divided by b, and r' is the remainder when a' is divided by b.

From equality (9), we know

$$a = bk + a'. \tag{12}$$

But from equality (11), we know that a' may be replaced by $bq' + r'$. Therefore,

$$a = bk + (bq' + r'), \quad 0 \leq r' < b. \tag{13}$$

Applying the appropriate associative, commutative, and distributive properties to (13), we write

$$a = b(q' + k) + r', \quad 0 \leq r' < b. \tag{14}$$

Now compare equalities (10) and (14). Each is derived from the division, $a \div b$, with remainder less than b. But this can be done in only one way. Hence, the two remainders must be equal; that is, $r = r'$.

This completes the proof, and we can state:

If two numbers a and a' differ by a multiple of b, then they yield equal remainders when divided by b.

Consider the numbers 10 and 22. They differ by 12, which is a multiple of 6. Therefore, we can be sure that 10 and 22 give equal remainders when divided by 6. (In fact, each gives a remainder of 4.)

It should be clear now that we have the following two results:

If $a \geq a'$ and $a - a' = bk$, then a and a' yield equal remainders when divided by b.

If a and a' yield equal remainders when divided by b, and $a \geq a'$, then $a - a'$ is a multiple of b.

7.4 EXERCISES

1. (a) What is the remainder when 28 is divided by 6?
   (b) List the set of whole numbers between 0 and 50 which yield a remainder of 2 when divided by 6.
   (c) Let S designate the set of all whole numbers yielding remainder 2 when divided by 6. Which of the following statements are true, and which are false?

$$104 \in S$$
$$6 \in S$$
$$0 \in S$$
$$2 \in S$$
$$2 + 6 \in S$$
$$2 + 6 + 6 \in S$$
$$2 + (6 \cdot 5) \in S$$
$$2 + 6k \in S \quad \text{(where } k \text{ is a whole number)}$$
$$6k \in S \quad \text{(where } k \text{ is a whole number)}$$

2. (a) List the set of possible remainders when 5 is used as divisor.
   (b) How many elements are contained in the set of possible remainders when each of the following numbers is used as divisor?

   5, 6, 100, 837, d

   (c) Use the roster method to indicate the set of possible remainders when the whole number d is used as divisor.
3. (a) Is 35 a multiple of 5? Explain.
   (b) Is 32 a multiple of 5? Explain.
   (c) Is any whole number a multiple of 1? Explain.
   (d) Is any whole number a multiple of itself? Explain.
4. (a) The difference between 30 and 24 is 6, which is a multiple of 1, of 2, of 3, and of 6. For what divisors do 30 and 24 yield equal remainders?
   (b) The difference between 12 and 25 is 13. For what divisors do 12 and 25 yield equal remainders?
   (c) If a and b are two whole numbers which differ by 18, for what divisors do a and b yield equal remainders?
   (d) If r and s are two whole numbers such that $r - s = 7$, for what divisors do r and s yield equal remainders?
5. Find two whole numbers which yield equal remainders when divided by 1, by 3, by 5, or by 15, and do not yield equal remainders when divided by any other number.
   (a) What is the difference between the two numbers? (Hint: The difference must be a multiple of 1, 3, 5, and 15, but not of any other number.)
   (b) If 40 is the smaller number, what is the larger?
   (c) If 90 is the larger number, what is the smaller?
   (d) If x represents one of the numbers, how may the other be represented?

We shall now make use of the above properties of remainders to formulate the definition of a new and important kind of mathematical relation called a *congruence relation.* For illustrative purposes, consider two numbers a and a' that yield equal remainders when divided by 5. This number, 5, in this context, will be called a *modulus.* We shall say that a and a' are congruent with respect to the modulus 5, or that they are "congruent (modulo 5)."

The selection of a modulus is arbitrary. Any whole number n (other than 0 or 1) may be chosen. Then the following definition of *congruence (modulo n)* is made:

DEFINITION: *Given two whole numbers a and a', a is* congruent to *a'* (modulo *n*) *if a and a' yield equal remainders when divided by n.*

The relation "a is congruent to a' (modulo n)" may be expressed more succinctly as follows:

$$a \equiv a' \pmod{n}$$

Note that, when indicating congruence of two numbers, it is essential to indicate also the modulus. We have seen that 21 and 16 are congruent (mod 5). However, it is not true that 21 and 16 are congruent (mod 4). Thus, if one simply writes "$21 \equiv 16$," the sentence can be judged neither true nor false, and so is useless.

Because we have already established that two numbers yield equal remainders upon division by n if and only if the difference of the two numbers is a multiple of n, congruence of two numbers may also be defined in the following way:

Given two whole numbers a and a' $(a > a')$, $a \equiv a' \pmod{n}$ *if* $a - a'$ *is a multiple of n; that is,* $a \equiv a' \pmod{n}$ *if* $a - a' = nk$, *where k is a whole number.*

In order to ensure an understanding of the above definitions, some examples of congruent numbers are given below.

EXAMPLE 6. $11 \equiv 27 \pmod{4}$
Both 11 and 27 give a remainder of 3 when divided by 4. Also, it may be noted that the difference $27 - 11$ is 16, which is a multiple of 4.

EXAMPLE 7. $6 \equiv 10 \pmod{2}$
Both 6 and 10 give a remainder of 0 when divided by 2. Or again, the difference between 10 and 6 is 4, which is a multiple of 2.

EXAMPLE 8. $6 \not\equiv 10 \pmod{3}$
6 and 10 do *not* give the same remainder when divided by 3. Also, the difference between 10 and 6 is not a multiple of 3.

7.6 PROPERTIES OF A CONGRUENCE RELATION

It seems almost trivial to say that any number a is congruent to itself (mod n), for if a is divided by n, there is precisely one remainder less than n which can be obtained. Then too, $a - a$ is 0, and 0 is a multiple of any whole number n. "Any number is congruent to itself" is then a property of a congruence relation. Thus we write:

$a \equiv a \pmod{n}$. REFLEXIVITY OF $\equiv$

Suppose $a \equiv b \pmod{n}$. This means that the numbers a and b yield equal remainders when divided by n. We can just as well write, then, "$b \equiv a \pmod{n}$." This property (being able to "reverse" the numbers in a congruence) we write as:

If $a \equiv b \pmod{n}$, *then* $b \equiv a \pmod{n}$. SYMMETRY OF $\equiv$

Next, suppose $a \equiv b \pmod{n}$ and $b \equiv c \pmod{n}$. Suppose further that dividing the numbers a, b, and c by the number n yields the remainders r, r', r'', respectively. Since $a \equiv b \pmod{n}$, we know their remainders are equal; that is, $r = r'$. And since $b \equiv c \pmod{n}$, we know their remainders are equal; that is, $r' = r''$. But if $r = r'$ and $r' = r''$, then $r = r''$; that is, a and c yield equal remainders when divided by n; therefore, $a \equiv c \pmod{n}$. This property of a congruence relation is expressed as follows:

If $a \equiv b \pmod{n}$ *and* $b \equiv c \pmod{n}$, *then* $a \equiv c \pmod{n}$.

TRANSITIVITY OF $\equiv$

Note well the three properties just discussed—reflexivity, symmetry, and transitivity. Recall that any relation which possesses these three properties is called an *equivalence relation* (section 1.13). Thus, a congruence relation (for any specified modulus) is an equivalence relation.

7.7 RESIDUE CLASSES (mod 3)

We have seen that a congruence relation is an equivalence relation; it has the three properties of reflexivity, symmetry, and transitivity. And it was noted in Chapter 1 that any equivalence relation partitions a set. It follows then that a congruence relation partitions the set of whole numbers. Let us see precisely how this partitioning is effected.

In order to begin with as concrete a case as possible, let us specify a modulus, say 3. Any two numbers which yield the same remainder when divided by 3 are congruent (mod 3). Let us first list the set of numbers which yield remainder 0 when divided by 3. This set is indicated below:

$$\{0, 3, 6, 9, 12, 15, \ldots\}$$

Any two elements of this set are congruent (mod 3). Each of them yields a remainder of 0 when divided by 3. The difference between any two of them is a multiple of 3. This set shall be designated C_0, the "0" subscript suggesting remainder 0. Hence, we write

$$C_0 = \{0, 3, 6, 9, 12, 15, \ldots\}.$$

Next we consider all numbers which give a remainder of 1 when divided by 3, and use the symbol C_1 to denote the set of all such numbers:

$$C_1 = \{1, 4, 7, 10, 13, 16, \ldots\}$$

Again, any two elements of this set are congruent (mod 3).

Finally, we consider the set of all numbers yielding a remainder of 2 when divided by 3:

$$C_2 = \{2, 5, 8, 11, 14, 17, \ldots\}$$

Observe that every whole number is in one of these sets—C_0, C_1, C_2. For if a whole number is divided by 3, the remainder is 0, 1, or 2. Furthermore, no whole number is in two different sets. We have then three disjoint subsets of the whole numbers. And again we see an equivalence relation—congruence (mod 3)—partitioning a set.

The three disjoint subsets C_0, C_1, C_2 are called *residue classes* (mod 3). We may refine our language then to say that the equivalence relation "congruent (mod 3)" partitions the set of whole numbers into three residue classes. Note that each of the residue classes contains an infinite number of elements.

7.8 RESIDUE CLASSES (mod n)

In the preceding section, the number 3 was selected as modulus, and three residue classes were determined. If modulus 5 had been specified, five residue classes would have resulted, as follows:

$$\begin{aligned} C_0 &= \{0, 5, 10, 15, 20, 25, \ldots\} \\ C_1 &= \{1, 6, 11, 16, 21, 26, \ldots\} \\ C_2 &= \{2, 7, 12, 17, 22, 27, \ldots\} \\ C_3 &= \{3, 8, 13, 18, 23, 28, \ldots\} \\ C_4 &= \{4, 9, 14, 19, 24, 29, \ldots\} \end{aligned}$$

There are five residue classes (mod 5), because when 5 is used as divisor, only the remainders 0, 1, 2, 3, 4 are obtainable. Hence, any whole number is an element of one and only one of the residue classes above.

In fact, any whole number n (except 0 or 1) may be selected as modulus, with the result that the whole numbers will be partitioned into n residue classes (mod n). These n classes correspond to the n possible remainders, 0, 1, 2, . . . , $n - 1$, when dividing by n. The classes may be indicated as follows:

$$\begin{aligned} C_0 &= \{\ 0,\ n,\ 2n,\ 3n,\ 4n,\ 5n, \ldots\} \\ C_1 &= \{\ 1,\ 1+n,\ 1+2n,\ 1+3n,\ 1+4n,\ 1+5n, \ldots\} \\ C_2 &= \{\ 2,\ 2+n,\ 2+2n,\ 2+3n,\ 2+4n,\ 2+5n, \ldots\} \\ &\vdots \\ C_{n-1} &= \{n-1, 2n-1, 3n-1, 4n-1, 5n-1, 6n-1, \ldots\} \end{aligned}$$

In any residue class, any two elements are congruent (mod n). Hence, any two elements must differ by a multiple of n. So, given an element of a residue class (mod n), other elements can be determined by progressively adding n.

We summarize the preceding discussion with the following compact theorem:

THEOREM: *The whole numbers are partitioned into n residue classes* (mod n).

7.9 EXERCISES

1. For each of the following statements, indicate whether it is true or false:
   (a) $6 \equiv 18 \pmod 3$
   (b) $6 \equiv 18 \pmod 2$
   (c) $6 \equiv 18 \pmod 6$
   (d) $6 \equiv 18 \pmod{18}$
   (e) $6 \equiv 18 \pmod 5$
   (f) $11 \equiv 22 \pmod 2$
   (g) $11 \equiv 11 \pmod 2$
   (h) $11 \equiv 11 \pmod 7$
   (i) $4 \equiv 4 \pmod 7$
   (j) $2 \equiv 2 + 5k \pmod 5$ (where k is a whole number)
2. Suppose that a and b are two whole numbers such that $a \equiv b \pmod 5$. State two relationships between the numbers a and b which must then be true.
3. (a) What is the number of residue classes (mod 3)?
   (b) Use the roster method to indicate the members of each of the residue classes (mod 3).
   (c) How many elements does each residue class (mod 3) contain?
   (d) Determine which residue class (mod 3) each of the following whole numbers is an element of:

   9, 10, 11, 12, 30, 31, 32, 33, 57, 58, 100, 333, 334

   (e) Is every whole number an element of one of the residue classes (mod 3)?
4. (a) What is the number of residue classes (mod 6)?
   (b) Use the roster method to indicate the members of each of the residue classes (mod 6).
   (c) Determine which residue class (mod 6) each of the following whole numbers is an element of:

   6, 7, 8, 24, 25, 26, 27, 28, 29, 60, 61, 65, 100, 6000
5. (a) What is the number of residue classes (mod 25)?
   (b) Determine which residue class (mod 25) each of the following whole numbers is an element of:

   25, 26, 50, 51, 100, 105, 150, 155, 200, 223, 225, 227
6. (a) What is the number of residue classes (mod n)?
   (b) Determine which residue class (mod n) each of the following whole numbers is an element of:

   $2,\ 2 + n,\ 2 + 2n,\ 3,\ 3 + 2n,\ 3 + n,\ 100n$ (assume $n > 3$)

Consider again residue classes (mod 3). As we have seen, there are three such classes; they are listed again below for reference:

$$C_0 = \{0, 3, 6, 9, 12, 15, \ldots\}$$
$$C_1 = \{1, 4, 7, 10, 13, 16, \ldots\}$$
$$C_2 = \{2, 5, 8, 11, 14, 17, \ldots\}$$

Suppose we wish to define the sum $C_1 + C_2$. In order to do this, select any element of C_1—say 4; and select any element of C_2—say 8. Now determine the sum $4 + 8$, which is 12. 12 is an element of C_0. Therefore, by definition, we say $C_1 + C_2 = C_0$. We leave it to the reader to verify the fact that the result is independent of the particular elements chosen; that is, if any element of C_1 is added to any element of C_2, then an element of C_0 is obtained. In this way, we may construct an addition table for residue classes (mod 3) as follows:

$+$	C_0	C_1	C_2
C_0	C_0	C_1	C_2
C_1	C_1	C_2	C_0
C_2	C_2	C_0	C_1

The above table shows that we have defined an operation (internal law of composition) over the set $\{C_0, C_1, C_2\}$. We have arbitrarily called this operation "addition" because of the way in which it was defined; however, it is not the same as addition of whole numbers since it is residue classes—not whole numbers—that are being "added" here.

In an earlier chapter, we saw that addition of whole numbers possesses certain properties, such as commutativity, associativity, and an identity element. Let us check each of these properties in turn to see if addition of residue classes (mod 3) also possesses them.

1) *Commutativity.* This property can be checked easily by simply investigating each possible sum; e.g.,

$$C_1 + C_2 = C_2 + C_1.$$

Also, the fact that the pattern of the addition table is symmetric about the diagonal running from upper left corner to lower right corner indicates that the operation is commutative.

2) *Associativity.* It takes a bit more brute force to investigate each possible case here. (There are 27 of them!) Consider one such case:

$$(C_1 + C_2) + C_1 = C_0 + C_1 = C_1$$
$$C_1 + (C_2 + C_1) = C_1 + C_0 = C_1$$

Thus,

$$(C_1 + C_2) + C_1 = C_1 + (C_2 + C_1)$$

and associativity is verified in this instance. Though we shall not take the space to do it here, it can be shown to hold in every other instance also.

3) *Identity Element.* From the table, it is easily seen that C_0 serves as an identity element for addition of residue classes (mod 3).

Hence, addition of residue classes (mod 3) is commutative and associative, and does possess an identity element.

This operation possesses another property which addition of whole numbers does not possess. Consider any element of the set—say C_1. Is there an element of the set which can be added to C_1 to obtain the identity element? C_2 is such an element, since $C_1 + C_2 = C_2 + C_1 = C_0$. Because of this, C_2 is said to be an *inverse element* of C_1 for the given operation. And so we are led to a fourth property of addition of residue classes (mod 3):

4) *Inverse Element.* From the table, it is observed that each element of the set possesses an inverse element. (Note that C_0 is its own inverse.)

These four properties have been emphasized for a reason; they are the defining properties of a mathematical structure called a *commutative group.* A commutative group is composed of a set of elements together with an operation defined for the set and such that the above four properties hold. (If the commutative property does not hold, but the other three properties do, then the structure is still identified as a group, but not a commutative group.) Thus, the residue classes (mod 3) constitute a commutative group under the operation of addition.

Multiplication of residue classes (mod 3) may be defined in a manner analogous to that in which addition was defined. Thus, the product $C_1 \cdot C_2$ may be determined by selecting any two elements of these residue classes—say 4 and 5, respectively. The product $4 \cdot 5$ is 20, and 20 is an element of C_2. Therefore, by definition, $C_1 \cdot C_2 = C_2$. Again it is emphasized that the result is independent of the particular element chosen from each residue class. Construction of a multiplication table and identification of properties of multiplication of residue classes (mod 3) are left for the exercises.

In this section, the residue classes (mod 3) were selected for illustrative purposes. Similar results would have been obtained had any other modulus been specified.

7.11 RESIDUE CLASSES AND MULTIPLES

Of special interest is the residue class C_0 (mod n). Recall that this class may be indicated as

$$C_0 = \{0, n, 2n, 3n, 4n, 5n, \ldots\}.$$

We notice immediately that this is simply the set of *multiples* of n; that is, the set of whole numbers which are multiples of n is equal to the residue class C_0 (mod n). This of course is consistent with the theory developed earlier. For, by definition, a multiple of n yields a remainder of 0 when divided by n. Hence, any multiple of n is congruent to 0 (mod n).

Suppose $a \equiv a'$ (mod n). Then we know that $a - a'$ is a multiple of n (assuming $a \geq a'$). Therefore, as in the preceding paragraph, $a - a'$ is an element of C_0 (mod n); that is to say, $a - a' \equiv 0$ (mod n). We state this precisely as follows:

If $a \equiv a'$ (mod n), *then* $a - a' \equiv 0$ (mod n).

A specific example here may help to clarify this statement. Let a be 19, a' be 13, and n be 3. $19 \equiv 13$ (mod 3) since each number yields a remainder of 1 when divided by 3. The difference between 19 and 13 is 6, which is a multiple of 3. Therefore, $6 \equiv 0 \pmod 3$. Or, $19 - 13 \equiv 0 \pmod 3$.

7.12 EXERCISES

1. Construct a multiplication table for the residue classes (mod 3).
   (a) Is this operation commutative?
   (b) Is this operation associative?
   Show that $(C_2 \cdot C_2) \cdot C_1 = C_2 \cdot (C_2 \cdot C_1)$ using the table you constructed.
   (c) What is the identity element for multiplication of the residue classes (mod 3)?
2. Construct a table for addition of residue classes (mod 4).
   (a) Using the table, show that $(C_2 + C_1) + C_3 = C_2 + (C_1 + C_3)$.
   (b) What is the identity element for the operation?
   (c) Determine the inverse element (if any) for each residue class.
   (d) Do the residue classes (mod 4) constitute a commutative group under addition?
3. Construct a table for multiplication of residue classes (mod 4).
   (a) What is the identity element for the operation?
   (b) Determine the inverse element (if any) for each residue class. (Remember that the product of each element and its inverse must be the identity element.)
   (c) Do the residue classes (mod 4) constitute a commutative group under multiplication?
4. (a) Given a set and an operation defined for the set, what properties must the operation have in order for the set to constitute a commutative group under the operation?
   (b) Consider the set of whole numbers and the operation of addition defined for this set. Why do the whole numbers *not* constitute a commutative group under addition?
5. If x and y are two whole numbers $(x > y)$ such that $x \equiv y \pmod n$, then to what number must $x - y$ be congruent $\pmod n$?

7.13 CLOCK ARITHMETICS

Certain finite mathematical systems, often called *clock arithmetics*, are sometimes confused with modular arithmetic. To be sure, there are certain similarities; but there are also important distinctions which should be understood. And so we turn our attention in this last section to clock arithmetic.

Consider the numbers represented on the face of a clock. There are precisely twelve such numbers: 1, 2, 3, 4, 5, 6, 7, 8, 9, 10, 11, 12. If the time is 9 o'clock, then 6 hours later it will be 3 o'clock. Thus, the statement "$9 + 6 = 3$" is not without some meaning in terms of clock time (we are ignoring A.M. and P.M. designations). In fact, a complete addition table could be set up for "clock addition."

To illustrate an addition table, let us consider a special clock of only four numbers. The face of such a clock is represented at the right. Here, addition is interpreted physically as a clock hand moving clockwise. Thus, if one begins at 1 and moves "one hour," he arrives at 2; that is, $1 + 1 = 2$. Similarly, $1 + 2 = 3$, and $1 + 3 = 0$. A complete addition table for this "clock arithmetic" is given below:

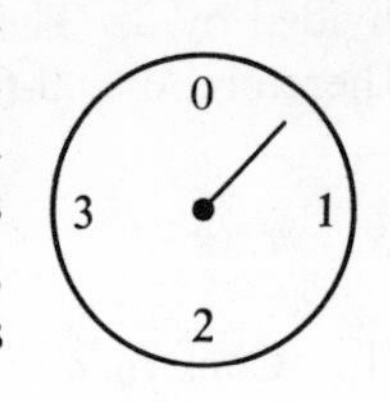

+	0	1	2	3
0	0	1	2	3
1	1	2	3	0
2	2	3	0	1
3	3	0	1	2

In order to construct a multiplication table for this clock arithmetic, imagine four "push buttons" installed below the face of the clock, as in the figure below. The number named on each button indicates how many positions the dial will move in a clockwise direction when that button is pushed. Thus, if the pointer is set at 0, and the "2" button is pushed once, the pointer moves to 2. In effect, $1 \times 2 = 2$. Had the "2" button been pushed twice in succession, the pointer would have moved first to 2, and then to 0; that is, $2 \times 2 = 0$. If the "2" button had been pushed 3 times in succession, the pointer would have come to rest at 2, indicating $3 \times 2 = 2$.

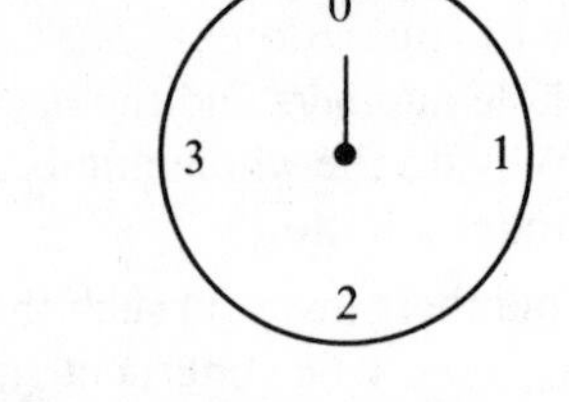

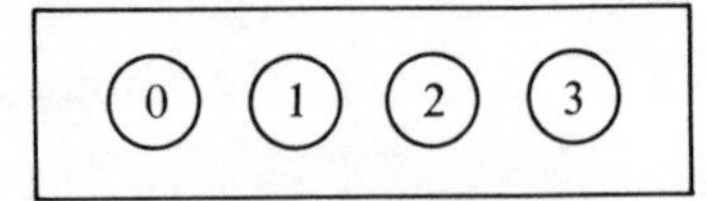

This physical appeal to a clock face and "push buttons" may be used to construct a complete multiplication table. (The buttons have different effects, of course. The "3" button results in an advance of three positions with each push, the "1" button in an advance of only one position, and the "0" button in no advance at all.) Actual construction of the table is left for the exercises.

One may work with a clock arithmetic based on a "clock" of any specified number of "hours." But there is an important distinction between a clock arithmetic and modular arithmetic. Consider the clock system above. There are precisely four elements—0, 1, 2, and 3. There is no such thing, for example, as "20 o'clock" in this system. Such a system is called a *finite system* because it contains a finite number—not an endless number—of elements.

On the other hand, we saw that modular arithmetic is an arithmetic of all the whole numbers. Given any modulus, every whole number is a member of one of the residue classes corresponding to that modulus. In subsequent chapters, we shall see that modular arithmetic has an important role to play in certain aspects of mathematics.

7.14 EXERCISES

1. Consider the addition table developed in the text for a clock arithmetic consisting of the elements {0, 1, 2, 3}.
   (a) Is the addition commutative?
   (b) Is the operation associative?
   (c) Is there an identity element for the operation?
   (d) Does each element have an inverse element?
   (e) Is this clock arithmetic a commutative group under addition?
2. Construct the multiplication table for a clock arithmetic based on a clock face with numerals 0, 1, 2, and 3. (Follow the suggestion in the text concerning use of "push buttons" to obtain products.)
   (a) Is this operation commutative?
   (b) Is this operation associative?
   (c) Is there an identity element for multiplication?
   (d) Does each element have an inverse element?
   (e) Do we have here an instance of a commutative group under multiplication?
3. Develop a clock arithmetic for a "clock" with numerals 0, 1, 2, 3, 4, 5, 6 on its dial by constructing appropriate addition and multiplication tables.
4. What is the most important distinction between the notions of *residue classes* and *clock arithmetic?*

7.15 REFERENCE QUESTIONS

1. Is division always possible in a modular system? For an answer to this question, and a full discussion of clock arithmetics and residue classes, see

   Mueller, Francis J. "Modular Arithmetic," *Enrichment Mathematics for the Grades* (27th yearbook). Washington, D.C.: National Council of Teachers of Mathematics, 1963. Chapter 4.
2. How is "casting out nines" related to modular arithmetic? See

   Haines, Margaret. "Modular Arithmetic," *The Arithmetic Teacher*, 9: 127–129; 1962.

8 TESTS FOR DIVISIBILITY

THERE ARE OCCASIONS *in mathematics when it is necessary to determine whether or not one number is divisible by another. Of course, this can always be determined by employing the division algorism. On the other hand, it is convenient to have rapid tests for divisibility by certain numbers, thus obviating the necessity of actually dividing. It is the purpose of this chapter to develop some of these divisibility tests. First, however, we must be sure that the meaning of the term "divisibility" is clear.*

8.1 MULTIPLES AND DIVISIBILITY

The meaning of "multiple" has already been established. For example, 12 is a multiple of 4 since $12 = 4 \cdot 3$. This in turn implies that the quotient $12 \div 4$ is 3; the remainder is 0, and we say "12 is *divisible by* 4." Note below the relationship between "multiple of" and "divisible by":

12 is a multiple of 4.

12 is divisible by 4.

12 is not a multiple of 5.

12 is not divisible by 5.

Suppose that a number a is a multiple of a number b. Then $a = bk$, where k is a whole number. Thus, $a \div b = k$, remainder 0, and a is divisible by b. On the other hand, if it is first known that $a \div b = k$, then $a = bk$. Hence, if a

is divisible by b, then a is a multiple of b. We conclude then that the following statements are equivalent (if one of them is true, then so is the other):

a is a multiple of b.

a is divisible by b.

By "divisibility test," we mean some method—hopefully, a time-saving one—of determining whether or not one number is divisible by another. In the following sections, we shall develop divisibility tests for certain numbers. Since these tests depend on the system of numeration, the reader may wish to review portions of Chapter 5 as needed.

8.2 DIVISIBILITY BY 10 AND BY 100

In this section, we develop tests for determining the divisibility of a number N by 10 and by 100. Consider a number N, and let its decimal nùmeral be $\overline{u_n \ldots u_2 u_1 u_0}$. Then

$$N = u_n 10^n + \cdots + u_2 10^2 + u_1 10^1 + u_0. \quad (1)$$

Applying the distributive property to equality (1), the following is obtained:

$$N = 10(u_n 10^{n-1} + \cdots + u_2 10 + u_1) + u_0 \quad (2)$$

If the use of the distributive property seems unclear here, observe that if each term in the parentheses in equality (2) is multiplied by the factor 10, then (1) is recovered. Note also that $10 \times 10^{n-1} = 10^n$.

Now (2) in turn implies

$$N - u_0 = 10(u_n 10^{n-1} + \cdots + u_2 10 + u_1). \quad (3)$$

Equality (3) shows that the difference between N and u_0 is a multiple of 10. (Why?) Thus, as established in Chapter 7, since N and u_0 differ by a multiple of 10, $N \equiv u_0 \pmod{10}$.

What is u_0? It is a digit—specifically, the units digit of the decimal numeral for N. Therefore, it is one of the following: 0, 1, 2, 3, 4, 5, 6, 7, 8, 9. Of these, only 0 gives a remainder of 0 when divided by 10. But since $N \equiv u_0 \pmod{10}$, N yields the same remainder as does u_0 when divided by 10. Therefore, if N is to yield a remainder of zero when divided by 10, so must u_0. This means that u_0 must be the digit 0. We conclude:

A number N is divisible by 10 *if and only if the units digit of its decimal numeral is* 0.

For example, the following represent numbers which are divisible by 10:

30, 500, 520, 18760, 18000;

and the following represent numbers which are *not* divisible by 10:

31, 502, 400003, 20202

The test for divisibility by 100 is derived in much the same way. Using the same notations as before,

$$N = u_n 10^n + \cdots + u_2 10^2 + u_1 10 + u_0.$$

This time, however, in applying the distributive property, we use 100 as a multiplier:

$$N = 100(u_n 10^{n-2} + \cdots + u_2) + u_1 10 + u_0 \tag{4}$$

Equality (4) implies

$$N - (u_1 10 + u_0) = 100(u_n 10^{n-2} + \cdots + u_2). \tag{5}$$

From equality (5), it is seen that the difference between N and the number $(u_1 10 + u_0)$ is a multiple of 100. This implies $N \equiv u_1 10 + u_0 \pmod{100}$. And this in turn implies that the numbers N and $u_1 10 + u_0$ yield equal remainders when divided by 100. But what is the number $u_1 10 + u_0$? It is the number named by the *last two digits* (the tens and units digits) of the decimal numeral for N. What are the possibilities for this number? Although we don't take space to list the complete set, we indicate it as follows:

$$\{00, 01, 02, \ldots, 10, 11, 12, \ldots, 20, 21, 22, \ldots, 90, 91, \ldots, 99\}$$

In effect, it is the set of all two-digit numbers. Now, if N is to yield remainder 0 when divided by 100, so must the number $u_1 10 + u_0$. In the above set, only 00 meets this requirement. Therefore, we can say:

> *A number N is divisible by* 100 *if and only if the last two digits of its decimal numeral are zeros.*

For example, 800, 234000, 503000, and 7700 are divisible by 100; but 70080, 87, and 1090 are not divisible by 100.

8.3 DIVISIBILITY BY 2 AND BY 5

In this section, we seek simple tests for divisibility of a number N by 2 and by 5. As in the preceding section, the number N may be expressed as

$$N = 10(u_n 10^{n-1} + \cdots + u_2 10 + u_1) + u_0, \tag{6}$$

which may be written simply as

$$N = 10q + u_0, \tag{7}$$

where q represents the expression in parentheses in equality (6). Thus

$$N - u_0 = 10q \tag{8}$$

and we now have an expression for the difference between N and u_0. We next make use of the fact that $10 = 2 \times 5$ to write

$$N - u_0 = (2 \times 5)q. \tag{9}$$

And the associative principle of multiplication enables us to write

$$N - u_0 = 2(5q). \tag{10}$$

Thus, N and u_0 differ by a multiple of 2. So, $N \equiv u_0 \pmod 2$, and N and u_0 yield equal remainders when divided by 2. The possibilities for u_0 are

0, 1, 2, 3, 4, 5, 6, 7, 8, 9.

Of these, the following give a remainder of 0 when divided by 2: 0, 2, 4, 6, 8. If, therefore, N is to be divisible by 2, u_0 must be one of the five digits listed immediately above. Stated as a divisibility test, we have:

> *A number N is divisible by* 2 *if and only if the units digit of its decimal numeral is an element of the following set:* {0, 2, 4, 6, 8}.

For example, 32, 7778, 110, and 258 are divisible by 2; but 447, 101, and 22223 are not divisible by 2.

Look again at equality (9). It may just as well be written as

$$N - u_0 = 5(2q). \tag{11}$$

It may be inferred from equality (11) that N and u_0 differ by a multiple of 5; they are therefore congruent (mod 5). Hence, if N is to be divisible by 5, the units digit u_0 must be divisible by 5. Of the ten possible digits, only 0 and 5 yield a remainder of 0 when divided by 5. We are led then to the following divisibility test:

> *A number N is divisible by* 5 *if and only if the units digit of its decimal numeral is an element of the following set:* {0, 5}.

For example, 35, 700, 875, and 9990 are divisible by 5, while 554, 100003, and 504 are not.

Referring to equality (4) of section 8.2, we recall that the number N with decimal numeral $\overline{u_n \ldots u_2u_1u_0}$ may be written as

$$N = 100(u_n10^{n-2} + \cdots + u_2) + u_110 + u_0, \tag{12}$$

which is of the form

$$N = 100q + (u_110 + u_0), \tag{13}$$

where q has replaced the expression in parentheses in equality (12). Now,

$$N - (u_110 + u_0) = 100q, \tag{14}$$

which may be written as

$$N - (u_110 + u_0) = (4 \times 25)q, \quad \text{or} \tag{15}$$

$$N - (u_110 + u_0) = 4(25q), \quad \text{or} \tag{16}$$

$$N - (u_110 + u_0) = 25(4q). \tag{17}$$

It should be borne in mind that the number $u_110 + u_0$ is the number named by the last two digits of the numeral for N. Equality (16) shows that the difference between this number and the number N is a multiple of 4. Therefore, they are congruent (mod 4) and yield the same remainder when divided by 4. Indicated below is the set of two-digit numbers which are divisible by 4:

$$\{00, 04, 08, 12, 16, 20, 24, 28, \ldots, 92, 96\}$$

A number divisible by 4 must have a decimal numeral ending in one of the "digit-pairs" above. We state the divisibility test in the following way:

A number N is divisible by 4 if and only if the number named by the last two digits of its decimal numeral is itself divisible by 4.

For example, 56428 is divisible by 4 since 28 is divisible by 4; but 44414 is not divisible by 4 because 14 is not.

In the same manner, equality (17) implies that the number N and the number $u_110 + u_0$ differ by a multiple of 25, are therefore congruent (mod 25), and therefore give equal remainders when divided by 25. Written below is the set of two-digit numbers divisible by 25:

$$\{00, 25, 50, 75\}$$

A number N is divisible by 25 if and only if its decimal numeral ends in one of these digit-pairs. Following is a statement of this divisibility test:

A number N is divisible by 25 if and only if the number named by the last two digits of its decimal numeral is itself divisible by 25.

For example, 777375 is divisible by 25 because 75 is divisible by 25; but 25257 is not divisible by 25 since 57 is not.

8.5 EXERCISES

1. (a) How many digits are contained in the numeral "3265"?
   (b) Use the expanded notation (powers of ten) to indicate the number named by "3265."
   (c) How many digits are contained in the numeral $\overline{u_3u_2u_1u_0}$?
   (d) Use expanded notation to indicate the number named by $\overline{u_3u_2u_1u_0}$.
   (e) How many digits are contained in the numeral $\overline{u_nu_{n-1}\ldots u_2u_1u_0}$?
   (f) Use expanded notation to indicate the number named by $\overline{u_nu_{n-1}\ldots u_2u_1u_0}$.
2. Explain the difference in meaning of the following two symbols: $\overline{u_1u_0}$; u_1u_0
3. If a and b are two whole numbers such that a is divisible by b and b is divisible by a, what conclusion can be drawn?
4. (a) Is every whole number divisible by 1? Explain.
   (b) Is every whole number divisible by itself? Explain.
5. For each number named in the left-hand column below, indicate by answering "yes" or "no" whether the number is divisible by 2, by 4, by 5, by 10, by 25, by 100:

Number	Divisible by 2	4	5	10	25	100
284						
275						
500						
3225						
3226						
3222						
3220						
8604						
19,675						
19,670						
19,600						
315,516						
315,525						
315,520						
315,500						
111,111						
444,444						
1,000,000,000						
1,000,000,016						
1,000,000,075						
1,000,000,030						

Before proceeding to the next divisibility tests, it is necessary to establish two simple theorems concerning a congruence relation.

Suppose $a \equiv b \pmod{n}$. Then $a - b = kn$; that is, the difference of the numbers is a multiple of n. Next, suppose the numbers a and b are each multiplied by the same number r, obtaining ra and rb. Are these numbers congruent (mod n)? We consider their difference and see that

$ra - rb = r(a - b)$	by the distributive principle.
But $a - b = kn$	as established above.
So $ra - rb = r(kn)$	by substitution and
$ra - rb = (rk)n$	by the associative principle.

The last equation shows clearly that the numbers ra and rb differ by a multiple of n. Therefore, they are congruent (mod n). We reached this conclusion by assuming $a \equiv b \pmod{n}$.

Therefore, we have proved the following theorem:

THEOREM: *If* $a \equiv b \pmod{n}$ *then* $ra \equiv rb \pmod{n}$ *where* r *is a whole number greater than zero.*

Verbally, one may think of multiplying two congruent numbers by the same number; the numbers so obtained are also congruent.

In order to establish the next theorem, we make two assumptions, as follows:

$$a \equiv b \pmod{n}, \qquad c \equiv d \pmod{n}$$

We then know that

$$a - b = kn \quad \text{and} \quad c - d = k'n.$$

Note that although the difference between a and b is a multiple of n and the difference between c and d is a multiple of n, they are not necessarily the same multiple; so two distinct symbols, k and k', are used.

Consider now adding the numbers a and c, and adding the numbers b and d. Are the resulting sums $a + c$ and $b + d$ congruent (mod n)? To answer this question, we need only check to see if their difference is a multiple of n.

$$\begin{aligned}(a + c) - (b + d) &= (a - b) + (c - d)\\ &= kn + k'n\\ &= (k + k')n\end{aligned}$$

Their difference is a multiple of n. Hence $a + c \equiv b + d \pmod{n}$.

Considering our initial assumptions, we have proved the following theorem:

THEOREM: *If* $a \equiv b \pmod{n}$, *and* $c \equiv d \pmod{n}$, *then* $a + c \equiv b + d \pmod{n}$.

Again we invoke the symbol $\overline{u_n u_{n-1} \ldots u_2 u_1 u_0}$ to represent the decimal numeral for a number N. We seek a test for divisibility of this number by 3. We begin by considering the following list of congruences (mod 3):

$$\begin{aligned} 1 &\equiv 1 \pmod{3} \\ 10 &\equiv 1 \pmod{3} \\ 100 &\equiv 1 \pmod{3} \\ 1000 &\equiv 1 \pmod{3} \\ &\vdots \\ 10^n &\equiv 1 \pmod{3} \end{aligned}$$

The list is derived from the fact that any power of 10 is congruent to 1 (mod 3). This is easily verified. As an example, consider the number 10^3, or 1000. One less than 1000 is 999, which is clearly divisible by 3. Therefore, if 1000 is divided by 3, a remainder of 1 results; that is, $1000 \equiv 1 \pmod{3}$. A similar argument applies to any power of 10.

Now, if $10^3 \equiv 1 \pmod{3}$, then $u_3 10^3 \equiv u_3 \pmod{3}$. This is true by virtue of the first theorem proved in the preceding section; that is, both of two congruent numbers have been multiplied by the same number u_3; so the resulting products are also congruent (mod 3). In fact, proceeding through the list of congruences (mod 3) above, we can make a new list, as follows:

$$\begin{aligned} u_0 &\equiv u_0 \pmod{3} \\ u_1 10 &\equiv u_1 \pmod{3} \\ u_2 10^2 &\equiv u_2 \pmod{3} \\ &\vdots \\ u_n 10^n &\equiv u_n \pmod{3} \end{aligned}$$

At this point, the second theorem of the preceding section is applicable; that is, the sum of the left members of the congruences above is congruent to the sum of the right members (mod 3). Specifically,

$$u_n 10^n + \cdots + u_2 10^2 + u_1 10 + u_0 \equiv u_0 + u_1 + \cdots + u_n \pmod{3}.$$

What is the significance of this last equation? On the left, we have the number N itself (recall the meaning of decimal notation). On the right, we have simply the sum of the digits used in the decimal numeral for N.

The conclusion then is that a number N is congruent (mod 3) to the sum of its digits. Therefore, a number N yields the same remainder when divided by 3 as does the number obtained by adding the digits used in writing the numeral for N. The divisibility test is stated as follows:

A number N is divisible by 3 if and only if the sum of the digits of its decimal numeral is itself divisible by 3.

To test whether 73842 is divisible by 3, we see that the sum of the digits, $7 + 3 + 8 + 4 + 2$, or 24, is divisible by 3; therefore, we conclude that 73842 is divisible by 3. But in testing the divisibility of 73843 by 3, we find the sum of the digits is 25, and therefore, we see that 73843 is not divisible by 3.

A divisibility test for 9 may be established in exactly the same manner as that in which the test for 3 was established. This results from the fact that 10^n, any power of 10, is also congruent to 1 (mod 9). Therefore, the list of the previous section can be repeated, this time with a modulus of 9. We simply state the conclusion:

> *A number N is divisible by 9 if and only if the sum of the digits of its decimal numeral is itself divisible by 9.*

For example, 87381 is divisible by 9 since the sum $8 + 7 + 3 + 8 + 1$, or 27, is divisible by 9.

8.8 CASTING OUT NINES

A process commonly known as "casting out nines" has long been a part of arithmetic textbooks, sometimes as standard fare and sometimes as "enrichment," but always as a means of "checking" arithmetic computations. Therefore, it is of interest to note that the process can be validated by invoking some of the conclusions of the preceding sections of this chapter. In order to see how this may be done, let us consider the following problem in addition:

$$\begin{array}{r} 38 \\ 48 \\ 25 \\ \underline{72} \\ 183 \end{array}$$

Considering the first addend, 38, we know $38 \equiv 11 \pmod 9$ because any number is congruent (mod 9) to the sum of the digits of its decimal numeral. $11 \equiv 2 \pmod 9$ for the same reason; and therefore, by the property of transitivity, $38 \equiv 2 \pmod 9$. The other addends can be treated in a similar way so that we have the following congruence:

$$\begin{aligned} 38 &\equiv 2 \pmod 9 \\ 48 &\equiv 3 \pmod 9 \\ 25 &\equiv 7 \pmod 9 \\ 72 &\equiv 0 \pmod 9 \end{aligned}$$

Next, applying the second theorem of section 8.6, we have

$$38 + 48 + 25 + 72 \equiv 2 + 3 + 7 + 0 \pmod 9.$$

Or, since $2 + 3 + 7 + 0 = 12$, and $12 \equiv 3 \pmod 9$,

$$38 + 48 + 25 + 72 \equiv 3 \pmod 9.$$

The sum of the addends, then, must be congruent to 3 (mod 9). So, in order to check the result 183 obtained earlier, it must be shown that $183 \equiv 3 \pmod 9$:

$$\begin{aligned} 183 &\equiv 12 \pmod 9 \\ 12 &\equiv 3 \pmod 9 \\ \text{So } 183 &\equiv 3 \pmod 9. \end{aligned}$$

Thus, the result 183 "checks."

How does the label "casting out nines" arise? The numbers 2, 3, 7, and 0 obtained above are the remainders when 38, 48, 25, and 72, respectively are divided by 9; for, if two numbers are congruent (mod 9), then they yield equal remainders when divided by 9. Thus, to obtain these numbers, one simply "casts out" as many 9's as possible from each addend, and then works with the remainders. The sum of these remainders must be congruent (mod 9) to the sum of the addends.

We introduce another example in addition to illustrate how quickly the process can be applied:

$$\begin{aligned} 87 &\equiv 6 \pmod 9 \\ 92 &\equiv 2 \pmod 9 \\ \underline{39} &\equiv \underline{3} \pmod 9 \\ 218 &\quad 11 \end{aligned}$$

$$218 \equiv 11 \pmod 9$$

since $\quad 2 \equiv 2 \pmod 9$

So the "check" is completed.

While the "casting out nines" process is not without merit, it is important to note that although a correct result is sure to check, so also will certain incorrect results. As one obvious instance, suppose in the example immediately above that the digits "2" and "1" had been transposed in recording the sum. Then 128 would have been recorded as the sum; and, since $128 \equiv 11 \pmod 9$, this incorrect result is accepted by the process.

Casting out nines may also be applied to other operations with whole numbers. The validation is much the same, however, and so we omit further discussion here but include some other operations in the exercises.

8.9 EXERCISES

1. (a) $5 \equiv 14 \pmod 3$. Multiply 5 and 14 each by 4, and show that the resulting products are also congruent (mod 3).
   (b) Multiply 5 and 14 each by 10, and show that the resulting products are also congruent (mod 3).
   (c) State the general theorem of which the results in parts (a) and (b) are specific instances.
2. (a) $31 \equiv 51 \pmod 4$ and $82 \equiv 50 \pmod 4$. Determine the sums $31 + 82$ and $51 + 50$, and show that these sums are also congruent (mod 4).
   (b) State the general theorem of which the result in part (a) is a specific instance.

3. Use the divisibility tests developed in the text to test each of the following numbers for divisibility by 3 and by 9:

870	871	872	873
874	333	3333	33,333
999	9999	99,999	1,435,352
1,435,353	1,435,354	1,435,355	1,435,356
1,000,000,000	1,000,000,011	1,011,111,111	

4. (a) 8754 is divisible by 3, since 6 is divisible by 3. Explain. (Hint: First apply the "sum of digits" test to 8754, and then apply the test again to the resulting number.)
   (b) Apply the "sum of digits" test as many times as possible to test divisibility of 873577 by 3.

5. Perform the following arithmetic computations, and check each by use of the "casting out nines" process.
   (a) $187 + 825 + 557 + 903$ (b) 752×38
   (c) $368 - 241$ (d) $812 - 572$

8.10 DIVISIBILITY BY 11

The last divisibility test which we shall develop in this chapter is one for divisibility by 11. In order to do this, consider first the following list of equalities:

$$10^0 - 1 = 11 \cdot 0$$
$$10^1 + 1 = 11 \cdot 1$$
$$10^2 - 1 = 11 \cdot 9$$
$$10^3 + 1 = 11 \cdot 91$$
$$10^4 - 1 = 11 \cdot 909$$
etc.

Each of these equalities can be verified by direct computation. But what should be especially noted is the following discernible pattern:

An *even* power of 10 *decreased by* 1 is a multiple of 11;
an *odd* power of 10 *increased by* 1 is a multiple of 11.

Thus, if p is any whole number, then $2p$ is an even number and $2p + 1$ is an odd number; and we have:

$10^{2p} - 1$ is a multiple of 11;
$10^{2p+1} + 1$ is a multiple of 11.

Returning now to the above list of equalities, both members of the first equality are multiplied by u_0, both members of the second equality are multiplied by u_1, both members of the third equality are multiplied by u_2, etc., where u_0, u_1, u_2, etc. are the digits of a decimal numeral, as used in previous sections of this chapter. We obtain the following results:

$$
\begin{aligned}
u_0 10^0 - u_0 &= 11 \cdot (0 \cdot u_0) \\
u_1 10^1 + u_1 &= 11 \cdot (1 \cdot u_1) \\
u_2 10^2 - u_2 &= 11 \cdot (9 \cdot u_2) \\
u_3 10^3 + u_3 &= 11 \cdot (91 \cdot u_3) \\
u_4 10^4 - u_4 &= 11 \cdot (909 \cdot u_4) \\
&\text{etc.}
\end{aligned}
$$

Again, we note that in each case the right member of the equality is some multiple of 11. (If a multiple of 11 is multiplied by some whole number, another multiple of 11 is obtained.) In general, then, any equality involving an even power of 10 is of the following form:

$$u_{2p} 10^{2p} - u_{2p} = \text{some multiple of } 11$$

And any equality involving an odd power of 10 is of the following form:

$$u_{2p+1} 10^{2p+1} + u_{2p+1} = \text{some multiple of } 11$$

If, in the last list of equalities, the right members are added and the left members are added, we have

$$u_0 10^0 - u_0 + u_1 10^1 + u_1 + u_2 10^2 - u_2 + u_3 10^3 + u_3 + \cdots = \text{multiple of } 11$$

since, on the right, if multiples of 11 are added, another multiple of 11 is obtained as the sum. This equality may be rewritten as

$$u_0 10^0 + u_1 10^1 + u_2 10^2 + u_3 10^3 + \cdots + (-u_0 + u_1 - u_2 + u_3 - \cdots) = \text{multiple of } 11.$$

Or,

$$u_0 10^0 + u_1 10^1 + u_2 10^2 + u_3 10^3 + \cdots - (u_0 - u_1 + u_2 - u_3 + \cdots) = \text{multiple of } 11.$$

The last equality above shows that any number N (represented in expanded form as $u_0 10^0 + u_1 10^1 + u_2 10^2 + u_3 10^3 + \cdots$) is congruent (mod 11) to the number obtained by adding each digit of an even power of 10 and subtracting each digit of an odd power of 10. (These numbers are congruent (mod 11) since their difference is a multiple of 11.)

EXAMPLE 1. Is the number 964,364,896 divisible by 11?

Solution: Consider the number $6 - 9 + 8 - 4 + 6 - 3 + 4 - 6 + 9$, or 11. The number 11 is divisible by 11. Therefore, the number 964,364,896 is divisible by 11.

The formal statement of the test for divisibility by 11 is stated in two parts as follows, where p is any whole number:

A number N whose decimal numeral is $\overline{u_{2p} \ldots u_2 u_1 u_0}$ *is divisible by* 11 *if*

$u_0 - u_1 + u_2 - \cdots + u_{2p}$ *is divisible by* 11.

A number N whose decimal numeral is $\overline{u_{2p+1} \ldots u_2 u_1 u_0}$ *is divisible by* 11 *if*

$u_0 - u_1 + u_2 - \cdots - u_{2p+1}$ *is divisible by* 11.

EXAMPLE 2. Test 48,357 for divisibility by 11.

Solution: $7 - 5 + 3 - 8 + 4 = 1$.
1 is not divisible by 11.
Therefore, 48,357 is not divisible by 11.

To avoid adding and subtracting alternately, we can write:

$$u_0 - u_1 + u_2 - u_3 + \cdots = (u_0 + u_2 + u_4 + \cdots) - (u_1 + u_3 + u_5 + \cdots) \qquad \text{(A)}$$

If the sum of the first expression in parentheses is less than the sum of the second, we can always add a multiple of 11 to the first sum so that it exceeds the second sum.

EXAMPLE 3. Is 988,152 divisible by 11?

Solution: $(2 + 1 + 8) - (5 + 8 + 9) = (11 + \textcircled{11}) - (22) = 0$.
Because 0 is divisible by 11, we may conclude that 988,152 is divisible by 11.

From the following example we see that "casting out elevens" may also be used as a check for computation since a number and the difference of the sums of its even and odd place digits are congruent modulus eleven.

EXAMPLE 4.

$$\begin{array}{rll} 684 \equiv & 2 \pmod{11} & (6 + 4) - (8) \\ 293 \equiv & 7 \pmod{11} & (2 + 3 + \textcircled{11}) - (9) \\ \underline{549} \equiv & \underline{10} \pmod{11} & (5 + 9) - (4) \\ 1526 \equiv & 19 \pmod{11} \equiv 8 \pmod{11} & \\ \Downarrow & & \end{array}$$

$$(6 + 5) - (2 + 1) = 8$$

8.11 NUMBERS, NUMERALS, AND DIVISIBILITY

In discussing the divisibility tests in this chapter, reference has frequently been made to the decimal system of numeration. Is such reference necessary, or are the divisibility tests independent of the system of numeration used?

In order to answer this question, consider the sets A and B below. Denote the cardinality of set A by the symbol "n(A)." And denote the cardinality of set B by the symbol "n(B)."

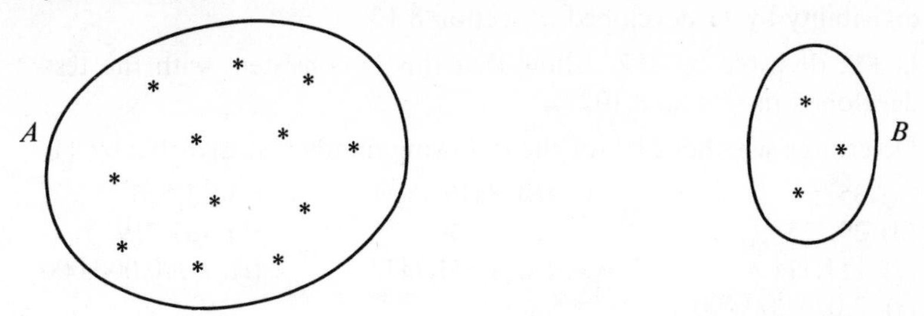

The number n(A) is divisible by the number n(B). In order to see the substantiation of this statement, consider the diagram below. It shows that set A may be partitioned into equivalent subsets (with no elements left over) such that each subset is equivalent to set B. This, in effect, is what is meant by divisibility.

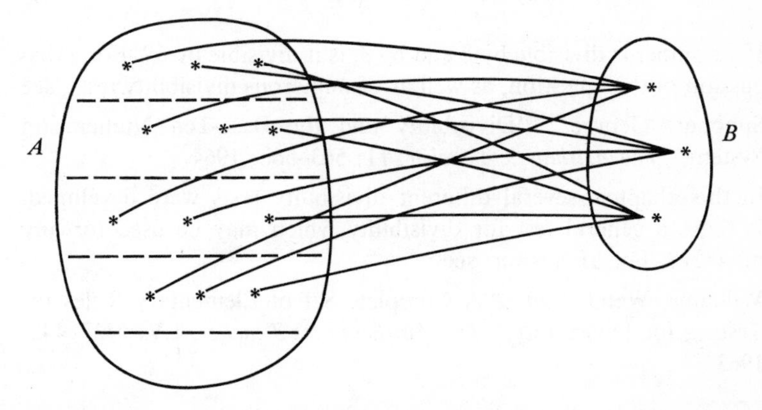

Now, in the decimal system of numeration, n(A) is 12, and n(B) is 3. Thus, we have a case of divisibility by 3; i.e., 12 is divisible by 3. Note that this is consistent with the test for divisibility by 3 which was developed earlier. The sum of the digits of "12" is 1 + 2, or 3; and 3 is divisible by 3.

Suppose, however, that a system of numeration using the base five is employed. Then n(A) is 22, and n(B) is 3. n(A) must still be divisible by n(B) since the sets A and B have not been altered. But the test for divisibility by 3 fails. The sum of the digits of "22" is 2 + 2, or 4; and 4 is not divisible by 3.

This single illustration points up the fact that the divisibility tests were developed by making use of *characteristics of the decimal system of numeration*, and are therefore not applicable to other systems of numeration. (It might be instructive to peruse the chapter again, noting the role of the decimal system of numeration in deriving the divisibility tests.)

We may summarize, then, by stating that divisibility tests are properties of a numeration system rather than properties of number.

We shall see in ensuing chapters that divisibility tests are of considerable assistance in such processes as determining factors of numbers, least common denominators, and greatest common factors.

8.12 EXERCISES

1. Is 99 divisible by 11? Show that this is consistent with the test for divisibility by 11 developed in section 8.10.
2. Is 132 divisible by 11? Show that this is consistent with the test developed in section 8.10.
3. Determine whether each of the following numbers is divisible by 11.

   (a) 3575 (b) 8419 (c) 15,696
   (d) 29,375 (e) 33,492 (f) 147,719
   (g) 111,111 (h) 1,111,111 (i) 2,200,000,000
   (j) 2,020,000,000
4. Show that if a numeration system to base seven is used, then the test for divisibility by 5 which was developed in the text is not applicable.

8.13 REFERENCE QUESTIONS

1. If a number is divisible by 2 and by 3, is it divisible by 6? For a discussion of this question, as well as of numerous divisibility tests, see

   Spooner, George. "Divisibility and the Base-Ten Numeration System," *The Arithmetic Teacher*, 11: 563–568; 1964.
2. In this chapter, several different divisibility tests were developed. Is there a general test for divisibility which may be used for any number? For an answer, see

   Williams, Wendell M. "A Complete Set of Elementary Rules for Testing for Divisibility," *The Mathematics Teacher*, LVI: 437–442; 1963.

9 PRIME NUMBERS AND FACTORS

In this chapter, we turn our attention to the problem of finding factors of whole numbers, particularly factors which we shall identify as prime factors. Throughout the chapter, we shall refer to this problem as one of "factoring a number." First, we must be sure that the meaning of the term "factor" is itself clear.

9.1 FACTORS

Just as the components of an indicated sum are called addends, so the components of an indicated product are called *factors*. Thus, for example, 6×3 is an indicated product, and 6 and 3 are factors of this product. Furthermore, since the product of 6 and 3 is 18, 6 and 3 are said to be *factors of* 18. Then, too, an individual factor may be singled out for attention; one may say "6 is a factor of 18" or "3 is a factor of 18."

Continuing with the example in the preceding paragraph, we note immediately that 6 and 3 are not the only factors of 18. 9 and 2 are also factors of 18 since $9 \times 2 = 18$. And 18 and 1 are factors of 18, since $18 \times 1 = 18$. In fact, the set of factors of 18 may be listed as follows:

$$F_{18} = \{1, 2, 3, 6, 9, 18\}$$

Each of the elements of the above set is a factor of 18.

Let us now consider the following question. Should 36 be included in this set of factors of 18, inasmuch as $36 \times \frac{1}{2} = 18$? Before answering, we must clearly understand the meaning of "factor." Whenever we speak of "factors," the set of elements from which factors may be selected must be specified. In this chapter, we are concerned only with the set of whole numbers and, hence, we are considering only whole number factors. (In later chapters other kinds of numbers will be discussed.) Hence the product $36 \times \frac{1}{2}$ is excluded from consideration because one of the factors, $\frac{1}{2}$, is not a whole number. In general, the problem of factoring a number is taken to mean determining factors each of which is the same kind of number as the number being factored. In the case given above, then, 36 is not a factor of 18 since it is impossible to find a *whole number* k such that $36 \times k = 18$.

On the basis of the discussion thus far, the following definition of factor is formulated:

DEFINITION: *If a and c are whole numbers, then a is a* factor *of c if there exists a whole number b such that*

$$a \times b = c.$$

In order to make sure that this definition says what we want it to say, let us consider another specific case: Is 7 a factor of 21? Referring to the definition, we seek a whole number b such that $7 \times b = 21$. There is such a whole number —the number 3—and so 7 is a factor of 21.

In the examples of the preceding paragraphs, only two factors were present in each indicated product. There is, however, no reason to restrict the number of factors to two. For example, since $3 \times 5 \times 4 = 60$, each of the numbers 3, 5, and 4 is a factor of 60. There is indeed no inconsistency here with the definition formulated above. 3 is a factor of 60 since there is a whole number— the number 5×4—such that $3 \times (5 \times 4) = 60$.

9.2 FACTORS AND EXPONENTS

In certain indicated products, a factor may occur more than one time; and in such a case, exponential notation (introduced in Chapter 4) may be used to advantage. As an example, consider the indicated product

$$2 \times 2 \times 2 \times 3 \times 3 \times 5.$$

A simpler name for this product is "360," and so the expression indicates that 2, 3, and 5 are factors of 360. The factor 2 occurs three times, however; and the factor 3 occurs twice. And so the expression may be written more succinctly with exponents as

$$2^3 \times 3^2 \times 5.$$

In such a case, we might refer to 2 and 3 as *multiple factors* since they occur more than one time. We might, for example, say that "2 is a factor of multiplicity three" and "3 is a factor of multiplicity two."

In Chapter 4 it was noted that the second power of a number is called the square of the number. That is, 36 is the square of 6 because $6 \times 6 = 36$. Either of the two equal factors of a number is called a *square root* of the number. Here 6 is a square root of 36. As another example, consider the number

$$2 \times 2 \times 2 \times 2 \times 3 \times 3 = 2^4 \times 3^2 = 144.$$

Here $2^2 \times 3 = 12$ is a square root of 144. When a number is expressed as an indicated product, can you tell from the exponents of the factors, or the multiplicity of the factors, whether the number is a square?

9.3 FACTORS AND DIVISIBILITY

Consider again the first example of this chapter, $6 \times 3 = 18$, from which it was noted that 6 is a factor of 18. There is a firm relationship between this language and the language used in earlier chapters. Since $6 \times 3 = 18$, we observe the following:

(1) 6 is a factor of 18. $(3 \cdot 6 = 18)$
(2) 18 is a multiple of 6.
(3) 18 is divisible by 6. $(18 \div 6 = 3)$

In effect, the three numbered statements above are equivalent; if any one of them is true, then so are the other two. In general, then, the following statements (where *a*, *b*, and *c* represent whole numbers) are equivalent:

a is a factor of *c*. $(a \cdot b = c)$
c is a multiple of *a*.
c is divisible by *a*. $(c \div a = b)$

For example, we may say

6 is a factor of 24.
24 is a multiple of 6.
24 is divisible by 6.

9.4 PRIME NUMBERS

We turn our attention next to certain whole numbers, called *prime numbers*, which play a particular important role in mathematics. As we shall see in the following development, every whole number greater than 1 either is a prime number or can be expressed as the product of prime numbers.

What is a prime number? Reference has already been made to the fact that the set of all factors of 18 is

$$F_{18} = \{1, 2, 3, 6, 9, 18\}.$$

In contrast to this statement, consider the number 13. The only two whole numbers whose product is 13 are the numbers 13 and 1. Therefore, 13 and 1 are the only factors of 13; and for this reason, 13 is said to be a prime number.

Consider any whole number n. It is true that $n \times 1 = n$ for any such number n. Thus, for any number n, n and 1 are factors—for example, 8 and 1 are factors of 8; 12 and 1 are factors of 12; 7 and 1 are factors of 7; etc. If it is the case that these are the only factors the number n has, then n is said to be *prime*. If n is not prime, then it is said to be *composite*. Thus, 13 and 1 are factors of 13, and they are the only factors; therefore 13 is a prime number. On the other hand, 18 and 1 are factors of 18, but they are not the only factors; therefore 18 is not a prime number, but is instead a composite number.

In classifying whole numbers as prime or composite, the number 1 is a special case. It is true, of course, that the only product of two whole numbers yielding 1 is 1×1. However, 1 is not considered to be a prime number. With this in mind, the definitions of prime number and composite number may be stated as follows:

DEFINITION: *A whole number n greater than* 1 *is said to be* prime *if its only factors are n and* 1. *A whole number greater than* 1 *that is not a prime number is a* composite *number. The number* 1 *is neither prime nor composite.*

9.5 LISTING PRIME NUMBERS

A common method for listing prime numbers up to any desired number is referred to as the "Sieve of Eratosthenes," the name being derived from that of the Greek mathematician credited with introducing the procedure. Suppose it is desired to list the prime numbers less than 50. First, all the whole numbers less than 50 (and greater than 1) are listed:

```
 2  3  4  5  6  7  8  9 10 11 12 13
14 15 16 17 18 19 20 21 22 23 24 25
26 27 28 29 30 31 32 33 34 35 36 37
38 39 40 41 42 43 44 45 46 47 48 49
```

We shall identify each prime number by drawing a "loop" around the numeral, while crossing out the numeral of each composite number. In this way, we shall eventually be left with only the prime numbers less than 50; these numbers can be said to have "passed through the sieve." In the first step, a loop is drawn around "2" and at the same time each multiple of 2 is eliminated. (If a number greater than 2 is a multiple of 2, it cannot be prime, for it has a factor other than itself and 1.)

(2) 3 ~~4~~ 5 ~~6~~ 7 ~~8~~ 9 ~~10~~ 11 ~~12~~ 13
~~14~~ 15 ~~16~~ 17 ~~18~~ 19 ~~20~~ 21 ~~22~~ 23 ~~24~~ 25
~~26~~ 27 ~~28~~ 29 ~~30~~ 31 ~~32~~ 33 ~~34~~ 35 ~~36~~ 37
~~38~~ 39 ~~40~~ 41 ~~42~~ 43 ~~44~~ 45 ~~46~~ 47 ~~48~~ 49

Next, the number 3 is indicated as prime, and each multiple of 3 is eliminated.

② ③ ~~4~~ 5 ~~6~~ 7 ~~8~~ ~~9~~ ~~10~~ 11 ~~12~~ 13
~~14~~ ~~15~~ ~~16~~ 17 ~~18~~ 19 ~~20~~ ~~21~~ ~~22~~ 23 ~~24~~ 25
~~26~~ ~~27~~ ~~28~~ 29 ~~30~~ 31 ~~32~~ ~~33~~ ~~34~~ 35 ~~36~~ 37
~~38~~ ~~39~~ ~~40~~ 41 ~~42~~ 43 ~~44~~ ~~45~~ ~~46~~ 47 ~~48~~ 49

Of course, some multiples of 3—such as 12—had already been eliminated as multiples of 2. This is of no concern, however. We want to cross off all composite numbers; so once 12 has been crossed off as composite, it is no longer of any interest.

We note 4 has been eliminated as a multiple of some smaller number (besides 1). So 5 is marked as prime while multiples of 5 (greater than 5) are eliminated (if they have not already been crossed out). We then have:

② ③ ~~4~~ ⑤ ~~6~~ 7 ~~8~~ ~~9~~ ~~10~~ 11 ~~12~~ 13
~~14~~ ~~15~~ ~~16~~ 17 ~~18~~ 19 ~~20~~ ~~21~~ ~~22~~ 23 ~~24~~ ~~25~~
~~26~~ ~~27~~ ~~28~~ 29 ~~30~~ 31 ~~32~~ ~~33~~ ~~34~~ ~~35~~ ~~36~~ 37
~~38~~ ~~39~~ ~~40~~ 41 ~~42~~ 43 ~~44~~ ~~45~~ ~~46~~ 47 ~~48~~ 49

6 has been eliminated as a multiple of some smaller number (besides 1). Therefore, the next prime number is 7. This is indicated below, and multiples of 7 are removed from the list.

② ③ ~~4~~ ⑤ ~~6~~ ⑦ ~~8~~ ~~9~~ ~~10~~ 11 ~~12~~ 13
~~14~~ ~~15~~ ~~16~~ 17 ~~18~~ 19 ~~20~~ ~~21~~ ~~22~~ 23 ~~24~~ ~~25~~
~~26~~ ~~27~~ ~~28~~ 29 ~~30~~ 31 ~~32~~ ~~33~~ ~~34~~ ~~35~~ ~~36~~ 37
~~38~~ ~~39~~ ~~40~~ 41 ~~42~~ 43 ~~44~~ ~~45~~ ~~46~~ 47 ~~48~~ ~~49~~

By now, the pattern should be clear. The numbers 2, 3, 5, and 7 have "passed through the sieve." They are not multiples of any smaller number (besides 1) and so are prime numbers. Continuation of the process indicates that we now have all the primes less than 50. Therefore, the set

$$\{x : x \text{ is a prime number less than } 50\}$$

may be indicated by the roster method as follows:

$$\{2, 3, 5, 7, 11, 13, 17, 19, 23, 29, 31, 37, 41, 43, 47\}$$

It is at once apparent that the sieve of Eratosthenes can be used to find all the primes less than 100, all the primes less than 1000, and indeed all the primes less than any specified number whatever.

9.6 EXERCISES

1. Indicate whether each of the following statements is true or false:
   (a) 4 is a factor of 30.
   (b) 5 is a factor of 30.
   (c) 1 is a factor of 30.
   (d) 30 is a factor of 30.
   (e) 9 is a factor of 82,782.
   (f) 1 is a factor of 82,782.
   (g) 82,782 is a factor of 82,782.
   (h) 3 is a factor of 87,931.
   (i) 25 is a factor of 44,375.
   (j) 1 is a factor of any whole number n.
   (k) For any whole number n, n is a factor of n.
2. Write the following indicated products using exponential notation:
   (a) $5 \times 5 \times 5 \times 5 \times 2$
   (b) $2 \times 2 \times 2$
   (c) $3 \times 3 \times 5$
   (d) $2 \times 2 \times 3 \times 3$
   (e) $a \cdot a \cdot a \cdot b \cdot b$
3. Indicate whether each of the following statements is true or false:
   (a) 3 is a factor of $2^3 \times 3^2$.
   (b) 3^2 is a factor of $2^3 \times 3^2$.
   (c) 3^3 is a factor of $2^3 \times 3^2$.
   (d) 5^2 is a factor of $3^2 \times 5^2 \times 7$.
   (e) a is a factor of $a^2 \cdot b^5$.
4. Identify each of these numbers as prime or composite (or neither):
   (a) 6 (b) 7 (c) 8 (d) 9
   (e) 17 (f) 19 (g) 21 (h) 1
   (i) 100 (j) 1,000,000 (k) 207 (l) $\frac{1}{2}$
5. Indicate whether each of the following statements is true or false:
   (a) A prime number is a whole number.
   (b) A prime number is greater than 1.
   (c) Any odd number is a prime number.
   (d) 2 is a prime number.
   (e) All prime numbers besides 2 are odd numbers.
   (f) If n is a whole number, then $2n$ is a composite number.
6. Use the Sieve of Eratosthenes procedure to compile a list of all prime numbers less than 100.
7. Two consecutive odd numbers which are both prime are known as *twin primes*. For example, 3 and 5 are twin primes. In the set of prime numbers less than 100, identify all pairs of twin primes.

9.7 PRIME FACTOR OF A COMPOSITE NUMBER

The sentence "$4 \times 3 = 12$" indicates that 4 and 3 are factors of 12; thus, "4×3" is said to be a *factorization* of 12. Observe that in the factorization 4×3, it is not the case that all the factors are prime numbers; specifically, in this instance, the factor 4 is not prime. On the other hand, $2 \times 2 \times 3$ is also a factorization of 12; and in this instance it is true that each factor is prime. A factorization of a whole number n in which each of the factors is a prime number is called a *complete factorization* of the number n; the number is said to be "completely factored." For example, 3×5 is a complete factorization of 15 because each of the factors is prime. Also, 2×3^2 is a complete factorization of 18. On the other hand, 3×6 is not a complete factorization of 18 because the factor 6 is not prime.

In earlier sections, it has been pointed out that every whole number greater than 1 is either prime or composite, but not both. The characteristic of a prime number is that it admits *only* itself and 1 as factors. Therefore, we need only consider the factorization of composite numbers. We shall now take a first step toward obtaining the complete factorization of a composite number.

Let a be a composite number, for example, 18. Being composite, the number a has factors other than a and 1. And this set of all factors of a can be ordered. For example,

$$F_{18} = \{1, 2, 3, 6, 9, 18\}.$$

Let us represent this ordered set as

$$F_a = \{f_1, f_2, f_3, \ldots, f_{r-1}, f_r\},$$

where each factor is less than the one that follows it (for example, $f_2 < f_3$). r then represents the number of factors that a has. Furthermore, 1 is a factor of a and must be the smallest factor; a is a factor of a and must be the greatest factor. Thus, we can replace f_1 by 1 and f_r by a as follows:

$$F_a = \{1, f_2, f_3, \ldots, f_{r-1}, a\}$$

Let us now consider a whole number x, not 1 or a, that is a factor of a; in other words, $x \in F_a$. Then

$$a = kx, \quad \text{for some whole number } k. \tag{1}$$

If x is not prime, then suppose that y is a factor of x ($y < x$). Then

$$x = k'y, \quad \text{for some whole number } k'. \tag{2}$$

From equality (2), we see that $k'y$ may be substituted for x in equality (1), giving

$$a = k(k'y) \tag{3}$$

or

$$a = (kk')y \quad \text{by associativity of multiplication.} \tag{4}$$

Then, since the product of the two whole numbers k and k' is another whole number—call it k'', we obtain

$$a = k''y, \quad \text{for the whole number } k''. \tag{5}$$

The steps above have shown the following to be the case. If x is a factor of a, and if in turn y is a factor of x, then y is also a factor of a. In other words, not only is it true that $x \in F_a$, but also $y \in F_a$. Furthermore, since $y < x$, y precedes x in the ordered set F_a.

Now consider the ordered set F_a. The factor f_2 is preceded only by the number 1. Hence, f_2 can have no factor other than itself and 1. For if it had another factor, this factor would also be a factor of a and would precede f_2 in the ordered set F_a (as shown above), contradicting the assumption that f_2 is the immediate successor of 1 in the list.

Therefore, the factor f_2 is a prime factor, and we have established that *any composite number, a, has at least one prime factor.*

In this section, we shall develop in an informal way a property that we need for the proof in the next section, a property that is also important in its own right. We shall do this principally by means of examples.

Consider the product $8 \cdot 3$. Since $8 \cdot 3$ is 24, and 6 is a factor of 24, it is correct to say that 6 is a factor of $8 \cdot 3$. This may also be demonstrated in the following way:

$$\begin{aligned} 8 \cdot 3 &= (4 \cdot 2) \cdot 3 \\ &= 4 \cdot (2 \cdot 3) \qquad \text{(Associative Principle of Multiplication)} \\ &= 4 \cdot 6 \end{aligned}$$

Note that in the steps above, the number 8 was "decomposed" into the factors $4 \cdot 2$; then the factor 2 was associated with the factor 3 to obtain 6. Thus the original product was decomposed in such a way as to bring to the surface *factors of* 6. We note that while 6 is a factor of $8 \cdot 3$, 6 is not a factor of 8 and 6 is not a factor of 3.

Hence, if 6 is a factor of a product ab, we cannot conclude that 6 is a factor of a or that 6 is a factor of b (just as above 6 is not a factor of 8 or of 3) because the numbers a and b may be decomposed so as to obtain factors of 6. Below is the set of multiples of 6:

$$\{6, 12, 18, 24, 30, 36, 42, \ldots\}$$

Any one of these numbers is divisible by 6. Yet any one of them can be expressed as a product of two numbers, neither of which is divisible by 6. Thus,

$9 \cdot 2$ $(= 18)$ is divisible by 6;

$10 \cdot 3$ $(= 30)$ is divisible by 6; etc.

The discussion above centered upon the number 6 for illustrative purposes, but the same could be said for any composite number. Consider, however, a prime number—say 7. Suppose 7 is a factor of a product ab. Then can the numbers a and b be decomposed so as to obtain factors of 7? Patently not, since 7 is prime and has no factors other than itself and one. Hence, if 7 is a factor of a product ab, then 7 must be a factor of a or of b. This fact is further emphasized by listing the multiples of 7:

$$\{7, 14, 21, 35, 42, 49, 56, \ldots\}.$$

It is impossible to express any of these numbers as a product in which neither factor is divisible by 7.

And the same conclusion applies to any prime number. Though our discussion here has been informal and not a proof, we state the result as follows:

If a prime number p is a factor of a product ab, then p is a factor of a or p is a factor of b (or both).

Furthermore, the result can be extended to more than two factors, as follows:

If a prime number p is a factor of a product abcd . . . , then p is a factor of at least one of the numbers a, b, c, d, . . .

9.9 FUNDAMENTAL THEOREM OF ARITHMETIC

We now return to the problem of obtaining a complete factorization of a composite number a. We shall in effect show that this can always be done, and furthermore, that it can be done in only one way.

As established in section 9.7, the composite number a has at least one prime factor. Let us denote this prime factor by b_1. Then

$$a = b_1 c_1, \quad \text{for some whole number } c_1. \tag{6}$$

If c_1 also happens to be prime, then we have a complete factorization of a (all factors prime). If, on the other hand, the factor c_1 is not prime, then it is composite, and therefore has at least one prime factor—call it b_2. Then

$$c_1 = b_2 c_2, \quad \text{for some whole number } c_2. \tag{7}$$

Substituting from equality (7) into equality (6), the result

$$a = b_1 b_2 c_2 \tag{8}$$

is obtained. Now, b_1 and b_2 are prime numbers. So, if c_2 also happens to be prime, then the complete factorization of a is accomplished. If c_2 is composite, then it has at least one prime factor, and the process is repeated as before. We know that the process must eventually come to an end, for the factors become continually smaller. (Why?) Therefore, we are assured that any composite number can be expressed as the product of prime factors; that is, any composite number can be completely factored.

We illustrate here by a numerical example that follows the chain of steps in the discussion above:

$$\begin{aligned} 36 &= 3 \times 12 \\ &= 3 \times 3 \times 4 \\ &= 3 \times 3 \times 2 \times 2 \end{aligned}$$

In each step, a composite number was expressed as a product of two other numbers, until finally each factor was prime. $3 \times 3 \times 2 \times 2$ is a complete factorization of 36. In the preceding example, the complete factorization may be expressed more concisely by use of exponents:

$$36 = 3^2 \times 2^2$$

It has been shown that any composite number can be factored completely. It remains to be shown that this can be accomplished in only one way—that is, that the complete factorization of a number is *unique*. In order to show this, suppose that a whole number a may be factored completely as follows:

$$a = x_1^{r_1} \cdot x_2^{r_2} \cdot x_3^{r_3} \ldots, \tag{9}$$

the exponents being used since a prime factor may occur more than once. (If not, then of course the exponent is simply 1.) Suppose that the following also represents a complete factorization of the same whole number a:

$$a = y_1^{s_1} y_2^{s_2} y_3^{s_3} \ldots \tag{10}$$

Then, since equality is transitive,

$$x_1^{r_1} x_2^{r_2} x_3^{r_3} \ldots = y_1^{s_1} y_2^{s_2} y_3^{s_3} \ldots. \tag{11}$$

x_1 is certainly a factor of the left member of (11). Therefore, it must also be a factor of the right member. But x_1 is a prime number, and the right member above is a product. Therefore, if x_1 is a factor of this product, it must be a factor of one of the numbers $y_1, y_2, y_3, \ldots$, as was noted in section 9.8. However, each of the numbers $y_1, y_2, y_3, \ldots$ is prime; so the only way in which x_1 can be a factor of one of these numbers is for x_1 to be equal to one of them. Similarly it can be shown that each factor on the left must be equal to one of the factors on the right; also of course it can be shown that any factor on the right must be equal to one of the factors on the left. In effect, then, what has been shown is that if two complete factorizations of a composite number a are recorded, they are actually the same (although, of course, the order of the factors may be altered). That is to say, there is one and only one way in which a composite number may be completely factored.

We have shown that the complete factorization of a number does exist and that it is unique. That is the substance of a mathematical theorem frequently called the *Fundamental Theorem of Arithmetic*, and we state it formally as follows:

Any composite number may be factored completely, and the complete factorization is unique (except for the order of the factors).

Thus, for example, $3^2 \times 2^2$ is the complete factorization of 36, and there is no other complete factorization of 36.

Finally, we recall the fact that every whole number greater than 1 is either prime or composite; and if it is composite, it may be expressed uniquely as the product of prime factors. Hence:

Every whole number greater than 1 *is either prime or uniquely expressible as the product of primes.*

Having considered some of the theory underlying complete factorization, we consider now the actual problem of determining the complete factorization of a given number.

For example, let us determine the complete factorization of 24.

$$\begin{aligned} 24 &= 2 \times 12 \\ &= 2 \times (3 \times 4) \\ &= (2 \times 3) \times 4 \\ &= (2 \times 3) \times (2 \times 2) \\ &= 2^3 \times 3 \end{aligned}$$

The complete factorization of a number such as 24 is a relatively simple task; the number is small enough to make its factors easily seen. By way of contrast, consider the problem of factoring completely the number 381.

The complete factorization of 381 is to contain only prime numbers as factors. Hence, we simply take the prime numbers in turn—2, 3, 5, etc.—testing to see whether or not 381 is divisible by each of them (and making use, incidentally, of the divisibility tests developed in the preceding chapter). Even so, the task of testing all primes less than 381 seems a formidable one. The task is considerably simpler than this, however, for we need test only *some* of the primes less than 381—not all of them. To see why this is so, let us digress for a moment and consider the number 36.

If one were to write all the pairs of factors of 36, the list would look like this:

$$\begin{aligned} 1 &\times 36 \\ 2 &\times 18 \\ 3 &\times 12 \\ 4 &\times 9 \\ 6 &\times 6 \\ 9 &\times 4 \\ 12 &\times 3 \\ 18 &\times 2 \\ 36 &\times 1 \end{aligned}$$

Notice that after the product 6×6, the factors are simply commuted; no new factors are introduced. Also note that each pair of factors (other than 6×6) contains one factor greater than 6 and one factor less than 6. In the product 6×6, the factors are equal, and 6 is of course a square root of 36 (section 9.2). Finally, then, each pair of numbers (other than 6×6) whose product is 36 contains one number greater than 6 and one number less than 6.

In order to place the ideas of the foregoing paragraph on firmer logical footing, let a be a whole number and let $\sqrt{a}$ represent the *square root* of a. Then let

$$\sqrt{a} = n.$$

Then $$n \cdot n = a. \tag{12}$$

Now let b and c be two whole numbers whose product is a; that is,

$$b \cdot c = a. \tag{13}$$

From equalities (12) and (13), and by virtue of the transitivity of equality, we have

$$b \cdot c = n \cdot n. \tag{14}$$

Of the two factors b and c, suppose one of them—say b—is greater than n. Then,

$$b > n. \tag{15}$$

Multiplying both sides of this inequality by n,

$$b \cdot n > n \cdot n. \tag{16}$$

But, from equality (14), we know "$b \cdot c$" may be substituted for "$n \cdot n$." Thus, equality (16) becomes

$$b \cdot n > b \cdot c. \tag{17}$$

And, finally, equality (17) and the cancellation law yield

$$n > c.$$

Hence, if $a = b \cdot c$ and $b > n$, then $n > c$, where $n = \sqrt{a}$. That is, if one of the factors of a number is greater than its square root, then the other is less than its square root. Clearly, the earlier discussion of the number 36 was a specific instance of this general result.

Let us return now to the problem of factoring completely the number 381, and see what role the above result plays there. We know that $20^2 = 400$ and $19^2 = 361$; $\sqrt{400} = 20$ and, therefore, we may assume that $\sqrt{381} < 20$. In seeking prime factors of 381, then, we do not need to test any prime greater than 20. For if 381 has a factor greater than its square root, there must be a corresponding factor less than its square root. And this corresponding factor will already have been tested. Following is the set of prime numbers which are possible factors of 381:

$$\{2, 3, 5, 7, 11, 13, 17, 19\}$$

381 is not divisible by 2. But 381 is divisible by 3; that is, $381 = 3 \times 127$. We have achieved a factorization of 381, then, without having to try all the candidates in the above set. However, we do not yet have the complete factorization, unless the number 127 is prime. We next turn our attention to 127, then, and the following primes are potential factors of 127:

$$\{2, 3, 5, 7, 11\}$$

Since $12^2 = 144$, we need test only primes less than 12:

127 is not divisible by 2.
127 is not divisible by 3.

127 is not divisible by 5.
127 is not divisible by 7.

(Note that we have not developed a simple divisibility test for 7; hence actual division is the method used here.)

127 is not divisible by 11.

Therefore, 127 is a prime number; and the complete factorization of 381 is:

$$381 = 3 \times 127$$

The technique of complete factorization is an important one. Therefore, additional examples, detailing each step but without the accompanying narrative, are given below:

EXAMPLE 1. Determine the complete factorization of 108.

Solution: 2 is a factor of 108; $108 = 2 \times 54$.
Next, consider the factor 54.
2 is a factor of 54; $54 = 2 \times 27$.
So, $108 = 2 \times 2 \times 27$.
2 is not a factor of 27.
3 is a factor of 27; $27 = 3 \times 9$.
2 is not a factor of 9.
3 is a factor of 9; $9 = 3 \times 3$.
Thus, $108 = 2 \times 2 \times 3 \times 3 \times 3$.
Or, $108 = 2^2 \times 3^3$.

EXAMPLE 2. Factor completely the number 255.

Solution: 2 is not a factor of 255.
3 is a factor of 255; $255 = 3 \times 85$.
2 is not a factor of 85. 3 is not a factor of 85.
5 is a factor of 85; $85 = 5 \times 17$.
2 is not a factor of 17. 3 is not a factor of 17.
Since $5^2 = 25$, no prime greater than 4 need be tested.
Thus, $255 = 3 \times 5 \times 17$.

EXAMPLE 3. Factor completely the number 149.

Solution: 2 is not a factor of 149. 3 is not a factor of 149.
5 is not a factor of 149. 7 is not a factor of 149.
11 is not a factor of 149.
There is no need to continue since $13^2 = 169$.
Therefore, 149 has no prime factor, and hence is itself prime.

The last example points up the fact that a prime number cannot be completely factored, in the usual sense, since its only factors are itself and 1. (For example, $149 = 149 \times 1$.) Thus we see, as the opening passage of the chapter noted, that every whole number either is itself prime or can be expressed as the product of prime factors.

9.11 EXERCISES

1. Indicate whether each of the following statements is true or false:
   (a) Any whole number may be expressed as the product of prime numbers.
   (b) Any composite number may be expressed as the product of prime numbers.
   (c) If a number is expressed as the product of numbers that have no factors in common, the number is said to have been factored completely.
   (d) If a number is expressed as the product of numbers, each of which is a prime number, the number is said to have been factored completely.
   (e) Except for order of the factors, the complete factorization of a number is unique.
   (f) If a and b are whole numbers, and 10 divides the product ab, then 10 divides a or 10 divides b.
   (g) If a and b are whole numbers, and 11 divides the product ab, then 11 divides a or 11 divides b.
2. State, in your own words, the Fundamental Theorem of Arithmetic.
3. (a) What is the greatest prime that could possibly be a factor of 68?
   (b) What is the greatest prime that could possibly be a factor of 148?
   (c) What is the greatest prime that could possibly be a factor of 10,000?
4. Determine the complete factorization of each of the following numbers. (Use exponential notation where applicable.)

(a) 30	(b) 50	(c) 98	(d) 31	(e) 144	(f) 191
(g) 200	(h) 244	(i) 324	(j) 325	(k) 433	(l) 500
(m) 540	(n) 625	(o) 629	(p) 128	(q) 243	(r) 47

9.12 INFINITUDE OF THE PRIMES

Earlier in the chapter, the Sieve of Eratosthenes was used to identify the prime numbers less than 50 and less than 100; and it was noted at the time that the process could be used to list all the primes less than any specified whole number. Is it the case then that the number of primes is infinite? Or is there, on the other hand, a *greatest* prime number?

Answers to these questions have been known for centuries; but before we attempt to detail an answer to them, let us consider the set of prime numbers less than or equal to 13:

$$\{2, 3, 5, 7, 11, 13\}$$

First, form the product of the elements of this set, as follows:

$$2 \cdot 3 \cdot 5 \cdot 7 \cdot 11 \cdot 13$$

Then increase this product by 1, calling the result r. Thus,

$$r = (2 \cdot 3 \cdot 5 \cdot 7 \cdot 11 \cdot 13) + 1.$$

We note the following characteristics of the number r with their supporting arguments following each characteristic:

1) $r > 13$.

First, $1 \cdot 13 = 13$. Also, $a \cdot 13 > 13$, for any whole number $a > 1$. But the number r is the product

$$(2 \cdot 3 \cdot 5 \cdot 7 \cdot 11) \cdot 13,$$

increased by 1. $(2 \cdot 3 \cdot 5 \cdot 7 \cdot 11)$ is a whole number greater than 1. Therefore, $r > 13$.

2) *The number r is not divisible by any prime up to, and including,* 13.

First, consider divisibility of r by 2.

$$r = 2 \cdot (3 \cdot 5 \cdot 7 \cdot 11 \cdot 13) + 1.$$

That is, r is of the form $2 \cdot k + 1$, where k is a whole number. Thus, if r is divided by 2, the quotient is k and the remainder is 1. Therefore, r is not divisible by 2.

Next, consider divisibility of r by 3. r may be expressed as $3 \cdot (2 \cdot 5 \cdot 7 \cdot 11 \cdot 13) + 1$. That is, r is of the form $3 \cdot k_1 + 1$, where k_1 is a whole number. Thus, if r is divided by 3, the quotient is k_1 and the remainder is 1. So r is not divisible by 3.

In the same way, it can be shown that division of r by any of the primes less than or equal to 13 yields a remainder of 1. Therefore, r is not divisible by any of them.

3) *If r is composite, it has a prime factor greater than* 13.

We know from section 9.7 that a composite number has at least one prime factor. We also know that none of the primes up to and including 13 is a factor of r.

It follows that r, if it is composite, must have a prime factor greater than 13.

The observations above concerning the number r were introduced primarily to help clarify the proof that the number of prime numbers is infinite, a proof which we now examine. If the number of primes were not infinite, then there would be a "stopping point" in the list of primes; for example, there would be a greatest prime number. For the sake of argument, let us suppose that somebody claims to have found such a number—call it p_n. The claim is then that the number p_n is the greatest prime number. We shall show that such a claim cannot be valid.

First, consider the set of all prime numbers (in order) up to and including p_n:

$$\{2, 3, 5, 7, 11, 13, 17, 19, \ldots, p_n\}$$

Next, form the product of the elements of this set, as follows:

$$2 \cdot 3 \cdot 5 \cdot 7 \cdot 11 \cdot 13 \cdot 17 \cdot 19 \cdot \cdots \cdot p_n$$

Finally, increase this product by 1, calling the result n. Thus,

$$n = (2 \cdot 3 \cdot 5 \cdot 7 \cdot 11 \cdot 13 \cdot 17 \cdot 19 \cdot \cdots \cdot p_n) + 1.$$

We shall now use the number n to invalidate the claim that p_n is the greatest prime number. We know that the number n must be either prime or composite; there is no other possibility.

First, suppose n is prime. Certainly $n > p_n$. Hence, if n is prime, the claim that p_n is the greatest prime must be rejected.

Second, suppose that n is composite. It can be shown that n is not divisible by 2, not divisible by 3, and indeed not divisible by any prime up to and including p_n. (Recall the argument for the second characteristic of r, earlier in this section.) We know, however, that if n is composite, it must have at least one prime factor. It follows then that n must have a prime factor that is greater than p_n. That is, there must be a prime number greater than p_n. Hence, if n is composite, the claim that p_n is the greatest prime must be rejected.

This completes the proof which shows that it is impossible to name a greatest prime number, and we have the following theorem:

THEOREM: *The set of prime numbers is an infinite set.*

★9.13 GOLDBACH'S CONJECTURE

A well known conjecture, first made by the mathematician Goldbach and serving as one illustration of the interest the prime numbers have generated through the years, concerns the even numbers greater than 2. It is as follows:

GOLDBACH'S CONJECTURE: *Any even number (greater than 2) is the sum of two prime numbers.*

Consider, for instance, the even numbers from 4 through 12; each of them can be expressed as the sum of two primes, as follows:

$$\begin{aligned} 4 &= 2 + 2 \\ 6 &= 3 + 3 \\ 8 &= 5 + 3 \\ 10 &= 7 + 3 \\ 12 &= 7 + 5 \end{aligned}$$

We have ended the list with the even number 12, but it could be continued. As a matter of fact, hundreds of thousands of even numbers have been used to test Goldbach's conjecture; and no number has been found which refutes his conjecture.

Why then is the word "conjecture" used in this case? The reason lies in the fact that nobody has been able (despite numerous attempts) to formulate a deductive proof that any even number greater than 2 can be expressed as the sum of two primes. Unless such a proof is devised, nobody can be really sure that there are not some even numbers (which just haven't been tested yet) that are *not* the sum of two prime numbers. In other words, a "conjecture" is something like an "educated guess"; it is borne out by all available observations, but lacks the conviction of a proved theorem.

9.14 EXERCISES

1. Explain why the number $(2 \cdot 3 \cdot 5) + 1$ is not divisible by 2, by 3, or by 5.
2. In what way does the number $(2 \cdot 3 \cdot 5 \cdot 7 \cdot 11 \cdot 13 \cdot 17 \cdot 19) + 1$ establish the fact that there is a prime number greater than 19?
3. Express each of the following even numbers as the sum of two prime numbers:

   (a) 14 (b) 16 (c) 18 (d) 20
   (e) 50 (f) 64 (g) 100 (h) 168
4. Can every odd number be expressed as the sum of two primes? Explain. Are there any odd numbers which can be expressed as the sum of two primes?
5. Goldbach's conjecture states that every even number greater than 2 can be expressed as the sum of two prime numbers, but it does not state that such a sum is unique. Name five even numbers which can be expressed as the sum of two primes in more than one way.
6. Consider the statement: The number of prime numbers is infinite. Is this statement a theorem or a conjecture? Explain.

9.15 REFERENCE QUESTIONS

1. Is the number of primes finite or infinite? Is a formula available for generating as many prime numbers as desired? See

   Tinnappel, Harold. "Using Sets to Study Odd, Even, and Prime Numbers," *Enrichment Mathematics for the Grades.* Washington, D.C.: National Council of Teachers of Mathematics, 1963. Pp. 266–268.
2. In this chapter, the Fundamental Theorem of Arithmetic was established. What is the content of this theorem? Are there systems in which a number may be factored into prime factors in more than one way? See

   Greenleaf, Newcomb and Wisner, Robert J. "The Unique Factorization Theorem," *The Mathematics Teacher*, LII: 600–603; 1959.
3. What is the relationship between prime numbers and arrays? See

   National Council of Teachers of Mathematics. *Topics in Mathematics for Elementary School Teachers* (29th yearbook). Washington, D.C.: NCTM, 1964. Pp. 173–176.

10 GREATEST COMMON FACTOR AND LEAST COMMON MULTIPLE

THE DIVISIBILITY TESTS *and the process of complete factorization developed in chapters 8 and 9 find application in mathematics in a variety of ways. In this chapter, we look at two such applications—determining the greatest common factor and the least common multiple—which are basic to the mathematics of the elementary school.*

10.1 GREATEST COMMON FACTOR

The number 3 is a factor of 12 and also a factor of 18; therefore, 3 is said to be a *common factor* of the numbers 12 and 18. Of course the numbers 12 and 18 may have common factors other than 3, and one way to identify all of them is to list all the factors of each number in turn. Let F_{12} represent the set of factors of 12:

$$F_{12} = \{1, 2, 3, 4, 6, 12\}$$

And let F_{18} represent the set of factors of 18:

$$F_{18} = \{1, 2, 3, 6, 9, 18\}$$

Then the set of common factors of 12 and 18 is $F_{12} \cap F_{18}$:

$$F_{12} \cap F_{18} = \{1, 2, 3, 6\}$$

Thus, the numbers 12 and 18 have a total of four common factors. In this set, the number 6 is easily seen to be the greatest number. Therefore, 6 is said to be the *greatest common factor* of 12 and 18.

To express this relationship we introduce the following symbols:

$$\text{GCF}(a, b) = c,$$

where a and b are two whole numbers, and c is their greatest common factor. Thus the example just cited may be expressed as

$$\text{GCF}(12, 18) = 6.$$

Among the common factors of two or more numbers, the greatest common factor is the one most likely to be sought. Provided that the numbers are reasonably small, the "roster" method used above for finding the greatest common factor is easily accomplished. (A more sophisticated technique, helpful when working with larger numbers, is developed in the next section.) Further examples of the greatest common factor of two or more numbers are given below.

EXAMPLE 1. What is the greatest common factor of 24, 36, and 48?

Solution: Let F_{24}, F_{36}, F_{48} be the set of factors of 24, 36, and 48, respectively. Then

$$F_{24} = \{1, 2, 3, 4, 6, 8, 12, 24\};$$
$$F_{36} = \{1, 2, 3, 4, 6, 9, 12, 18, 36\};$$
$$F_{48} = \{1, 2, 3, 4, 6, 8, 12, 16, 24, 48\}.$$

The intersection of these three sets is $\{1, 2, 3, 4, 6, 12\}$; and this is the set of common factors of the three numbers. 12 is easily seen to be the greatest common factor.

EXAMPLE 2. Determine the greatest common factor of 8 and 24.

Solution: $F_8 = \{1, 2, 4, 8\}$
$F_{24} = \{1, 2, 3, 4, 6, 8, 12, 24\}$
The intersection is $\{1, 2, 4, 8\}$.
Thus, $\text{GCF}(8, 24) = 8$.

From Example 2 we see that the greatest common factor of two numbers may be one of the numbers themselves.

EXAMPLE 3. What is the greatest common factor of 9 and 16?

Solution: $F_9 = \{1, 3, 9\}$
$F_{16} = \{1, 2, 4, 8, 16\}$
$\text{GCF}(9, 16) = 1$.

Thus, the greatest common factor of two numbers may be 1. In such a case, the numbers are said to be *relatively prime;* 1 is their only common factor. (The numbers themselves are not necessarily prime numbers, however; neither 9 nor 16 is prime, but they are relatively prime.)

As discussed in the previous section, the problem of determining the greatest common factor of two or more numbers is simple indeed when the numbers are relatively small and their factors easily listed. A more efficient method is desirable, however, when the numbers are larger, and it is the purpose of this section to develop such a method.

In order to introduce the technique, we shall consider the greatest common factor of two relatively small numbers, 30 and 42, and then apply the technique to more challenging problems. Factor completely the number 30:

$$30 = 2 \times 3 \times 5$$

Thus we form the set

$$P_{30} = \{2, 3, 5\},$$

the product of whose elements represents the complete factorization of 30. Next, factor completely the number 42:

$$42 = 2 \times 3 \times 7$$

Form the set

$$P_{42} = \{2, 3, 7\},$$

the product of whose elements represents the complete factorization of 42. Since $30 = 2 \times 3 \times 5$, (2×3) is a factor of 30. And since $42 = 2 \times 3 \times 7$, (2×3) is a factor of 42. Thus, 2×3 is a common factor of 30 and 42. Furthermore, it is the greatest common factor since we have "pulled out" all the common factors from the complete factorizations. We notice further that 2 and 3 are the elements of $P_{30} \cap P_{42}$; that is,

$$P_{30} \cap P_{42} = \{2, 3\}.$$

In summary, then, the greatest common factor of 30 and 42 is simply the product of the elements of $P_{30} \cap P_{42}$.

EXAMPLE 4. Determine GCF(42, 70).

Solution: $P_{42} = \{2, 3, 7\}$ because $2 \times 3 \times 7$ is the complete factorization of 42.

$P_{70} = \{2, 5, 7\}$ because $2 \times 5 \times 7$ is the complete factorization of 70.

$P_{42} \cap P_{70} = \{2, 7\}$

Therefore, $\text{GCF}(42, 70) = 2 \times 7 = 14$.

We see, then, that this technique for determining the greatest common factor reduces the problem to the previously solved problems of complete factorization and set intersection.

Next, we apply the process to a problem in which multiple factors occur in the complete factorizations. Consider, for example, determination of GCF(18, 90). The complete factorization of 18 is

$$18 = 2 \times 3 \times 3.$$

However, we do *not* write $P_{18} = \{2, 3\}$ because the product of the elements of this set is not 18. Also, we do *not* write $P_{18} = \{2, 3, 3\}$ since this clearly violates our agreement that an element of a set be listed precisely once. We must keep in mind that the elements of P_{18} are *factors* of 18, and 3 occurs as a factor twice —there is a first factor 3 and there is a second factor 3. We might identify these as "3_1" and "3_2" and then write

$$P_{18} = \{2, 3_1, 3_2\}.$$

In the same way, the complete factorization of 90 is written

$$90 = 2 \times 3 \times 3 \times 5$$

and so

$$P_{90} = \{2, 3_1, 3_2, 5\}.$$

Again, to determine GCF(18, 90), we consider the elements of

$$P_{18} \cap P_{90} = \{2, 3_1, 3_2\}$$

and form their product. Thus, the product is to have a factor 2, a first factor 3, and a second factor 3; that is,

$$\text{GCF}(18, 90) = 2 \times 3 \times 3 = 18.$$

This is another instance of a case in which the greatest common factor of two numbers is one of the numbers themselves.

EXAMPLE 5. Determine GCF(504, 180).

Solution:

$$P_{504} = \{2_1, 2_2, 2_3, 3_1, 3_2, 7\}$$
$$(504 = 2 \times 2 \times 2 \times 3 \times 3 \times 7)$$

$$P_{180} = \{2_1, 2_2, 3_1, 3_2, 5\}$$
$$(180 = 2 \times 2 \times 3 \times 3 \times 5)$$

$$P_{504} \cap P_{180} = \{2_1, 2_2, 3_1, 3_2\}$$

Therefore, GCF(504, 180) $= 2 \times 2 \times 3 \times 3 = 36$.

A familiar method for determining the greatest common factor of two numbers has survived since the work of Euclid, who first employed it. The method makes use of repeated executions of the division algorism, and we explain it by means of examples.

EXAMPLE 6. Determine GCF(12, 32).

Solution:

$$12\overline{)32}\quad 2,\quad 32-24=8$$

So, $32 = 2(12) + 8$ or $32 - 2(12) = 8$.
Therefore, any factor common to 12 and 32 can be "factored out" of the left member of the last equality by the distributive law. Therefore, any such factor must also be a factor of 8; that is, any factor of 12 and 32 is also a factor of 8. This means that we can reduce the problem to one of finding GCF(8, 12).

$$8\overline{)12}\quad 1,\quad 12-8=4$$

So, $12 = 1(8) + 4$ or $12 - 1(8) = 4$.
Thus, if any number is a factor of both 12 and 8, the distributive law tells us that it is a factor of the left member of the last equality. Hence, it must also be a factor of the right member, 4. So, the problem is reduced to finding GCF(8, 4).

$$4\overline{)8}\quad 2,\quad 8-8=0$$

Thus, $8 = 2(4)$.
That is, 4 is a factor of 8, and there can be no greater common factor of 4 and 8. Therefore, GCF(8, 4) = 4.
But GCF(8, 4) = GCF(8, 12) = GCF(12, 32) as detailed in earlier steps.
Finally, then, GCF(12, 32) = 4.

EXAMPLE 7. Use the Euclidean algorism to determine GCF(28, 64).

Solution: $64 = 2(28) + 8$
or $64 - 2(28) = 8$
So, GCF(28, 64) = GCF(28, 8).

$$28\overline{)64}\quad \text{quotient } 2,\ 56,\ \text{remainder } 8$$

$28 = 3(8) + 4$
or $28 - 3(8) = 4$
So, GCF(8, 28) = GCF(8, 4).

$$8\overline{)28}\quad \text{quotient } 3,\ 24,\ \text{remainder } 4$$

$8 = 2(4)$
Therefore,
GCF(8, 4) = 4
GCF(8, 28) = 4
GCF(28, 64) = 4.

$$4\overline{)8}\quad \text{quotient } 2,\ 8,\ \text{remainder } 0$$

As you can see, this process ferrets out pairs of successively smaller numbers whose greatest common factor is the same as that of the pair whose GCF is being sought. The process terminates when a remainder of zero is obtained.

The notion of the greatest common factor is useful in elementary mathematics. Later when we discuss fractions, an application of the greatest common divisor will be helpful in determining the simplest fraction equivalent to a given fraction (section 12.2).

10.4 EXERCISES

1. If a and b are relatively prime numbers, what is GCF(a, b)? Cite three different pairs of relatively prime numbers.
2. If r and s are two numbers such that s is a multiple of r, what is GCF(r, s)? Give three such pairs of numbers.
3. Concerning the set $P_{12} = \{2_1, 2_2, 3\}$, which of the following statements is more defensible?
   (a) "2_1" and "2_2" represent different numbers.
   (b) "2_1" and "2_2" represent different factors.
4. List the elements of the following sets:
   (a) P_{32} (b) P_{26} (c) P_{50} (d) P_{100} (e) P_{250}
5. Determine the following, using the technique of section 10.2:
   (a) GCF(8, 12) (b) GCF(13, 32) (c) GCF(44, 28)
   (d) GCF(110, 385) (e) GCF(42, 147) (f) GCF(375, 1050)
   (g) GCF(297, 700) (h) GCF(297, 270) (i) GCF(1000, 256)
   (j) GCF(441, 105) (k) GCF(381, 190)
6. Use the Euclidean algorism to determine the following:
   (a) GCF(34, 72) (b) GCF(36, 150) (c) GCF(256, 108)
   (d) GCF(20, 41) (e) GCF(9, 34)

The number 48 is a multiple of both 6 and 8, and hence is a *common multiple* of 6 and 8. There are other common multiples of 6 and 8, and some of them are identified by listing the set of multiples of each number in turn. Thus,

$$\text{Multiples of } 6 = \{6, 12, 18, 24, 30, 36, 42, 48, \ldots\},$$

and

$$\text{Multiples of } 8 = \{8, 16, 24, 32, 40, 48, 56, 64, \ldots\}.$$

Of course, each of these sets contains an endless number of elements and so we must be content with only a partial listing. Multiples that are common to 6 and 8 are elements of the intersection of these two sets:

$$\{24, 48, 72, \ldots\}$$

Again, we have only a partial listing of such elements, but it is sufficient to identify 24 as the *least common multiple* of 6 and 8. We indicate this as follows:

$$\text{LCM}(6, 8) = 24$$

Generally, let a and b be two whole numbers whose least common multiple is c and we have

$$\text{LCM}(a, b) = c.$$

It is with the notion of least common multiple that the remainder of this chapter is concerned.

EXAMPLE 8. Determine the least common multiple of 6, 8, and 10.

Solution: Let A, B, and C represent the set of multiples of 6, 8, and 10 respectively. Then

$A = \{6, 12, 18, 24, 30, 36, 42, 48, 54, 60, 66, 72, 78, 84, 90, 96, 102, 108, 114, 120, 126, 132, \ldots\}$

$B = \{8, 16, 24, 32, 40, 48, 56, 64, 72, 80, 88, 96, 104, 112, 120, 128, 136, \ldots\}$

$C = \{10, 20, 30, 40, 50, 60, 70, 80, 90, 100, 110, 120, 130, \ldots\}$

Perusal of these set listings indicates that 120 is the least common multiple of 6, 8, and 10.

The above example also serves to point up the fact that this method of simply listing the sets of multiples is an inefficient one, for many numbers may have to be listed before a common multiple is found. A more efficient method is discussed in the next section.

DETERMINING LEAST COMMON MULTIPLE

In this section, we develop an alternative process to the inefficient process discussed in the last section. In order to do this, consider the problem of determining the least common multiple of the numbers 10 and 21. The complete factorizations of these numbers are as follows:

$$10 = 2 \times 5$$

$$21 = 3 \times 7$$

Therefore, as in section 10.2, the following sets may be formed:

$$P_{10} = \{2, 5\} \qquad P_{21} = \{3, 7\}$$

Now the number

$$2 \times 5 \times 3 \times 7$$

is certainly a multiple of 10 since $2 \times 5 \times 3 \times 7 = (2 \times 5) \times 3 \times 7$, and it is also a multiple of 21 since $2 \times 5 \times 3 \times 7 = 2 \times 5 \times (3 \times 7)$; it is therefore a common multiple of 10 and 21. Furthermore, it is the *least common multiple*. If either 2 or 5 were omitted as factors, the number would not be a multiple of 10; if either 3 or 7 were omitted, the number would not be a multiple of 21. Hence, the set

$$\{2, 5, 3, 7\}$$

represents the "minimum" set of factors which can be used to form a common multiple of 10 and 21. We note, however, that

$$\{2, 5, 3, 7\} = P_{10} \cup P_{21}.$$

In summary, then, the least common multiple of 10 and 21 is simply the product of the elements of $P_{10} \cup P_{21}$.

Following are some examples of determining least common multiple by the complete factorization process.

EXAMPLE 9. Determine LCM(30, 42).

Solution: $P_{30} = \{2, 3, 5\}$ $\qquad (30 = 2 \times 3 \times 5)$

$P_{42} = \{2, 3, 7\}$ $\qquad (42 = 2 \times 3 \times 7)$

$P_{30} \cup P_{42} = \{2, 3, 5, 7\}$

$2 \times 3 \times 5 \times 7 = 210$

Therefore, $210 = \text{LCM}(30, 42)$.

EXAMPLE 10. Determine the least common multiple of 6, 8, and 10.

Solution: $P_6 = \{2, 3\}$ $P_8 = \{2_1, 2_2, 2_3\}$ $P_{10} = \{2, 5\}$

$P_6 \cup P_8 \cup P_{10} = \{2_1, 2_2, 2_3, 3, 5\}$

Therefore, the least common multiple of 6, 8, and 10 is $2 \times 2 \times 2 \times 3 \times 5$, or 120.

In this example, it might have been clearer to list P_6 as $\{2_1, 3\}$ and P_{10} as $\{2_1, 5\}$, to indicate that each number contains only a single factor 2. Thus, it is clear that 2_1 is an element of each of the three sets P_6, P_8, and P_{10}. Compare the solution of Example 10 with the more cumbersome solution to the same problem, Example 8, in section 10.5.

10.7 EUCLIDEAN ALGORISM FOR LCM

Euclid also developed an algorism for finding the LCM of two or more numbers. This is accomplished by dividing the numbers successively by the prime factors 2, 3, 5, 7, . . . , until all common prime factors have been uncovered from each of the numbers and the successive quotients.

We illustrate the method by finding LCM(60, 84). First we uncover the factor 2, and the quotients are (30, 42). From these we again remove a factor 2,

2	60	84
2	30	42
3	15	21
5	5	7
7	1	7
	1	1

and the quotients are (15, 21). From these quotients we remove (uncover) the factor 3, and the new quotients are (5, 7). It is easily seen that these are prime factors. Hence,

$$\text{LCM}(60, 84) = 2 \times 2 \times 3 \times 5 \times 7 \quad \text{or} \quad 420.$$

Note that this procedure is merely another way of finding the union of the prime factors from the complete factorization of each number.

EXAMPLE 11. Find, by the Euclidean algorism, the LCM(30, 28, 35).

Solution: Remove the factor 2. Since 35 does not have factor 2, rewrite it in the second line. Remove the factor 2 again

2	30	28	35
2	15	14	35
3	15	7	35
5	5	7	35
7	1	7	7
	1	1	1

rewriting 15 and 35, neither of which has the factor 2. Continue with the factors 3, 5, and 7. Then,

$$\text{LCM}(30, 28, 35) = 2 \times 2 \times 3 \times 5 \times 7 = 420.$$

The notion of least common multiple, like that of greatest common factor, finds application in even the most elementary mathematical processes. One such application will be used later when we discuss addition of fractions where the least common multiple will be helpful in finding a "common denominator" for fractions with unlike denominators (section 13.16).

In summary, the similarity between this process for determination of the least common multiple and that developed earlier for determination of the greatest common factor is at once apparent. A general statement of both of these processes is given below.

Given two whole numbers a and b:

GCF(a, b) *is the product of the elements of*

$P_a \cap P_b$;

LCM(a, b) *is the product of the elements of*

$P_a \cup P_b$.

10.8 EXERCISES

1. Use the "complete factorization" process of section 10.6 to determine the following:

   (a) LCM(8, 12) (b) LCM(5, 10) (c) LCM(14, 24)
   (d) LCM(7, 13) (e) LCM(1, 20) (f) LCM(36, 48)
   (g) LCM(48, 72) (h) LCM(100, 64) (i) LCM(256, 108)
   (j) LCM(100, 256) (k) LCM(64, 128) (l) LCM(1, 128)

2. If LCM$(a, b) = b$, what is the relationship between a and b?

3. If a and b are relatively prime, what is LCM(a, b)?

4. Use the Euclidean algorism to determine the following:

   (a) LCM(36, 16) (b) LCM(54, 72) (c) LCM(98, 72)
   (d) LCM(36, 54) (e) LCM(108, 64) (f) LCM(100, 108)

5. For each of the following pairs of numbers, determine both the least common multiple and the greatest common factor.

   (a) 24; 32 (b) 144; 72 (c) 84; 63 (d) 32; 27 (e) 32; 28

10.9 REFERENCE QUESTIONS

1. As noted in this chapter, determination of least common multiples is important in developing the skill of adding fractions. For another discussion of this role of the least common multiple, see

   Paige, Donald D. "Primes and Factoring," *The Arithmetic Teacher*, 9: 449–452; 1962.

2. Many texts present methods for determining greatest common factor and least common multiple which differ from those presented in this chapter in that they do not make such explicit use of sets. As a reference, consult

   National Council of Teachers of Mathematics. *Topics in Mathematics for Elementary School Teachers* (29th yearbook). Washington, D.C.: NCTM, 1964. Pp. 195–201.

11 CARDINALS AND SEGMENTS

IN THIS CHAPTER *we shall unite the study of arithmetic and geometry through the use of segments and cardinal numbers. First we shall consider operations on segments, and then a new operation involving number and segment. Finally, a new entity is created which is called a fraction.*

11.1 ADDITION AND SUBTRACTION OF SEGMENTS

In Chapter 6 the meaning of a line, and of a segment, a part of the line bounded by two points, was developed. Consider a line l such as shown in the figure.

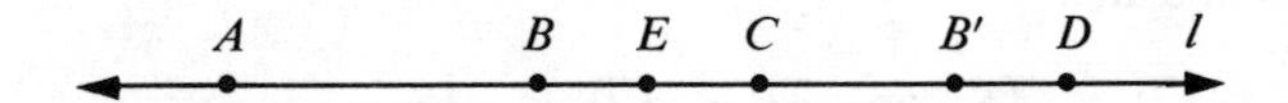

Then if we select any two points, such as A and B, they determine a segment $\overline{AB}$. Thus on the line there are an infinite number of segments. For example, in the figure, we can name $\overline{AE}$, $\overline{BE}$, $\overline{EC}$, $\overline{ED}$, $\overline{AD}$, etc. Note that $\overline{AB} = \overline{BA}$ for they are the same set of points.

Recall (section 2.1) that the symbol "=" implies that the names flanking it refer to *exactly* the same thing. Thus $5 = 5$, $5 = 2 + 3$, $\overline{AB} = \overline{BA}$ are correct statements. However, $\overline{AB} = 3$ is false, since $\overline{AB}$ refers to a set of points and 3 to a number, and a number is not a set of points. However, in the figure *something* appears to be the same about $\overline{AB}$ and $\overline{CD}$. If we slide $\overline{CD}$ along the line without stretching or shrinking it, until point C reaches point A, and then find that point D is on point B, we say that

segment AB is *congruent* to segment CD

and write

$\overline{AB} \cong \overline{CD}$.

We can also think of the entire line as sliding along itself, without stretching, shrinking, or any other deformation, and if eventually $\overline{CD}$ comes to occupy the same set of points that $\overline{AB}$ previously occupied, then $\overline{AB} \cong \overline{CD}$. We say $\overline{CD}$ has been *translated* into $\overline{AB}$ and call the correspondence a *translation*. (Note that in a drawing, the translation can be made by the use of a pair of compasses.) Congruency of segments, then, means that to every point of $\overline{AB}$ there is assigned a point of $\overline{CD}$ so that C corresponds to A, D to B, and each interior point of $\overline{CD}$ to an interior point of $\overline{AB}$.

By this intuitive approach, it is easily seen that congruency of segments is an *equivalence relation;* that is, it is reflexive, symmetric, and transitive:

(a) $\overline{AB} \cong \overline{AB}$. REFLEXIVITY OF $\cong$

(b) If $\overline{AB} \cong \overline{CD}$ then $\overline{CD} \cong \overline{AB}$. SYMMETRY OF $\cong$

(c) If $\overline{AB} \cong \overline{CD}$ and $\overline{CD} \cong \overline{EF}$, then $\overline{AB} \cong \overline{EF}$. TRANSITIVITY OF $\cong$

This relation separates all the segments on a line into disjoint equivalence classes. In any equivalence class each segment is congruent to every other segment in the class. In a sense, these segments are all the same, and from now on we shall speak of the segments of an equivalence class as being "equal" to each other; that is, congruent segments are equal and equal segments are congruent:

$$\overline{AB} \cong \overline{CD} \Rightarrow \overline{AB} = \overline{CD}\dagger$$

In the figure below, suppose we translate $\overline{AB}$ so that A corresponds to (or coincides with) E, and then point B corresponds to a point in the interior

A 'B E C B' D l

of $\overline{ED}$, such as B'. In this case we shall say tnat segment $\overline{ED}$ is greater than segment $\overline{AB}$ and write:

$$\overline{ED} > \overline{AB} \quad \text{or} \quad \overline{AB} < \overline{ED}$$

Also, whenever $AB < AC$, for example, there exists a segment AE such that

$$AB < AE < AC.$$

In the work that follows, we shall translate a segment along a given line. We shall assume that this translation always selects another segment (at some desired position on the line) which is equal to the given segment. We shall also use a single capital letter near the end of the alphabet, such as T, U, V, W, X, Y, Z, to name a segment as well as the form $\overline{AB}$, etc., in which we use the initial letters of the alphabet.

Consider the figure at the top of the next page. Suppose there are two segments on the line,

$$\overline{AB} = U \quad \text{and} \quad \overline{CD} = V.$$

---

† In Chapter 15 on measure, the use of "=" for "$\cong$" for segments is further justified.

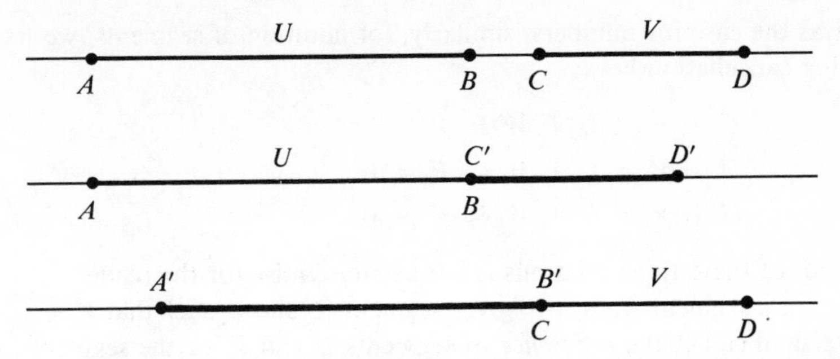

To the ordered pair (U, V) we assign the segment X, determined as follows. Translate V so that the point C coincides with B, call it C', and D occupies the point D'. Then the intersection of $\overline{AB}$ and $\overline{C'D'}$ is the single point B. We call the segment $\overline{AD'} = X$ the sum of the segments U and V and write

$$U + V = X.$$

If any other segments in the equivalence class of U, and of V, had been used for U and V, the sum would be in the same equivalence class as X. Hence addition of segments is unique.

Addition is a binary operation on the set of all segments of a line. Instead of adding V to U, we could start with V and translate U until point B coincided with point C. It is evident that the segment $\overline{A'D} = \overline{AD'} = X$ so that addition of segments is commutative. Thus we have

$$U + V = V + U. \qquad \text{COMMUTATIVITY OF } + \text{ OF SEGMENTS}$$

Similarly, as an exercise, the reader may prove that addition of segments is associative, that is,

$$(U + V) + W = U + (V + W). \qquad \text{ASSOCIATIVITY OF } + \text{ OF SEGMENTS}$$

As before (section 3.7), $U + V + W = (U + V) + W$, and so on.

Let us consider a segment $\overline{AA}$ in which the boundary points are the same point. In reality this segment is a point. We agree to call it the *null segment* or *zero segment* and write

$$\overline{AA} = \overline{BB} = \mathbb{O}.$$

The null segment can be any single point of the line and we may have

$$\overline{AB} + \overline{BB} = \overline{AB}$$

or

$$\overline{AB} + \mathbb{O} = \overline{AB}.$$

A U B
BB

Thus the null segment becomes the identity element for addition of segments and we have

$$U + \mathbb{O} = \mathbb{O} + U = U. \qquad \text{IDENTITY PRINCIPLE OF } + \text{ OF SEGMENTS}$$

As was the case for numbers, similarly, for addition of segments, we have the following cancellation laws:

$$U + V < U + W \Leftrightarrow V < W$$
$$U + V = U + W \Leftrightarrow V = W$$
$$U + V > U + W \Leftrightarrow V > W$$

The proof of these three relations is left as an exercise for the reader.

If there is a segment X, for two given segments U and V, such that $V + X = U$, then we shall call X the *difference* of segments U and V, or the segment formed by *subtracting* V from U. Thus we have

$$V + X = U \Rightarrow X = U - V. \qquad U \geq V$$

If $U = V$, then $X = \mathbb{O}$.

If $U < V$, then X does not exist.

U

V $\quad U - V = \mathbb{O}$

U

V $\quad U - V$ is impossible.

Note that if $V > U$, then by translation, U is equal to a subset of V. Thus U cannot be congruent to $V + X$, and subtraction becomes impossible in this case.

11.2 EXERCISES

On a line select three segments, U, V, and W, with $U > V$.

1. Construct $U + V$
2. Construct $U - V$
3. Construct $U + (V + W)$
4. Construct $(U + V) + W$
5. Show that in Exercises 3 and 4, the result is the same.
6. Show that $U + W > V + W$.
7. If possible, find X such that $V + X = W$; if not, find Y such that $W + Y = V$.
8. Prove that addition of segments is associative.
9. Prove the following three relations:

   $U + V < U + W \Leftrightarrow V < W$
   $U + V = U + W \Leftrightarrow V = W$
   $U + V > U + W \Leftrightarrow V > W$

10. Given two segments R and S, not congruent. Show that either $R - S$ or $S - R$ exists, but not both.

11. What is the complement of segment $\overline{AC}$ with respect to $\overline{AB}$ if C is an interior point of $\overline{AB}$?

★12. A *semigroup* is a set of elements for which a binary operation is defined that has an identity element and is associative. Show that the set of all segments of a line is a semigroup. What additional properties does this group have?

11.3 MULTIPLICATION OF A SEGMENT BY A CARDINAL NUMBER

We now introduce a new binary operation, in which to each ordered pair consisting of a segment and a cardinal number, as (U, n), there is assigned, as the result, a segment V. We shall call the operation scalar multiplication of segments. We shall use our intuitive feeling of this kind of multiplication to determine the product which we shall call the scalar product. In this case, we write the multiplier first, as $n \cdot U$.

Scalar Multiplication

$$\underbrace{\underset{\text{Ordered pair}}{(U, n)} \qquad \underset{\text{Scalar product}}{V}}_{n \cdot U = V}$$

What would $2 \cdot U$ be most likely to mean? Just as 2 times 3 means $3 + 3$, we feel $2 \cdot U$ ought to be $U + U$ and we shall agree to give this meaning to *scalar multiplication*. Then $3 \cdot U = U + U + U$, and generally:

$$n \cdot U = \underbrace{U + U + \cdots + U}_{n \text{ addends}}$$

From this definition we also agree that if $aU = bU$, then $a = b$. Thus, we have the cancellation law:

$$aU = bU \Rightarrow a = b$$

The identity element of this multiplication is 1 since

$$1 \cdot U = U$$ IDENTITY PRINCIPLE OF SCALAR ·

We agree that multiplying U by zero will give the null segment and we have

$$0 \cdot U = \text{①}.$$ ZERO PRINCIPLE OF SCALAR ·

Note that in scalar multiplication the result is a segment, and not a number.

Addition and scalar multiplication of segments have properties similar to those of the whole numbers. The multiplication of scalars is associative. Thus, as shown in the diagram, if we first form $2U$, and then multiply the result by 3 to form

$$3(2U),$$

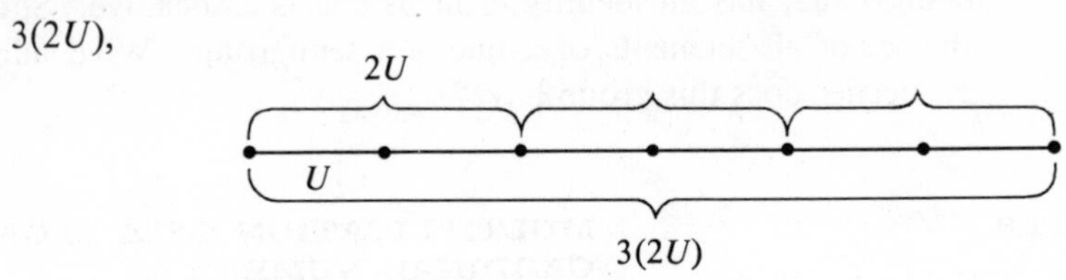

the result is the same as $(3 \cdot 2)U$ or $6U$. Quite generally, if we first determine

$$b \cdot U = \underbrace{U + U + \cdots + U}_{b \text{ addends}}$$

and then multiply the result by a, to find

$$a(bU) = \underbrace{\underbrace{(U + U + \cdots + U)}_{b \text{ addends}} + (U + U + \cdots + U) + \cdots + (U + U + \cdots + U)}_{a \text{ addends}},$$

then

$$a(bU) = (ab)U. \qquad \text{ASSOCIATIVITY OF SCALAR} \cdot$$

Scalar multiplication is distributive over the addition of segments. Given two segments U, V, we form the sum $U + V$. If we multiply the sum by n and

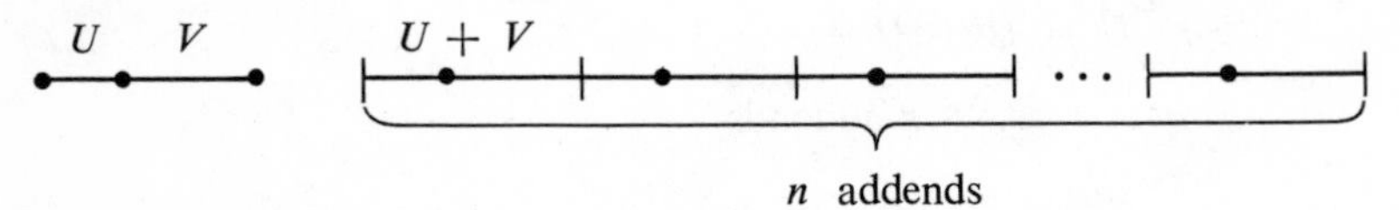

rearrange the segments by translation, we have a sequence of n congruent U-segments followed by a sequence of n congruent V-segments, so that

$$n(U + V) = nU + nV. \qquad \text{DISTRIBUTIVITY FOR SCALAR} \cdot \text{ OVER } + \text{ OF SEGMENTS}$$

It is left as an exercise for the reader to prove that

$$(a + b)U = aU + bU. \qquad \text{DISTRIBUTIVITY FOR SCALAR} \cdot \text{ OVER } + \text{ OF NUMBERS}$$

From the above results, since scalar multiplication is unique, we can prove the additional property, namely

$$(ba)U = (ca)U \Rightarrow b = c,$$

because $(ba)U = b(aU)$ and $(ca)U = c(aU)$, and then $b = c$.

In summary, we note that we have defined two internal laws of composition, addition of segments and scalar multiplication, for which the following properties hold:

1. $U + V = V + U$ — COMMUTATIVITY OF + OF SEGMENTS
2. $U + (V + W) = (U + V) + W$ — ASSOCIATIVITY OF + OF SEGMENTS
3. $U + \mathbb{O} = \mathbb{O} + U = U$ — IDENTITY PRINCIPLE OF + OF SEGMENTS
4. $1 \cdot U = U$ — IDENTITY PRINCIPLE OF SCALAR ·
5. $0 \cdot U = \mathbb{O}$ — ZERO PRINCIPLE OF SCALAR ·
6. $a(bU) = (ab)U$ — ASSOCIATIVITY OF SCALAR ·
7. $a(U + V) = aU + aV$ — DISTRIBUTIVITY FOR SCALAR · OVER + OF SEGMENTS
8. $(a + b)U = aU + bU$ — DISTRIBUTIVITY FOR SCALAR · OVER + OF NUMBERS

These principles are not only fundamental to the understanding of fractions, which follows, but also to the development of a type of geometry of a plane, or of 3-dimensions and even of n-dimensions, called *affine geometry*.

11.4 CHARACTERISTICS OF CARDINAL NUMBERS

In the development of the cardinal numbers their essential property was that of indicating the size or plurality of a set of things. Thus the cardinal numbers were used to answer the question "How many?" A system of numeration for these numbers provided us with an algorism for counting to determine the size of a set. Thus we consider the cardinal numbers as a *system of counting numbers*.

Now consider any cardinal number, say 4. If we select a segment U and form the product $4U$, we can think of the number 4 as an operator, which operating

U $\qquad$ U $\quad 4U = V$

on U *stretches* it to the segment V. If we had selected a different segment U', then $4U' = V'$ is obtained by stretching U' so that V' is the sum of four U'. Thus for *any* segment, the number 4 multiplying the segment stretches it to a

U' $\qquad$ U' $\quad 4U' = V'$

unique new segment. We say that the segment U has been transformed into the segment V by the operator 4. Generally, for any cardinal number n, each segment U is transformed or stretched into a new segment V, where $V = n \cdot U$.

In this way we can look upon the cardinal numbers as *multipliers*, or as *stretchers*, which operating on a segment transform it into another segment. Special cases are the numbers 1 and 0. When we multiply a segment by 1, we obtain the same segment, and we call this the identity stretcher, or multiplier. When we multiply a segment by 0, we obtain the null segment ⦶, and we say the 0 operator causes the segment to *vanish*. Thus 0, operating on any segment, gives the same result, namely the null segment ⦶. We can call 0 the vanishing stretcher, or multiplier. Thus the cardinal numbers can be considered as a *system of operators* which *transform segments* into other segments.

Again, consider a ray $\overrightarrow{OR}$ and select $\overline{OU}$ as a unit segment. To multiply $\overline{OU}$

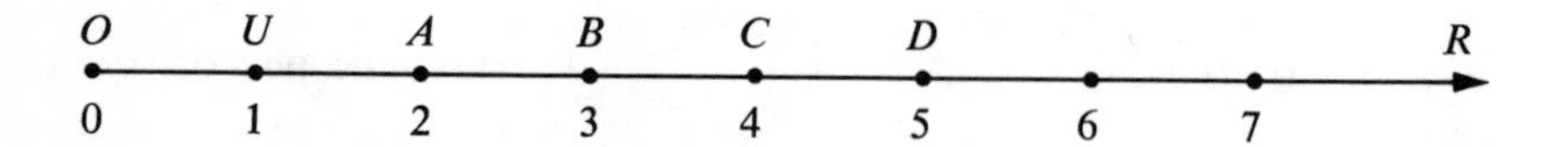

by 2 we obtain the segment $\overline{OA} = 2\overline{OU}$. Similarly we can multiply $\overline{OU}$ by 3, 4, 5, . . . , to obtain the segments $\overline{OB}$, $\overline{OC}$, $\overline{OD}$, and so on. To multiply $\overline{OU}$ by 1 is to transform it into itself and to multiply $\overline{OU}$ by 0 is to produce the null segment $\overline{OO}$ or ⦶. Now, to each of the terminal points $O, U, A, B, C, \ldots$, assign the cardinal number which was the multiplier of $\overline{OU}$ that produced the segment $\overline{OO}$, $\overline{OU}$, $\overline{OA}$, etc. Thus to each of certain points on the ray we have assigned a cardinal number, and to each cardinal number we have assigned a unique point. If we consider the vertex O as an origin, we say that points $O, U, A, B, C, \ldots$ *calibrate* the ray and that the cardinal numbers associated with these points act as a *system of reference*.

Thus we have three ways of looking upon the set of cardinal numbers:

(1) as a system of *counting*

(2) as a system of transformation *operators*

(3) as a system of *reference* points

Later we shall see a fourth way encompassing all three of these ways, namely as a system of measure.

11.5 EXERCISES

Select segments U, V, W, Z, no two congruent to each other.

1. Using U, illustrate $3(2U) = (3 \cdot 2)U$.
2. Using U and V, illustrate $3(U + V) = 3U + 3V$.
3. Using W, illustrate $(3 + 4)W = 3W + 4W$. Then prove that $(a + b)U = aU + bU$.

4. Using a self-winding tape measure, and one inch as a segment U, illustrate by "stretching" or "pulling":
   (a) $1 \cdot U$ (b) $5 \cdot U$
   (c) $36 \cdot U$ (d) $0 \cdot U$
5. (a) Show that $4 \cdot (0 \cdot U) =$ ⦶.
   (b) Show that $0 \cdot (4U) =$ ⦶.
   (c) Can a null segment be "stretched" to produce a nonnull segment?
   (d) What is $0 \cdot$ ⦶?
6. Consider all segments of a line and a constant number n. Let n operate on each segment of the line. Then there is possible a mapping of the set of original segments to the set of transformed segments. Illustrate by writing several ordered pairs of the mapping for $n = 2$. What kind of mapping results? If $n = 0$, what is the result?
7. Give two practical illustrations or applications of the cardinal numbers as a system of reference numbers.
8. Instead of a segment, we could use a physical quantity such as a pound of butter as a unit. Explain the use of cardinal numbers as operators on the pound of butter. Generalize this to the transformation of a unit of any physical entity.

11.6 DIVIDING A SEGMENT BY A CARDINAL NUMBER

In plane geometry, we learn how to bisect a segment, or to divide it into three, four, or any number of congruent parts. If we are given segment $\overline{OA}$, we draw any ray $\overrightarrow{OX}$ forming a convenient acute angle with $\overrightarrow{OA}$. Then we calibrate the

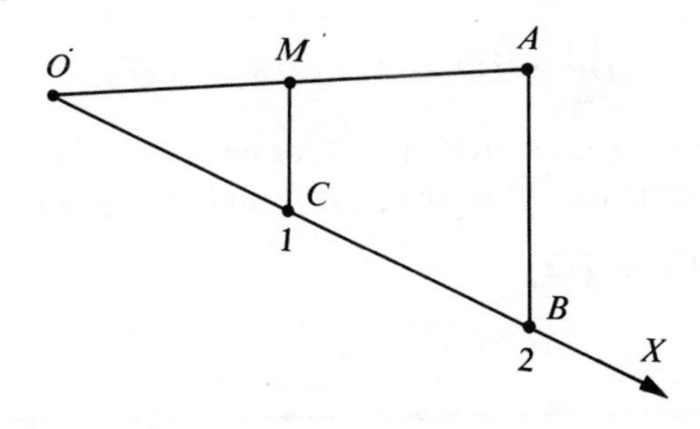

ray $\overrightarrow{OX}$ using any convenient segment U as the unit segment. To bisect $\overline{OA}$, we connect the reference point 2, labeled B, with A and through reference point 1 labeled C draw a line parallel to $\overleftrightarrow{BA}$ meeting $\overline{OA}$ at point M. Then M is the midpoint of $\overline{OA}$ and we write

$$2 \cdot \overline{OM} = \overline{OA}, \quad \text{where 2 is an operator.}$$

Similarly, if we connect reference point n labeled D to A, and through reference point 1 labeled C draw a line parallel to $\overleftrightarrow{DA}$, intersecting $\overline{OA}$ at N, we say $\overline{ON}$ is one of the n congruent segments of $\overline{OA}$ and write

$$n \cdot \overline{ON} = \overline{OA}, \quad \text{where } n \text{ is an operator.}$$

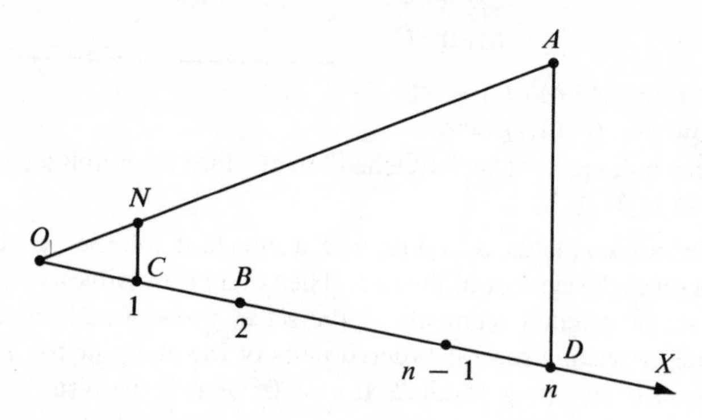

In the first case, when we bisect the segment $\overline{OA}$, we say we have divided the segment $\overline{OA}$ by 2. We may also say that we have operated on the segment $\overline{OA}$ to *shrink* it to segment $\overline{OM}$, in a manner such that

$$2\overline{OM} = \overline{OA} \Leftrightarrow \overline{OM} = 2^{-1} \cdot \overline{OA}.$$

Here, 2^{-1} is a new kind of operator, read "two to the negative one power." We can also write the same operator in the form $(\frac{1}{2})$, which is read "one half," and write

$$\overline{OM} = \tfrac{1}{2}\,\overline{OA}.$$

So we see that 2^{-1} and $(\frac{1}{2})$ are different forms for the same operator.

Similarly, if we operate on $\overline{OA}$ by 3^{-1} (or by $\frac{1}{3}$) we have a shrinking effect on $\overline{OA}$ such that

$$\overline{OA} = 3\,\overline{OP} \Leftrightarrow \overline{OP} = 3^{-1} \cdot \overline{OA} = \tfrac{1}{3}\,\overline{OA}.$$

We can also say $\overline{OA}$ has been divided by 3, or one third of $\overline{OA}$ yields $\overline{OP}$. Quite generally, if we operate on $\overline{OA}$ so that it is shrunk to $\overline{ON}$ and

$$n \cdot \overline{ON} = \overline{OA},$$

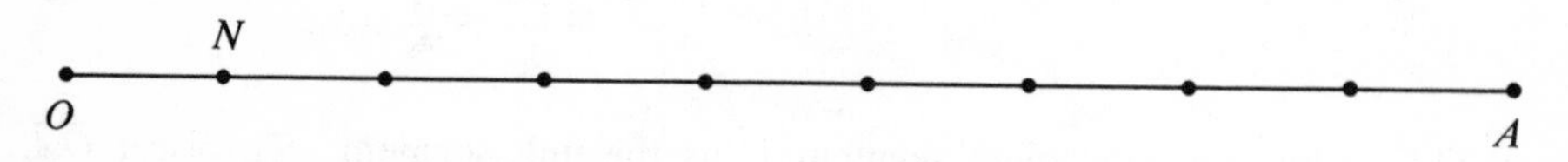

then $\overline{OA}$ has been operated upon by n^{-1} $\left(\text{or } \frac{1}{n}\right)$ and

$$\overline{ON} = n^{-1} \cdot \overline{OA} = \frac{1}{n}\,\overline{OA}.$$

Now, for each of the cardinal numbers 1, 2, 3, . . . , n, . . . we have a new set of operators 1^{-1}, 2^{-1}, 3^{-1}, . . . , n^{-1}, . . . which we shall call *shrinkers*, or *dividers*. Note that the operator 1^{-1} is the same as 1, because

$$1 \cdot \overline{OA} = \overline{OA} \Leftrightarrow \overline{OA} = 1^{-1}\,\overline{OA}.$$

Note also that the cardinal number 0 as an operator transforms every segment into the null segment, ⦶. It is impossible to multiply the null segment, or to subdivide it, by using any cardinal number so that $n \cdot$ ⦶ will give OA. Hence 0^{-1} is meaningless.

If $n \cdot U = V$, we shall call V a multiple of U, and since $n^{-1}V = U$, we shall call U a submultiple of V. Thus $3 \cdot U = V$ means V is a multiple of U, in fact $3 \cdot U$; and $3^{-1}V = U$ means U is a submultiple of V, in fact one of the three congruent segments of V.

Finally we note that n and n^{-1} are inverse operators (compare section 7.10). We shall show that if n operating on U yields nU, then n^{-1} operating on the result, or $n^{-1}(nU)$, yields the segment U. Let $n^{-1}(nU) = V$. This means

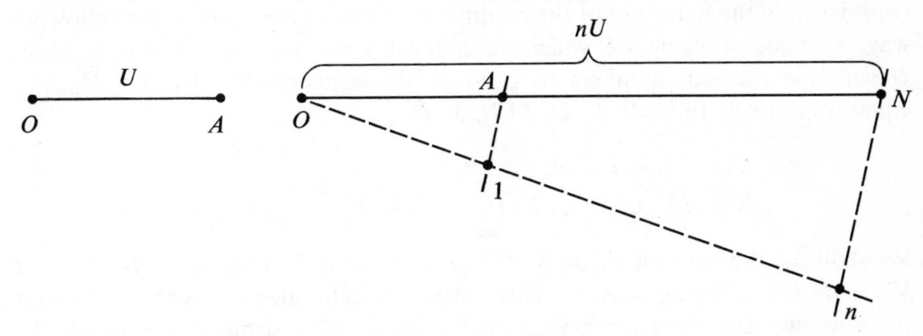

$$nU = nV \quad \text{or} \quad U = V.$$

Thus,

$$n^{-1}(nU) = U, \quad \text{and} \quad n^{-1} \cdot n = 1;$$

also,

$$n \cdot n^{-1} = 1.$$

We shall also say:

> *To operate on a segment by n^{-1} is the same as to divide the segment by n or*
>
> $$V \div n = n^{-1} \cdot V.$$

11.7 EXERCISES

1. Select a segment $\overline{OA}$, and construct:
   (a) $2^{-1}\,\overline{OA}$ (b) $4^{-1}\,\overline{OA}$ (c) $5^{-1}\,\overline{OA}$
2. Show that $2^{-1}\,\overline{OA} > 3^{-1}\,\overline{OA}$; $5^{-1}\,\overline{OA} < 3^{-1}\,\overline{OA}$.

3. Write all the operators $4^{-1}, 3^{-1}, 2^{-1}, 1^{-1}, 0, 1, 2, 3, 4$, in an order of the transformation they produce on a unit segment U.
4. By the use of a segment, show that $3^{-1}(3U) = 3(3^{-1}U)$. What is the result in either case?
5. Show that $4^{-1}(2U) = 2^{-1}U$.
6. If on a reference ray, OU is the unit segment and the number 1 is assigned to A, find the points to assign the operators 2^{-1}, 3^{-1}, and 10^{-1}.
7. What is the meaning of $\frac{1}{3}$? of $\frac{1}{5}$? of $\frac{1}{n}$?

11.8 COMMENSURABLE SEGMENTS

First, it is necessary to talk of the *measure* of a segment. For the present we shall consider only the naive use of the cardinal numbers as measures in the following way. Consider a segment U which we shall call a *unit segment*. Now operate on U with the cardinal numbers to produce the segments $V_0, V_1, V_2, V_3, \ldots$ equal respectively to $0 \cdot U, 1 \cdot U, 2 \cdot U, 3 \cdot U, \ldots$.

$$C = \{0, 1, 2, 3, 4, \ldots, n, \ldots\}$$
$$S = \{0 \cdot U, 1 \cdot U, 2 \cdot U, 3 \cdot U, 4 \cdot U, \ldots, n \cdot U, \ldots\}$$

We shall say the segment $V_3 = 3 \cdot U$ has the *measure* 3. In general, the segment $V_a = a \cdot U$ has the *measure* a. Then, using the calibrated ray with U as a unit segment, we can construct a segment, or mark off a segment, for which the measure is any given cardinal number. In fact, this is the way a ruler edge is used to measure a line drawing or to mark off a given number of inches.

Now, if $V = aU$, V has the measure a, and if $V' = bU$, then V' has the measure b. Adding the segments V and V', we obtain

$$V + V' = aU + bU = (a + b)U,$$

and the sum of the segments has as its measure the sum of the measures of each segment. Note that the *measure* of a segment is a *number*, while the segment itself is a set of points.

Suppose we have two segments V and V' which are unequal. Also, suppose there are two cardinal numbers a and b, of such a nature that

$$a \cdot V = b \cdot V' = W.$$

V V'

W } aV

W } bV'

We shall prove that *in this case* there is a unit segment U which measures both V and V', that is, that V and V' are *commensurable*.

As an illustration from common experience, suppose we have two pieces of wire, V and V', one measuring $\frac{3}{4}$ inch, the other $\frac{1}{2}$ inch. Then 8 of the larger pieces measure 6 inches and 12 of the smaller pieces also measure 6 inches, so that

$$8V = 12V'.$$

Then we see that both V and V' have a common unit of measure U, namely $\frac{1}{4}$ inch.

Returning to the general case, we know that

$$a \cdot V = b \cdot V' = W.$$

Now we divide W by the number ab, or operate on W by $(ab)^{-1}$, that is, divide W into ab congruent segments. Let one of these segments be U. Then we have

$$(ab)^{-1}W = U \quad \text{or} \quad (ab)U = W,$$

and

$$aV = (ab)U \quad \text{or} \quad aV = a(bU);$$

and by the cancellation principle,

$$V = bU.$$

Thus, the measure of V is b, where the unit is U and $U = (ab)^{-1}W$. Similarly,

$$bV' = (ab)U \quad \text{or} \quad bV' = b(aU);$$

hence

$$V' = aU.$$

In summary, we may state the following theorem:

THEOREM: *Given two segments V and V', not congruent, if two numbers a and b exist, for which $aV = bV'$, then V and V' are commensurable.*

In the illustration, $8V = 12V'$, but also $2V = 3V'$. Therefore a common unit of measure of V and V' may be found by taking $U = \frac{1}{3}V = \frac{1}{2}V'$.

On the other hand, as will be shown later, there can be two segments for which no common unit segment of measure exists, for example, the side of a square V, and its diagonal $V' = \sqrt{2}\,V$. There are *no whole numbers a* and b for which $aV = bV'$ in this case; that is, *any* segment serving as a unit of measure for V cannot serve as a unit of measure for V'.

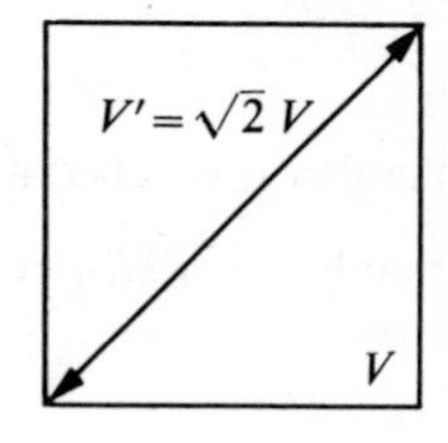

11.9 TRANSFORMATIONS OF COMMENSURABLE SEGMENTS

Suppose we have two commensurable segments V and V', such that

$$a \cdot V = b \cdot V'. \tag{I}$$

We ask the question: "How can we transform one segment into the other?" The answer to this problem will give us a new kind of operator which we shall call a *fraction.*

If we multiply V by a, we obtain a segment congruent to V' multiplied by b, which we call W, and thus

$$aV = W. \tag{II}$$

If we divide W by ab (or operate on it by $(ab)^{-1}$) we obtain a segment U such that

$$(ab)U = W. \tag{III}$$

Substituting (III) for W in (II), we have

$$aV = (ab)U = b(aU). \tag{IV}$$

Now divide both sides of (IV) by b (or operate on it by b^{-1}) and obtain

$$(b^{-1})(aV) = b^{-1}[b(aU)] = aU \tag{V}$$

since $b^{-1}b = 1$.

From section 11.8 we know $aU = V'$; hence

$$(b^{-1})(aV) \quad \text{or} \quad a(b^{-1}V) = V'. \tag{VI}$$

To transform V into V', where $aV = bV'$, we

(1) multiply V by a, and divide the result by b,

or

(2) divide V by b, and multiply the result by a.

The transformation involves two operations, but the order of the operations is independent of the result, i.e., the operations are commutative.

The number a is called the multiplier of the transformation.

The number b is called the divisor of the transformation.

The pair of operators (a, b), which can also be written as $a \cdot b^{-1}$ or $\frac{a}{b}$, is called a *fraction.*

The number a is called a multiplier, a stretcher, or a *numerator.*

The number b, *which is never zero*, is called a divider, a shrinker, or a *denominator.*

It is customary in writing a fraction to write the numerator first and the denominator second, so that no confusion can arise.

DEFINITION: *A* fraction *is an ordered pair of numbers, in which the first number is called the* numerator *(or* multiplier*) and the second number, non-zero, is called the* denominator *(or* divisor*).*

EXAMPLE 1. Show how to obtain $\frac{2}{3}V$ from the given segment V.

Solution 1: Given V as segment ———, we multiply by 2 to obtain ——————, which is $2V$. Then we divide (shrink) the result by 3 to obtain ——, which is $\frac{2}{3}V$.

Solution 2: We divide V by 3 to obtain —. We multiply the result by 2 to obtain ——, which is $\frac{2}{3}V$.

This example shows that we can conceive of $\frac{2}{3}$ as stretching to double (2) and shrinking the result to one-third (3^{-1} or $\frac{1}{3}$), or shrinking the given amount to one-third and doubling the result. Thus

$\frac{a}{b}$ operating on any quantity may be conceived as producing

1. one of the b congruent parts of a times the quantity, or
2. a of the b congruent parts of the quantity.

EXAMPLE 2. Explain how $2 \cdot 3^{-1}$ differs from $(2 \cdot 3)^{-1}$.

Solution: $2 \cdot 3^{-1}$ is the same as $\frac{2}{3}$ (see Example 1 above) $(2 \cdot 3)^{-1}$ is 6^{-1} or $\frac{1}{6}$ and hence 1 of the 6 equal parts of a given segment.

EXAMPLE 3. If $4V = 6V'$ where V is a given segment, find V'.

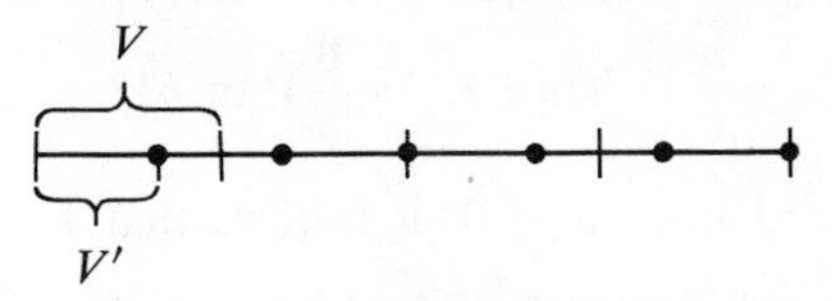

Solution: We first multiply V by 4. We then divide the resulting segment by 6. One of the resulting parts is $(4V) \div 6$ or $6^{-1}(4V)$ or $\frac{1}{6}(4V)$ or $\frac{4}{6}V$. This is V'.

Check: $6(\frac{4}{6}V) = (6 \cdot 6^{-1})4V = 4V$; i.e., $6V'$ is equal to $4V$.

11.10 EXERCISES

1. Show that the operator 3^{-1} is equivalent to the fraction $\frac{1}{3}$.
2. The operators $\{0, 1, 2, \ldots, n, \ldots\}$ calibrate a ray. Show how the operators $\{2^{-1}, 4^{-1}, 8^{-1}, 16^{-1}\}$ calibrate the unit segment.
3. Show how the fractions $\{\frac{0}{10}, \frac{1}{10}, \frac{2}{10}, \ldots, \frac{9}{10}, \frac{10}{10}\}$ calibrate the unit segment.
4. If $5V = 3V'$, where V and V' are nonequal segments,
   (a) show how to construct V' from V.
   (b) show how to construct V from V'.
   Illustrate your answers.
5. A boy desired $\frac{3}{8}$ of a pound of beef. Illustrate, in two ways, how $\frac{3}{8}$ as an operator explains the amount desired.
6. The meaning of a fraction was developed through the use of segments. In place of segments we could use any entity such as ice cream. Let the figure represent a portion of ice cream. Explain the meaning of operating on this entity by:
   (a) 1 (b) 3 (c) 2^{-1} (d) $\frac{2}{3}$ (e) $\frac{7}{4}$
7. Show that the operators $\frac{2}{3}$ and $\frac{4}{6}$ are equivalent; that is, operating on the same segment they produce the same result.
8. Show how, given $aV = bV'$, to transform V' into V.

11.11 THE SET OF FRACTIONS

We have defined $\frac{a}{b}$, where a is a whole number and b is a nonzero whole number, as a fraction which, operating on a segment V, produces the segment V', such that

$$V' = \frac{a}{b}V \qquad \text{or} \qquad aV = bV'.$$

Among these fractions, some are equivalent to cardinal number operators.

1. Let $a = 0$ in $V' = \frac{a}{b}V$. Then $V' = \frac{0}{b}V$ or $bV' = 0V$. Since $0 \cdot V = \obar$, we have $bV' = \obar$, and since $b \neq 0$, it follows that $V' = \obar$. Hence $\frac{0}{b}$, for every b, produces the null segment, and we have

$$\frac{0}{b}V = \obar \quad \text{for every value of } b.$$

Hence $\frac{0}{b}$ is equivalent to the cardinal number 0.

2. Let $b = 1$ in $V' = \frac{a}{b} V$. Then $\frac{a}{1} V = V'$ or $aV = 1V'$. Since $1V' = V'$, we have $aV = V'$. Hence:

$$\frac{a}{1} V = aV \quad \text{for every value of } a,$$

and $\frac{a}{1}$, for every a, produces the same segment as the cardinal number a.

3. Let $a = 1$ in $V' = \frac{a}{b} V$. Then $\frac{1}{b} V = V'$ or $V = bV'$, which in turn is the same as $V' = b^{-1}V$. Thus $\frac{1}{b}$ operating on a segment shrinks it to *one* of the b equal segments of V and is not equivalent to any cardinal number operator. We call the fraction $\frac{1}{b}$ a *unit fraction*. When $b = 1$,

$$V = 1 \cdot V' \qquad \text{and} \qquad V' = 1^{-1}V.$$

Since $V = 1 \cdot V'$, we have $V = V'$ and $1 \cdot V = V'$. Substituting $1 \cdot V = V'$ in $V' = 1^{-1}V$, we have

$$1 \cdot V = 1^{-1}V \qquad \text{or} \qquad 1^{-1} = 1.$$

4. Let a be a multiple of b, that is, $a = m \cdot b$, in $V' = \frac{a}{b} V$. Then $V' = \frac{mb}{b} V$ or $(mb)V = bV'$ or $mV = V'$. We thus have

$$\frac{mb}{b} V = mV,$$

and the operator $\frac{mb}{b}$ is equivalent to the cardinal number m for every value of b. If $m = 1$, we have $\frac{b}{b}$, which is equivalent to the operator 1 for every b.

5. Let a and b be relatively prime. Then

$$V' = \frac{a}{b} V \Rightarrow aV = bV'$$

and the segments are commensurable. There is a common unit of measure U, such that $aU = V'$ and $bU = V$, and $\frac{a}{b}$ is a fraction not equivalent to any cardinal number operator.

We can now exhibit the set of fractions as follows. In the first row we write all the fractions with numerator 0; then in the second row all with numerator 1, then 2, and so on forever, giving us:

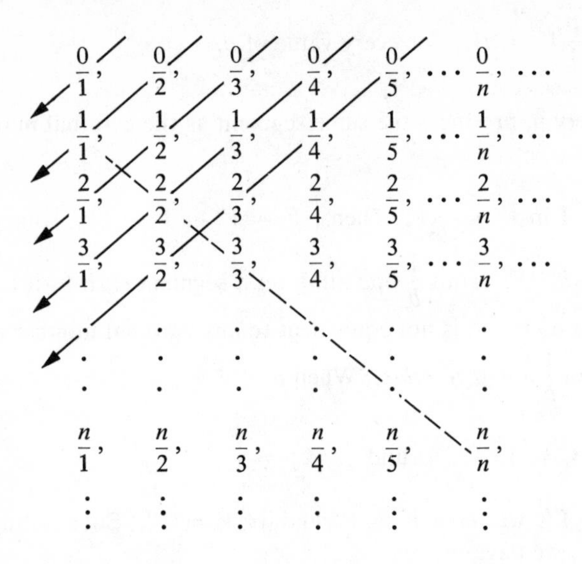

The first column gives fractions equivalent to the cardinal numbers, and the broken diagonal line indicates the identity fractions. If we now rewrite the fractions in the order indicated by the solid arrows, going from left to right, we have the set of all the fractions in this form:

$$F = \left\{\frac{0}{1}, \frac{0}{2}, \frac{1}{1}, \frac{0}{3}, \frac{1}{2}, \frac{2}{1}, \frac{0}{4}, \frac{1}{3}, \frac{2}{2}, \frac{3}{1}, \frac{0}{5}, \ldots, \right.$$

$$\left. \frac{0}{n}, \frac{1}{n-1}, \frac{2}{n-2}, \ldots, \frac{n-1}{1}, \ldots\right\}$$

11.12 EXERCISES

1. Explain the meaning of $V + V'$; $V - V'$; aV; and $\frac{a}{b} V$.
2. List the fundamental principles for the operations $V + V'$ and $a \cdot V$.
3. List the fundamental principles for the operation $\frac{a}{b} V$.
4. Distinguish between equal segments and congruent segments.
5. A null segment is a point. Explain this statement.
6. State three different uses of the cardinal numbers.
7. State the meaning given to a fraction in this chapter.
8. Show that for every cardinal a, $a \cdot a^{-1} = 1$.

9. What is meant by a "transformation of a segment U"?
10. The cardinals, 2, 3, 4, . . . , as operators produce a segment greater than the segment on which they operate. Explain the transformation effected by 1, $\frac{1}{2}$, $\frac{1}{3}$, $\frac{1}{4}$, $\frac{1}{10}$, $\frac{1}{100}$, and 0, and illustrate on a given segment.
11. Explain the equivalence of the words "shrinker," "divider," and "denominator." Of the words "stretcher," "multiplier," and "numerator."
12. If $3V = V'$, are V and V' commensurable? If so, what is a common unit segment of the given segments?
13. Illustrate segments V and V' for which $8V = 12V'$. What is the largest possible common unit segment?
14. If two segments have a common unit segment U, is $2^{-1}U$ also a common unit segment? $3^{-1}U$? $n^{-1}U$? Explain.
15. In the set of fractions F, in section 11.11, discover a pattern or common property that exists by considering the first fraction, the next two fractions, the next three fractions, etc. What is this principle for "the next eight fractions"? For what fractions is the sum of numerator and denominator 12?

★16. Explain the statement "The number of fractions is countable."

11.13 REFERENCE QUESTION

What is meant by saying that a cardinal number, acting as an operator, *transforms* one segment into another? (Refer to the discussion in this chapter.) If you are interested in a more detailed discussion of transformations in general, see

Sensiba, Daniel E. "Geometry and Transformations," *Enrichment Mathematics for the Grades.* Washington, D.C.: NCTM, 1963. Chapter 23.

12 FRACTIONS AND RATIONAL NUMBERS

IN THE PREVIOUS CHAPTER *we developed the concept of a fraction as an operator. In this chapter we shall study fractions as a set of mathematical beings in themselves, independent of segments or other magnitudes. However, we shall do this by abstracting the properties of fractions from their definition as operators.*

12.1 EQUIVALENT FRACTIONS

Let a fraction $\frac{a}{b}$, operating on a segment U, transform it into segment V. Now suppose there is another fraction $\frac{c}{d}$, where $a \neq c$ and $b \neq d$, such that $\frac{c}{d}U$ also yields the segment V; that is,

$$\frac{a}{b}U = \frac{c}{d}U = V.$$

Then $\frac{a}{b}$ and $\frac{c}{d}$ have the same effect as operators, and we say they are *equivalent;* that is, $\frac{a}{b}$ is equivalent to $\frac{c}{d}$, which is written in symbols as

$$\frac{a}{b} \sim \frac{c}{d}.$$

First, we shall seek the relationship that exists between the four cardinals a, b, c, d, for equivalent fractions. By definition of the fraction as an operator, we have

$$\frac{a}{b}U = \frac{c}{d}U = V.$$

Then $\quad \frac{a}{b} U = V \Rightarrow aU = bV$

and $\quad \frac{c}{d} U = V \Rightarrow cU = dV.$

We can multiply each side of the last equalities by d and b respectively, to obtain:

$$\begin{aligned} d(aU) &= d(bV) \\ b(cU) &= b(dV) \end{aligned} \quad \text{or} \quad \begin{aligned} (ad)U &= (bd)V \\ (bc)U &= (bd)V \end{aligned}$$

From the last two equalities, it follows that

$$(ad)U = (bc)U \quad \text{or} \quad ad = bc.$$

Hence, if $\frac{a}{b}$ and $\frac{c}{d}$ are equivalent, as operators, then $ad = bc$; that is,

$$\frac{a}{b} U = \frac{c}{d} U \Rightarrow ad = bc.$$

It can also be shown that

$$ad = bc \Rightarrow \frac{a}{b} U = \frac{c}{d} U.$$

Now, dropping the idea of operators, we make the following definition:

DEFINITION: *Two fractions* $\frac{a}{b}$ *and* $\frac{c}{d}$ *are* equivalent *if and only if the product ad is equal to the product bc. That is,*

$$\frac{a}{b} \sim \frac{c}{d} \Leftrightarrow ad = bc.$$

The numbers a and d are sometimes called the extremes, *and b and c, the* means.

EXAMPLE 1. Is $\frac{3}{5} \sim \frac{9}{15}$?

Solution: Since $3 \times 15 = 5 \times 9$, the two fractions are equivalent.

EXAMPLE 2. From $4 \times 9 = 3 \times 12$, form pairs of equivalent fractions.

Solution: The 4 and 9 can come first and last. The numbers 3 and 12 are the means. Hence we have the following pairs:

$$\frac{4}{3} \sim \frac{12}{9}, \quad \frac{4}{12} \sim \frac{3}{9}, \quad \frac{9}{3} \sim \frac{12}{4}, \quad \frac{9}{12} \sim \frac{3}{4}$$

Note that we do *not* say that the fraction $\frac{4}{3}$ is *equal* to $\frac{12}{9}$, we say it is *equivalent* to $\frac{12}{9}$. However, we do say the whole number 4×9 is equal to the whole number 3×12. Thus 3×12 and 4×9 are the same number, but $\frac{4}{3}$ and $\frac{12}{9}$ are equivalent fractions.

To show that we use the word "equivalent" rightfully, we must prove that the relation is reflexive, symmetric, and transitive. That is, we must prove:

1. $\frac{a}{b} \sim \frac{a}{b}$ REFLEXIVITY

   Proof: $ab = ba$

2. If $\frac{a}{b} \sim \frac{c}{d}$, then $\frac{c}{d} \sim \frac{a}{b}$. SYMMETRY

   Proof:
$$ad = bc$$
$$cb = da$$
$$\frac{c}{d} \sim \frac{a}{b}$$

3. If $\frac{a}{b} \sim \frac{c}{d}$ and $\frac{c}{d} \sim \frac{e}{f}$, then $\frac{a}{b} \sim \frac{e}{f}$. TRANSITIVITY

   Proof:
$$ad = bc$$
$$cf = de$$
$$(ad)(cf) = (bc)(de)$$
$$(af)(cd) = (be)(cd)$$
$$af = be$$
$$\frac{a}{b} \sim \frac{e}{f}$$

The reader should supply the reason for each step in each of the foregoing proofs.

EXAMPLE 3. Is $\frac{2}{3} \sim \frac{4}{5}$?

Solution: Since $2 \times 5 \neq 3 \times 4$, the fractions are not equivalent.

12.2 THE SIMPLEST OF ALL EQUIVALENT FRACTIONS

Let $\frac{p}{q}$ be any given fraction, and consider the fraction formed from this one by multiplying both numerator and denominator by the same number n, not equal to zero, that is, the fraction $\frac{pn}{qn}$. Thus, we have the following theorem:

THEOREM: $\frac{pn}{qn} \sim \frac{p}{q}$ *where n is a cardinal number, $n \neq 0$.*

Proof:

$pnq = qnp$ Commutativity

$(pn)q = (qn)p$ Associativity

$\frac{pn}{qn} \sim \frac{p}{q}$ Definition

In this way one can find many fractions equivalent to a given fraction as exhibited in the following example.

EXAMPLE 4. $\frac{3}{5} \sim \frac{2 \cdot 3}{2 \cdot 5}$ or $\frac{6}{10}$, also $\frac{3}{5} \sim \frac{5 \cdot 3}{5 \cdot 5}$ or $\frac{15}{25}$, and so on.

To *simplify* a fraction means to find an equivalent fraction whose terms (numerator and denominator) are less than those of the given fraction. Thus the fraction $\frac{4}{6}$ is simpler than the fraction $\frac{24}{36}$, which is the same as $\frac{4 \cdot 6}{6 \cdot 6}$, and which, by the previous paragraph, is equivalent to $\frac{4}{6}$. However, $\frac{4}{6}$ is *not* the *simplest* fraction.

DEFINITION: *The* simplest fraction *equivalent to a given fraction is one whose terms are relatively prime to each other; that is, the numerator and denominator have no common factor.*†

To find the simplest fraction from a given fraction, we proceed as follows: Let $\frac{a}{b}$ be any given fraction. Find the GCF of a and b (sections 10.2 and 10.3), and suppose it is f. Then $a = pf$ and $b = qf$, where p and q are now relatively prime. Thus

$$\frac{a}{b} = \frac{pf}{qf} \sim \frac{p}{q}.$$

Then $\frac{p}{q}$ is the simplest fraction equivalent to the given fraction $\frac{a}{b}$. In the above example, the GCF of 24 and 36 is 12. Then $24 = 2 \cdot 12$ and $36 = 3 \cdot 12$. Thus

$$\frac{24}{36} = \frac{2 \cdot 12}{3 \cdot 12} \sim \frac{2}{3},$$

and $\frac{2}{3}$ is the *simplest* fraction.

EXAMPLE 5. Given $\frac{60}{84}$, we know the GCF of 60 and 84 is 12. Then $60 = 5 \times 12$ and $84 = 7 \times 12$. Thus

$$\frac{60}{84} = \frac{5 \times 12}{7 \times 12} \sim \frac{5}{7},$$

and $\frac{5}{7}$ is the simplest fraction equivalent to $\frac{60}{84}$.

Thus, it may be seen that a set of equivalent fractions will have one simplest fraction because no matter what fraction is chosen from the set its simplest fraction can be found by this process to be the same as that found for all the other fractions in the set. Therefore, in a set of equivalent fractions there is one, and only one, which is simplest.

† The simplest fraction is frequently called *irreducible* because the terms of the fraction cannot be transformed into smaller numbers and still give an equivalent fraction.

We now ask the question: "Is it possible, given a fraction, to find the set of *all* fractions equivalent to the given fraction?" The answer is yes. First, we prove the following theorem:

THEOREM: *If a fraction is equivalent to a simplest fraction, then its terms are the same multiple of the terms of the simplest fraction.*

Proof: Let $\frac{a}{b}$ be a simplest fraction. Then a and b have no common divisor. Suppose $\frac{a}{b} \sim \frac{x}{y}$ where $x \neq a$, and $y \neq b$. By an earlier theorem

$$\frac{a}{b} \sim \frac{x}{y} \Leftrightarrow ay = bx; \qquad \text{(I)}$$

that is, the whole number ay and the whole number bx are the same. Now a divides bx because it divides its equal ay. Since a has no factor in common with b, and a divides bx, a must divide x. There is thus a whole number f, $f \neq 0$, such that $x = f \cdot a$. Substituting for x in (I), we have $ay = b \cdot f \cdot a$ or $y = b \cdot f$. Hence x and y are the same multiple, f, of a and b respectively.

As an example of the above proof, suppose $\frac{3}{7} \sim \frac{30}{70}$. Then $3(70) = 7(30)$. Since 3 divides the left side exactly, it must divide the right side exactly. But 3 does not divide 7; hence it is a factor of thirty, in fact $3 \times 10 = 30$. Replacing 30 by 3×10, we have $3(70) = 7(3 \times 10)$, and canceling 3 from each side, we have $70 = 7 \times 10$. Hence both 3 and 7 have been multiplied by the same factor 10 to obtain the equivalent fraction $\frac{30}{70}$. Study this example with the above general proof until you can apply it to any given simplest fraction.

Now we are in a position to create the set of all fractions equivalent to a given fraction. First, if the given fraction is not the simplest fraction, we find the simplest equivalent fraction. Then, by multiplying both its numerator and denominator successively by $1, 2, 3, \ldots, n, \ldots$, we shall obtain a set of all fractions equivalent to the given fraction. For example, if we are given $\frac{30}{42}$, we first obtain the simplest fraction by finding the GCF of 30 and 42, which is 6, and write

$$\frac{30}{42} = \frac{5 \cdot 6}{7 \cdot 6} \sim \frac{5}{7}.$$

Now multiplying $\frac{5}{7}$ successively by the whole numbers (not zero) we obtain

$$\left\{\frac{5}{7}, \frac{10}{14}, \frac{15}{21}, \frac{20}{28}, \frac{25}{35}, \frac{30}{42}, \ldots, \frac{n \cdot 5}{n \cdot 7}, \ldots\right\}.$$

Quite generally, let $\frac{a}{b}$ be any given fraction. Find the GCF of a and b and let it be f, so that $a = pf$ and $b = qf$. Then the simplest fraction is $\frac{p}{q}$. The set of all fractions equivalent to $\frac{a}{b}$ is then

$$\left\{\frac{p}{q}, \frac{2p}{2q}, \frac{3p}{3q}, \ldots, \frac{f \cdot p}{f \cdot q}\left(\text{or } \frac{a}{b}\right), \ldots, \frac{n \cdot p}{n \cdot q}, \ldots\right\}.$$

12.3 EXERCISES

1. Show, by taking a given segment and operating on it, that $\frac{3}{4} \sim \frac{6}{8}$.
2. Express each of the following in its simplest equivalent form:
   (a) $\frac{84}{108}$ (b) $\frac{34{,}786}{74{,}256}$ (c) $\frac{4{,}920}{28{,}044}$ (d) $\frac{535{,}533}{689{,}689}$
3. Find a number which added to the numerator and denominator of a given fraction will produce an equivalent fraction.
4. How many fractions are there that are equivalent to, yet simpler than, $\frac{10}{15}$? What is the simplest equivalent fraction?
5. Find the set of all fractions equivalent to:
   (a) $\frac{4}{7}$ (b) $\frac{28}{42}$ (c) $\frac{52}{91}$ (d) $\frac{x}{x+1}$
6. (a) Is $\frac{4}{7} \sim \frac{205}{451}$? (b) Is $\frac{0}{5} \sim \frac{0}{9}$?
7. What is the simplest fraction equivalent to:
   (a) $\frac{0}{7}$ (b) $\frac{1}{6}$ (c) $\frac{7}{11}$ (d) $\frac{24}{24}$ (e) $\frac{257}{43}$

12.4 FRACTIONS AS MEASURES

In Chapter 11 we regarded the cardinal numbers as different systems according to the way they were applied. These applications included:

(a) a system of reference for the size of discrete sets
(b) a system of operators for transforming segments
(c) a system of reference for calibrating a ray
(d) a system of measures for telling the length of a segment

We can now look upon the set of fractions as having properties that constitute analogous systems.

In Chapter 11 a fraction was introduced as an operator, which transforms a given segment into another segment. In this sense a fraction is a $\frac{\text{stretcher}}{\text{shrinker}}$, or $\frac{\text{multiplier}}{\text{divider}}$, and each fraction $\frac{a}{b}$ assigns to a given segment the transformed segment. Thus, for any given segment, there is assigned to it the transformed segment created by each of the fractions operating on the given segment. *The fractions are a system of operators.*

Now consider the ray $\overrightarrow{OX}$, and a segment $\overline{OA}$. Consider the set of fractions

$$\left\{\frac{0}{10}, \frac{1}{10}, \frac{2}{10}, \ldots, \frac{9}{10}, \frac{10}{10}\right\}$$

each operating on $\overline{OA}$. The first shrinks the segment to ⓘ. The second fraction, $\frac{1}{10}$, shrinks the segment to $\overline{OA}_1$, the third to $\overline{OA}_2$, etc., until the last, $\frac{10}{10}$, assigns

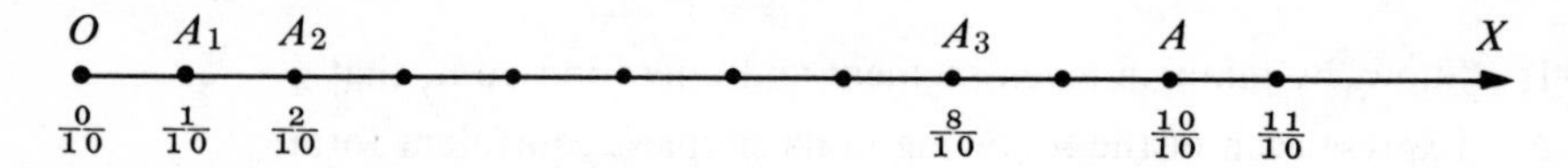

the segment $\overline{OA}$ to itself. All of the divisions of $\overline{OA}$ are congruent and there are ten such segments. If we assign to the end point of each of these transformed segments the fraction which generated the segment, we have a one-to-one correspondence (bijection) between the fractions and certain points of the ray. We say the segment has been calibrated into tenths. Similarly we could continue this calibration into the fractions $\frac{11}{10}$, $\frac{12}{10}$, etc., until the entire ray is calibrated into tenths.

Thus the fractions with denominator 10 and numerator 0, 1, 2, . . . *calibrate the ray into reference points.*

We could, however, use all the fractions with denominator 5 and calibrate the ray into fifths, or generally for any cardinal > 1, we can calibrate the ray into halves, thirds, fourths, and so on.

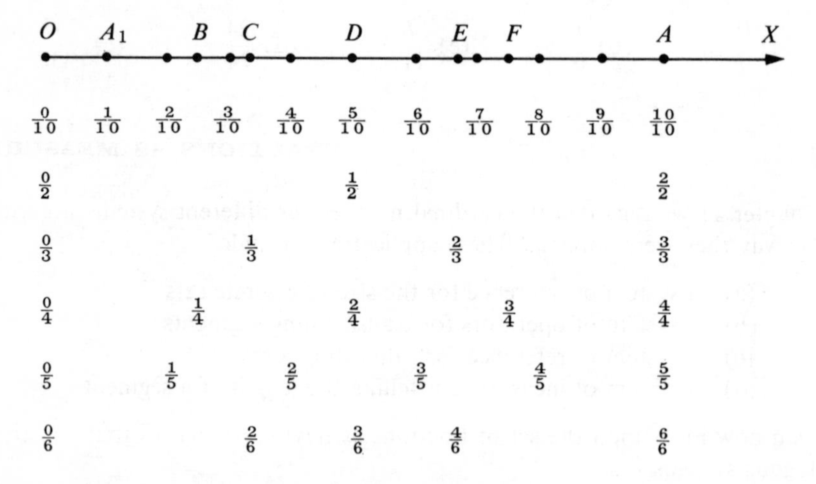

If we agree to give the value $\frac{10}{10}$ as a measure of the segment $\overline{OA}$, then the other reference numbers can also serve as the measure of the segment for which the corresponding point is the terminal point. For example, we write

$$m(\overline{OA}_1) = \tfrac{1}{10}; \quad m(\overline{OC}) = \tfrac{1}{3}; \quad m(\overline{OF}) = \tfrac{3}{4}.$$

In this way *the fractions serve as a system of measures.* This will be further expanded in Chapter 15.

In section 12.4, note that point D on ray $\overrightarrow{OX}$ had assigned to it both the fractions $\frac{1}{2}$ and $\frac{2}{4}$. Continuing the process of calibration, we will find that every fraction of the equivalence class

$$\left\{\frac{1}{2}, \frac{2}{4}, \frac{3}{6}, \ldots, \frac{k}{2 \cdot k}, \ldots\right\}$$

is assigned to the point D. Thus many fractions can be used to designate the point D of segment $\overline{OA}$. Since D is a unique point, it would seem natural to assign a unique number to this point, such that it calibrates the ray, or measures $\overline{OD}$. To do this, we say

DEFINITION: *An entire equivalence class represents one number, called a* rational number. *Any member of the class may be used to name this number.*

Thus the number which represents the bisection of segment $\overline{OA}$ is the rational number designated by any element of the set

$$\left\{\frac{1}{2}, \frac{2}{4}, \frac{3}{6}, \ldots, \frac{k}{2k}, \ldots\right\}.$$

We shall generally name this number by the simplest name, that is, one-half ($\frac{1}{2}$). Similarly the number which represents point E is the rational number designated by

$$\left\{\frac{2}{3}, \frac{4}{6}, \frac{6}{9}, \ldots, \frac{2k}{3k}, \ldots\right\},$$

and generally we name it by the simplest name, two-thirds ($\frac{2}{3}$). However, any other element of the set can be used just as well to name the rational number corresponding to the point E.

Now recall the theorem (see Chapter 1) on the partitioning of a set into discrete equivalence classes, by an equivalence relation. In section 12.1 we proved that equivalence of fractions was an equivalence relation. If this relation is placed on the set of all fractions

$$F = \left\{\frac{0}{1}, \frac{0}{2}, \frac{1}{1}, \frac{0}{3}, \frac{1}{2}, \frac{2}{1}, \frac{0}{4}, \frac{1}{3}, \frac{2}{2}, \frac{3}{1}, \ldots, \frac{0}{p}, \frac{1}{p-1}, \frac{2}{p-2}, \ldots, \frac{p-1}{1}, \ldots\right\},$$

it will partition them into a number of discrete equivalence classes.

These classes are:

$$\left\{\frac{0}{1}, \frac{0}{2}, \frac{0}{3}, \frac{0}{4}, \ldots, \frac{0}{n}, \ldots\right\}$$

$$\left\{\frac{1}{1}, \frac{2}{2}, \frac{3}{3}, \frac{4}{4}, \ldots, \frac{n}{n}, \ldots\right\}$$

$$\left\{\frac{1}{2}, \frac{2}{4}, \frac{3}{6}, \frac{4}{8}, \ldots, \frac{n}{2n}, \ldots\right\}$$

$$\left\{\frac{2}{1}, \frac{4}{2}, \frac{6}{3}, \frac{8}{4}, \ldots, \frac{2n}{n}, \ldots\right\}$$

. . . .

Each of these sets designates (or is assigned to) a unique point on the ray. Each of these sets represents a rational number. The set of rational numbers can then be designated by the simplest element of its equivalence class to obtain the set of rational numbers:

$$R = \left\{\frac{0}{1}, \frac{1}{1}, \frac{1}{2}, \frac{2}{1}, \frac{1}{3}, \frac{3}{1}, \frac{1}{4}, \frac{2}{3}, \frac{3}{2}, \frac{4}{1}, \frac{1}{5}, \frac{5}{1}, \ldots\right\}$$

Of course any other equivalent fraction could be used to name the same rational number. When we write

$$\frac{1}{2} \sim \frac{3}{6} \quad \text{or} \quad \frac{a}{b} \sim \frac{c}{d},$$

we are considering the entities as fractions. The fractions are equivalent. However, since $\frac{1}{2}$ and $\frac{3}{6}$ name the same rational number, we can now write

$$\frac{1}{2} = \frac{3}{6} \quad \text{or} \quad \frac{a}{b} = \frac{c}{d},$$

and here we are considering the fractions as names of rational numbers. Thus $\frac{1}{2}$ and $\frac{3}{6}$ are two ways of designating the same rational number. They are not two ways of designating the same fraction. They are two equivalent fractions.

A novel way of illustrating all the rational numbers, and the equivalence classes which represent them, is by the use of coordinates (see Chapter 17). We reproduce only the first quadrant, but the enterprising teacher can see how to extend this to the other quadrants. In the diagram, each ray has the simplest name as vertex, and contains all the points which represent its equivalence class. Note that if every ray were extended backward, it would pass through the origin and thus $\frac{0}{0}$ would be a name for every rational number. This is one reason for ruling zero out as a denominator.

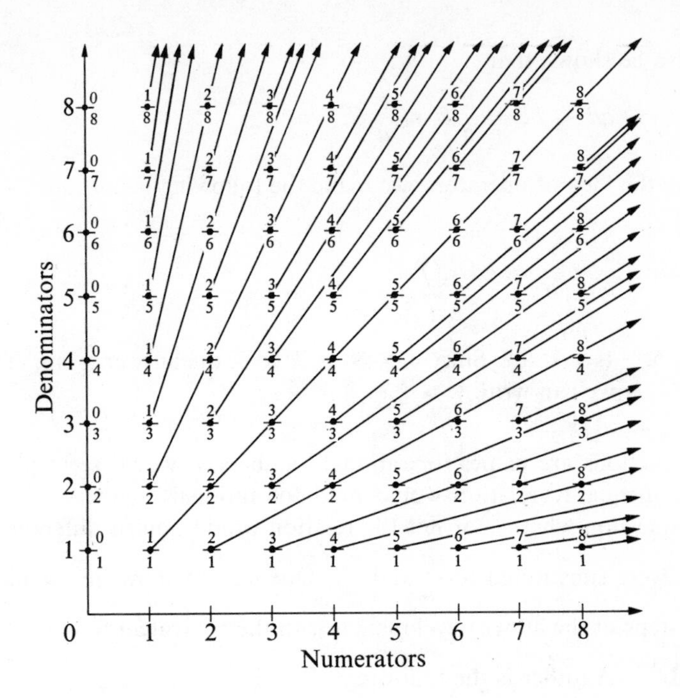

12.6 INEQUALITY OF FRACTIONS AND RATIONAL NUMBERS

We seek a relationship of the cardinals a, b, c, d for inequality of fractions, corresponding to that of equivalence in section 12.1. Let a segment U be given, and let $\frac{a}{b}$ and $\frac{c}{d}$ be two fractions, such that

$$\frac{a}{b}U < \frac{c}{d}U$$

and, hence (section 11.1),

$$\frac{a}{b}U < V < \frac{c}{d}U. \tag{II}$$

From (II) we obtain

$$aU < bV \qquad \text{and} \qquad dV < cU.$$

Multiplying each side of these inequalities by d and b respectively, we obtain

$$adU < bdV \qquad \text{and} \qquad bdV < bcU. \tag{III}$$

By the transitivity of the inequality of segments we have, from (III),

$$adU < bcU,$$

which by the cancellation law of inequalities implies $ad < bc$. Thus,

$$\frac{a}{b}U < \frac{c}{d}U \Rightarrow ad < bc.$$

It can also be shown that

$$ad < bc \Rightarrow \frac{a}{b}\,U < \frac{c}{d}\,U.$$

Dropping the idea of operators, we make the following definition:

DEFINITION: $\frac{a}{b} < \frac{c}{d} \Leftrightarrow ad < bc.$

EXAMPLE 6. Is $\frac{4}{7} < \frac{5}{9}$? Since $4 \times 9 > 7 \times 5$, the answer is no. Then we can write $\frac{4}{7} > \frac{5}{9}$ or $\frac{5}{9} < \frac{4}{7}$.

Since fractions are names for rational numbers, it would seem plausible that the same inequality relation would hold for rational numbers. However, we can still question whether or not the relation would hold if different equivalent fractions were substituted for $\frac{a}{b}$ and $\frac{c}{d}$. One way to show this would be to repeat the steps of the above development with the equivalent fractions substituted for $\frac{a}{b}$ and $\frac{c}{d}$. Another is the following:

Suppose $\frac{a}{b} < \frac{c}{d}$ and $\frac{a}{b} \sim \frac{p}{q}$ and $\frac{c}{d} \sim \frac{r}{s}$. Then we know (1) $ad < bc$, (2) $aq = bp$, and (3) $cs = dr$. From (2) and (3) by multiplication we have

$$aqdr = bpcs.$$

Now if we divide these equal numbers by ad and bc respectively, the quotients are qr and ps. Since the divisor ad is less than the divisor bc by (1), the quotient qr is greater than the quotient ps; that is,

$$ps < qr, \text{ which implies } \frac{p}{q} < \frac{r}{s}.$$

Hence the inequality relation holds for rational numbers, no matter which equivalent names are used to represent the numbers.

Another way to compare fractions is to transform each to equivalent fractions which have the same denominator. Then the order relation of the numerators will be the order relation of the fractions. To transform fractions to the same (or common) denominator, we first recall (section 10.6) the following:

Given any two unequal numbers b and d, we can always find two other numbers b' and d' so that $bb' = dd' =$ LCM (b, d). In other words, if g is the LCM of two numbers b and d, then

$$g \div b = b' \quad \text{and} \quad g \div d = d' \quad \text{and} \quad g = bb' = dd'.$$

Now, given fractions $\frac{a}{b}$ and $\frac{c}{d}$, with $b \neq d$, we find LCM (b, d) and then multiply the terms of the first fraction by b' and those of the second fraction by d'. Thus

$$\frac{a}{b} \sim \frac{ab'}{bb'} \quad \text{and} \quad \frac{c}{d} \sim \frac{cd'}{dd'}$$

and the fractions $\frac{ab'}{bb'}$ and $\frac{cd'}{dd'}$ have the same denominator. We now order the fractions according to the numerators.

EXAMPLE 7. Compare $\frac{3}{7}$ and $\frac{5}{6}$.

Solution: We have

$$\frac{3 \cdot 6}{7 \cdot 6}, \frac{5 \cdot 7}{6 \cdot 7}, \text{ or } \frac{18}{42}, \frac{35}{42} \text{ and } 18 < 35 \Rightarrow \frac{3}{7} < \frac{5}{6}.$$

EXAMPLE 8. Compare $\frac{5}{42}$ and $\frac{4}{30}$.

Solution: We have

$$\frac{5 \cdot 5}{42 \cdot 5}, \frac{4 \cdot 7}{30 \cdot 7} \Rightarrow \frac{25}{210}, \frac{28}{210} \text{ and } 25 < 28 \Rightarrow \frac{5}{42} < \frac{4}{30}.$$

Here the least common multiple of $42 = 2 \cdot 3 \cdot 7$ and $30 = 2 \cdot 3 \cdot 5$ is $2 \cdot 3 \cdot 5 \cdot 7 = 210$. Then the multipliers are $210 \div 42 = 5$, and $210 \div 30 = 7$, respectively.

If there are more than two fractions, we can proceed in the same way to establish their order. Let $\frac{a}{b}, \frac{c}{d}, \frac{e}{f}$, and $\frac{g}{h}$ be given. Let m be the LCM of b, d, f, and h. Then we can find four numbers b', d', f', and h' such that $m = bb' = dd' = ff' = hh'$. The fractions equivalent to the given fractions are

$$\frac{ab'}{bb'}, \frac{cd'}{dd'}, \frac{ef'}{ff'}, \text{ and } \frac{gh'}{hh'}.$$

Since the denominators are equal, the order of the numerators gives the order of the fractions.

EXAMPLE 9. Order the fractions $\frac{5}{6}, \frac{11}{14}, \frac{13}{15}$.

Solution: Find the LCM of 6, 14, 15, which is 210. Then

$$\frac{5}{6} \sim \frac{5 \cdot 35}{6 \cdot 35}, \frac{11}{14} \sim \frac{11 \cdot 15}{14 \cdot 15}, \frac{13}{15} \sim \frac{13 \cdot 14}{15 \cdot 14} \text{ or } \frac{175}{210}, \frac{165}{210}, \frac{182}{210}.$$

Hence $\frac{11}{14} < \frac{5}{6} < \frac{13}{15}$.

There is a subset of the rational numbers that have properties very similar to those of the cardinal numbers and that behave similarly. These rational numbers can be signaled out of the totality of rationals by their properties as operators on segments, or calibrators of a ray. For example, as an operator, the rational number designated by the set

$$\left\{\frac{0}{n} : n > 0\right\} \Rightarrow 0$$

because it behaves exactly as the cardinal number zero. The set

$$\left\{\frac{n}{n} : n > 0\right\} \Rightarrow 1$$

because it behaves exactly as the cardinal number 1. Similarly

$$\left\{\frac{2n}{n} : n > 0\right\} \Rightarrow 2, \quad \left\{\frac{3n}{n} : n > 0\right\} \Rightarrow 3, \ldots, \quad \left\{\frac{kn}{n} : n > 0\right\} \Rightarrow k.$$

In this manner a one-to-one correspondence can be established between the cardinals and a subset of the rational numbers. We shall call this subset the *rational integers*, or the *rational whole numbers*. The rational whole numbers can be used in place of the cardinal numbers both as operators and as referents on a calibrated ray. They can also be used as a set of measures.

Thus, we have the following relation between the two sets:

$$\begin{array}{lcllllllll} \text{Cardinals} & = & \{0, & 1, & 2, & 3, & \ldots, & k, & \ldots\} \\ & & \updownarrow & \updownarrow & \updownarrow & \updownarrow & & \updownarrow & \\ \begin{array}{l}\text{Integral}\\ \text{Rationals}\end{array} & = & \left\{\frac{0}{n},\right. & \frac{n}{n}, & \frac{2n}{n}, & \frac{3n}{n}, & \ldots, & \frac{kn}{n}, & \left.\ldots\right\} \end{array}$$

or named differently with denominators of 1:

$$\begin{array}{lcllllllll} \text{Cardinals} & = & \{0, & 1, & 2, & 3, & \ldots, & k, & \ldots\} \\ & & \updownarrow & \updownarrow & \updownarrow & \updownarrow & & \updownarrow & \\ \begin{array}{l}\text{Integral}\\ \text{Rationals}\end{array} & = & \left\{\frac{0}{1},\right. & \frac{1}{1}, & \frac{2}{1}, & \frac{3}{1}, & \ldots, & \frac{k}{1}, & \left.\ldots\right\} \end{array}$$

In the next chapter we shall study the fundamental operations on rationals. There we shall find that the one-to-one correspondence is maintained for the results of the fundamental operations.

12.8 EXERCISES

1. On a ray $\overrightarrow{OX}$ select a point U, and using $\overline{OU}$ as a unit segment, calibrate it into:

   (a) Fifths (b) Halves (c) Fourths (d) Eighths

2. Explain how a ray calibrated into fourths may be used to measure a line segment.

3. Show that $2 \cdot \overline{OU}$ and $\frac{8}{4}\,\overline{OU}$ give the same reference point on $\overrightarrow{OX}$.

4. If $3U$ and $\frac{6}{2}U$ are transformations of U, prove they are congruent.

5. Explain why a ray $\overrightarrow{OX}$ with given unit $\overline{OU}$ calibrated to tenths is a better measuring instrument than the ray calibrated by the whole numbers.

6. Find the set of all fractions equivalent to:

   (a) $\frac{3}{4}$ (b) $\frac{14}{35}$ (c) $\frac{36}{42}$ (d) $\frac{2121}{3535}$

7. Given $\frac{3}{7} \sim \frac{18}{42}$ and $\frac{4}{9} \sim \frac{60}{135}$, we know $\frac{3}{7} < \frac{4}{9}$. Prove $\frac{18}{42} < \frac{60}{135}$.

8. If $\dfrac{a}{b}$ and $\dfrac{c}{d}$ are simplest fractions such that $\dfrac{a}{b} < \dfrac{c}{d}$, and $\dfrac{a}{b} \sim \dfrac{x}{y}$ and $\dfrac{c}{d} \sim \dfrac{w}{z}$, prove that $\dfrac{x}{y} < \dfrac{w}{z}$. (Hint: $x = k \cdot a$, $y = k \cdot b$, and $w = k' \cdot c$, etc.)

9. Order the rational numbers $\frac{2}{3}$, $\frac{5}{8}$, $\frac{13}{20}$, and $\frac{7}{12}$.

10. (a) Tell how to transform two fractions to like numerators. Use $\dfrac{a}{b}$ and $\dfrac{c}{d}$, with $a \neq c$.

    (b) Transform $\frac{5}{6}$ and $\frac{14}{17}$ to like numerators.

11. Tell how two fractions can be compared (ordered) by transforming them to like numerators. (Hint: If $\overline{OA}$ is shrunk to different sizes so that $V < V'$, then is $nV < nV'$?)

12. Give an illustration of a ray $\overrightarrow{OX}$ with $\overline{OU}$ and $\overline{OV} = 2 \cdot \overline{OU}$. Calibrate $\overline{OV}$ by halves, thirds, fourths, . . . , tenths. For each referent point write all the names for the rational number assigned, up to tenths.

13. Find the value of x, for which each of the following fractions has either a least or a greatest value.

    (a) $\dfrac{x}{x+1}$ (b) $\dfrac{x+1}{x}$ (c) $\dfrac{x}{2x+1}$ (d) $\dfrac{2x}{2x+1}$

    (e) $\dfrac{2x+1}{2x^2+2x}$

14. $\frac{2}{3}$ is irreducible. Show that $\dfrac{2+3}{2 \cdot 3}$, $\dfrac{3-2}{2 \cdot 3}$, $\dfrac{2 \cdot 3}{2^2+3^2}$, and $\dfrac{2+3}{2^2+2 \cdot 3+3^2}$ are all simplest fractions.

15. Generalize Exercise 14 for $\dfrac{a}{b}$ with $a < b$.

By the use of segments, and the notions of operator, transformation, and calibration, using a segment $\overline{OU}$ of ray $\overrightarrow{OX}$ we devised a meaning for a fraction. Using the results of these abstractions from a physical representation, we can now construct a pure theory of fractions and rational numbers that is logically consistent and independent of physical verification. We shall merely sketch the steps of this pure arithmetic and indicate how it can be extended in the next chapter on operations on fractions.

1. We start with the set of cardinal numbers, whose properties, possible operations, and principles of operation are known:

$$C = \{0, 1, 2, \ldots, n, \ldots\}$$

2. We form the product set of the cardinals with the cardinals with zero removed. This product set gives us ordered pairs (a, b) which we shall write in the form $\frac{a}{b}$. We thus create a set of elements called fractions:

$$F = \left\{\frac{x}{y} : x \in C \text{ and } y \in C,\ y \neq 0\right\}$$

3. We define an equivalence relation for fractions by

$$\frac{x}{y} \sim \frac{w}{z} \Leftrightarrow xz = yw.$$

This relation is proved to be reflexive, symmetric, and transitive.

4. The equivalence relation partitions all the fractions into disjoint equivalence classes. Each equivalence class has a simplest fraction. This class of equivalent fractions is a rational number

$$R = \left\{\frac{x}{y} : \frac{a}{b} \sim \frac{x}{y} \text{ and } \frac{a}{b} \text{ is the simplest fraction}\right\}.$$

5. Using the simplest fractions to name rational numbers, the *law of Trichotomy* holds; that is, only one of the following three cases is true:

$$\frac{a}{b} = \frac{c}{d},\quad \frac{a}{b} < \frac{c}{d},\quad \text{or}\quad \frac{a}{b} > \frac{c}{d} \qquad \text{(exclusive } or\text{)}$$

6. It is easy to determine which is the case by the rule

$$\frac{a}{b} \leq \frac{c}{d} \Leftrightarrow ad \leq bc.$$

7. Among the rational numbers, there is an ordered subset, represented by

$$I = \left\{\frac{0}{1}, \frac{1}{1}, \frac{2}{1}, \frac{3}{1}, \ldots, \frac{n}{1}, \ldots\right\},$$

which is in one-to-one correspondence, in order, with the set of cardinal numbers.

In the next chapter, we shall define operations on the rational numbers (or fractions) and show how the properties P_1 to P_{10} listed in Chapter 3 are all satisfied, with the exception of one property.

12.10 REFERENCE QUESTIONS

1. A fraction is defined by some authors as simply a symbol, or numeral. Compare such a definition with that given in this chapter. In this connection, see

   Mueller, Francis J. "On the Fraction as a Numeral," *The Arithmetic Teacher*, 8: 234–238; 1961.

2. State in full the definition of fraction presented in this chapter. Compare this definition with that to be found in the following reference:

   National Council of Teachers of Mathematics. *Topics in Mathematics for Elementary School Teachers* (29th yearbook). Washington, D.C.: NCTM, 1964. Pp. 215–223.

13 OPERATIONS ON RATIONAL NUMBERS

IN AN EARLIER CHAPTER, *operations with cardinal numbers were discussed. Having defined a rational number in Chapter 12, we are now in a position to discuss operations with rational numbers. In this chapter, the concept of rational number shall continue to be associated closely with that of a fraction as an operator; for, as we shall see, the definitions for operations with rational numbers will be suggested by consideration of fractions operating on segments. However, once these definitions are formulated, they may be divorced from the notions of segments and operators; thus, by the end of this chapter, we shall be able to consider the arithmetic of rational numbers in a completely abstract way.*

13.1 RATIONAL NUMBERS; EQUALITY

In the previous chapter, a rational number was defined to be an equivalence class of fractions. Thus, the class

$$\left\{\frac{1}{2}, \frac{2}{4}, \frac{3}{6}, \frac{4}{8}, \ldots, \frac{k}{2k}, \ldots\right\},$$

in which any two of the fractions are equivalent to each other, defines a rational number. It is clumsy indeed to indicate this class of fractions each time we wish to refer to the rational number. Hence, we shall speak simply of "the rational number $\frac{1}{2}$." To speak of the *fraction* $\frac{1}{2}$ is to speak of the operator (stretcher and shrinker) developed in Chapter 12; to speak of the *rational number* $\frac{1}{2}$ is to speak of the number which is the class of all fractions equivalent to the fraction $\frac{1}{2}$. In practice, this dual role of the symbol "$\frac{1}{2}$" seldom causes confusion.

To indicate that the rational number $\frac{1}{2}$ is an equivalence class of fractions, we may write

$$\frac{1}{2} = \left\{\frac{1}{2}, \frac{2}{4}, \frac{3}{6}, \frac{4}{8}, \ldots, \frac{k}{2k}, \ldots\right\}.$$

We have spoken of this rational number as the number $\frac{1}{2}$ since the simplest fraction of the equivalence class is the fraction $\frac{1}{2}$. However, the number may just as well be named by any other fraction in the class. For example, we may speak of the rational number $\frac{2}{4}$, and write

$$\frac{2}{4} = \left\{\frac{1}{2}, \frac{2}{4}, \frac{3}{6}, \frac{4}{8}, \ldots, \frac{k}{2k}, \ldots\right\}$$

or of the rational number $\frac{10}{20}$, and write

$$\frac{10}{20} = \left\{\frac{1}{2}, \frac{2}{4}, \frac{3}{6}, \frac{4}{8}, \ldots, \frac{k}{2k}, \ldots\right\}.$$

In other words, the rational number $\frac{1}{2}$ is the same as the rational number $\frac{2}{4}$; they are precisely the same equivalence class of fractions. So, if we are dealing with rational numbers, it is correct to state

$$\frac{1}{2} = \frac{2}{4}.$$

In the same way, the following statements are valid:

$$\frac{1}{2} = \frac{10}{20}, \frac{2}{4} = \frac{10}{20}, \frac{3}{6} = \frac{12}{24}, \text{ etc.}$$

Clearly, the remarks made above about the rational number $\frac{1}{2}$ may be applied to any rational number. As one more example, the rational number

$$\left\{\frac{5}{6}, \frac{10}{12}, \frac{15}{18}, \frac{20}{24}, \ldots, \frac{5k}{6k}, \ldots\right\}$$

may be referred to as "the rational number $\frac{5}{6}$," "the rational number $\frac{10}{12}$," "the rational number $\frac{15}{18}$," etc. "$\frac{5}{6} = \frac{10}{12}$" is a true statement about rational numbers.

Thus, it is easy to see that the definition of *equal rational numbers* is a direct consequence of the definition previously made for equivalent fractions.

DEFINITION: $\frac{a}{b} = \frac{c}{d}$ *if and only if* $ad = bc$, *where* $\frac{a}{b}$ *and* $\frac{c}{d}$ *are rational numbers.*

Let $\frac{a}{b}$ and $\frac{c}{d}$ be two fractions such that the following conditions hold:

(1) $\frac{a}{b}$, operating on a segment U, transforms U into V. Thus,

$$\frac{a}{b}U = V$$

or

$$aU = bV.$$

(2) $\frac{c}{d}$, operating on the segment V, transforms V into W. Thus,

$$\frac{c}{d}V = W$$

or

$$cV = dW.$$

Note that these two conditions may be described as follows: $\frac{a}{b}$ operates on U, producing V; $\frac{c}{d}$ then operates on this result V, producing W. In effect, we may think of U being transformed into W by the successive application of two operators—operator $\frac{a}{b}$ followed by operator $\frac{c}{d}$. In this sense, V is a sort of intermediate step in the transformation of U into W.

Referring to the conditions (1) and (2) stipulated in the preceding paragraph, we note the following equations:

$$aU = bV$$
$$cV = dW$$

Multiplying both members of the first equation by c, and multiplying both members of the second equation by b, we obtain the following two equations:

$$acU = bcV$$
$$bcV = bdW$$

Thus, by the transitive property of "=,"

$$acU = bdW.$$

This last equation, however, is equivalent to the statement

$$\left(\frac{ac}{bd}\right) U = W.$$

That is, it is equivalent to stating that the fraction $\frac{ac}{bd}$ operates on segment U to produce segment W. In this sense, then, it is possible to eliminate the "intermediate" segment V.

The ideas of the two preceding paragraphs may now be summarized as follows:

If segment U is operated on by $\frac{a}{b}$, *and the result of this transformation is in turn operated on by* $\frac{c}{d}$, *the final result is the same as that produced by the single fraction* $\frac{ac}{bd}$ *operating on U.*

The notion of one operator following another is one which we shall associate with multiplication of fractions. Thus, the notation $\frac{a}{b} \times \frac{c}{d}$ shall be used to indicate operator $\frac{a}{b}$ *followed by* operator $\frac{c}{d}$. With this in mind, we may write

$$\left(\frac{a}{b} \times \frac{c}{d}\right) U = \left(\frac{ac}{bd}\right) U,$$

which in turn implies

$$\frac{a}{b} \times \frac{c}{d} = \frac{ac}{bd}.$$

From the above discussion, we abstract the following definition of *multiplication of fractions:*

DEFINITION: *If* $\frac{a}{b}$ *and* $\frac{c}{d}$ *are fractions*

$$\frac{a}{b} \times \frac{c}{d} = \frac{ac}{bd}.$$

EXAMPLE 1. Determine the product $\frac{2}{3} \times \frac{4}{5}$.

Solution: By definition,

$$\frac{2}{3} \times \frac{4}{5} = \frac{2 \times 4}{3 \times 5} = \frac{8}{15}.$$

In terms of transformations, this product may be interpreted as follows: If U is operated on by $\frac{2}{3}$ and the result is in turn operated on by $\frac{4}{5}$, the final result is the same as that obtained when U is operated on by $\frac{8}{15}$.

13.3 MULTIPLICATION OF RATIONAL NUMBERS; DEFINITION

Inasmuch as a rational number has been defined as an equivalence class of fractions, it would seem that the definition for multiplication of rational numbers might be based upon the definition for multiplication of fractions given in section 13.2. Let us see how this might work. Consider the rational number

$$\left\{\frac{2}{3}, \frac{4}{6}, \frac{6}{9}, \frac{8}{12}, \ldots, \frac{2k}{3k}, \ldots\right\},$$

which is commonly called simply "the rational number $\frac{2}{3}$." And consider the rational number

$$\left\{\frac{2}{5}, \frac{4}{10}, \frac{6}{15}, \frac{8}{20}, \ldots, \frac{2k}{5k}, \ldots\right\},$$

or, more briefly, the "rational number $\frac{2}{5}$." To determine the product of these two rational numbers, it might seem reasonable to select a fraction from each class, determine the product of these fractions and define the equivalence class of which this product is a member to be the rational number which is the product of the two given rational numbers. We must be sure, however, that such a procedure does not depend on the particular fractions selected to represent the rational numbers; for we are concerned here not with the product of two specific fractions but rather with the product of two rational numbers, each of which is an equivalence class of fractions.

In order to clear up this ambiguity, let us consider the question in a general way before returning to the specific problem posed above. Let $\frac{a}{b}$ and $\frac{a'}{b'}$ be any two equivalent fractions; thus, $\frac{a}{b} \sim \frac{a'}{b'}$, and "$\frac{a}{b}$" and "$\frac{a'}{b'}$" are two names for the same rational number, which we shall call the rational number $\frac{a}{b}$. In a similar way, let $\frac{c}{d}$ and $\frac{c'}{d'}$ be equivalent fractions, each a name for the rational number $\frac{c}{d}$. The problem is to determine the product of the rational numbers $\frac{a}{b}$ and $\frac{c}{d}$. Suppose the fractions "$\frac{a}{b}$" and "$\frac{c}{d}$" are selected to represent these numbers, and are multiplied as fractions. Then

$$\frac{a}{b} \times \frac{c}{d} = \frac{ac}{bd}.$$

And it would seem that the equivalence class to which $\frac{ac}{bd}$ belongs might be defined as the product of the rational numbers. But suppose the fractions "$\frac{a'}{b'}$" and "$\frac{c'}{d'}$" had been chosen to represent the rational numbers. Then the product of fractions would have been as follows:

$$\frac{a'}{b'} \times \frac{c'}{d'} = \frac{a'c'}{b'd'}$$

Does this suggest a different product? Or is it the case that $\frac{ac}{bd} \sim \frac{a'c'}{b'd'}$ so that in each case the same rational number is determined? We may argue as follows:

$$ab' = ba' \quad \text{since} \quad \frac{a}{b} \sim \frac{a'}{b'},$$

and

$$cd' = dc' \quad \text{since} \quad \frac{c}{d} \sim \frac{c'}{d'}.$$

Therefore,

$$(ab')(cd') = (ba')(dc')$$

or

$$(ac)(b'd') = (bd)(a'c')$$

by associativity and commutativity of multiplication of whole numbers.

Thus,

$$\frac{ac}{bd} \sim \frac{a'c'}{b'd'}.$$

By virtue of the above argument, the product of any two rational numbers $\frac{a}{b}$ and $\frac{c}{d}$ may be determined by the following definition:

DEFINITION: *If $\frac{a}{b}$ and $\frac{c}{d}$ are rational numbers,*

$$\frac{a}{b} \times \frac{c}{d} = \frac{ac}{bd},$$

where it is understood that any fraction in the equivalence class $\frac{a}{b}$ and any fraction in the equivalence class $\frac{c}{d}$ may be used to determine the product.

Let us return now to the problem of finding the product of the rational numbers

$$\frac{2}{3} = \left\{\frac{2}{3}, \frac{4}{6}, \frac{6}{9}, \frac{8}{12}, \ldots, \frac{2k}{3k}, \ldots\right\}$$

and

$$\frac{2}{5} = \left\{\frac{2}{5}, \frac{4}{10}, \frac{6}{15}, \frac{8}{20}, \ldots, \frac{2k}{5k}, \ldots\right\}.$$

By the definition on page 228, the product may be determined by selecting *any* two fractions from the respective equivalence classes. Suppose "$\frac{4}{6}$" and "$\frac{6}{15}$" are selected. Then

$$\frac{4}{6} \times \frac{6}{15} = \frac{24}{90},$$

and so the product of the two rational numbers is the rational number $\frac{24}{90}$. On the other hand, the two simplest fractions, $\frac{2}{3}$ and $\frac{2}{5}$, might have been selected. Then

$$\frac{2}{3} \times \frac{2}{5} = \frac{4}{15},$$

and the product is the rational number $\frac{4}{15}$. Of course, the results in the two instances are identical; the rational number $\frac{24}{90}$ is the same as the rational number $\frac{4}{15}$ since the fractions "$\frac{24}{90}$" and "$\frac{4}{15}$" are elements of the same equivalence class.

13.4 MULTIPLICATION OF RATIONAL NUMBERS; PROPERTIES

From the definition of multiplication of rational numbers (in section 13.3), it is apparent that, given any two rational numbers, one may assign to them a unique third rational number called their product. Thus, for example,

$$\left(\frac{1}{2}, \frac{2}{3}\right) \to \frac{2}{6} \quad \text{since} \quad \frac{1}{2} \times \frac{2}{3} = \frac{2}{6},$$

and

$$\left(\frac{3}{7}, \frac{5}{2}\right) \to \frac{15}{14} \quad \text{since} \quad \frac{3}{7} \times \frac{5}{2} = \frac{15}{14}.$$

With this in mind, and arbitrarily letting Q represent the set of rational numbers, we see that multiplication of rational numbers may be considered as a map $Q \times Q \to Q$; and this is consistent with the definition given earlier for operations on cardinal numbers. Furthermore, it is easily seen that multiplication of rational numbers is a binary operation.

We next seek properties of multiplication of rational numbers. It seems reasonable to investigate the properties of multiplication of cardinal numbers, determining whether or not these properties hold also for multiplication of rational numbers. So we consider first the property of commutativity. If $\frac{a}{b}$ and $\frac{c}{d}$ are any two rational numbers,

$$\frac{a}{b} \times \frac{c}{d} = \frac{ac}{bd}, \qquad \frac{c}{d} \times \frac{a}{b} = \frac{ca}{db}.$$

However, a, c, b, and d are cardinal numbers; and commutativity of multiplication of cardinal numbers has already been established. Therefore, $ac = ca$ and $bd = db$, so that the two results above are in fact the same. We formally state then the following property:

If $\frac{a}{b}$ *and* $\frac{c}{d}$ *are rational numbers, then*

$$\frac{a}{b} \times \frac{c}{d} = \frac{c}{d} \times \frac{a}{b}. \qquad \text{COMMUTATIVITY OF } \times \text{ FOR } Q$$

Alternatively, one may say that the operation of multiplication of rational numbers assigns precisely the same number to the pairs $\left(\frac{a}{b}, \frac{c}{d}\right)$ and $\left(\frac{c}{d}, \frac{a}{b}\right)$.

As with the cardinal numbers, so with the rational numbers, if the product of three rational numbers $\frac{a}{b}$, $\frac{c}{d}$, and $\frac{e}{f}$ is indicated as

$$\frac{a}{b} \times \frac{c}{d} \times \frac{e}{f},$$

one must associate either the first two factors or the last two factors since multiplication of rational numbers is a binary operation. The point of interest is whether different results are obtained by the two different associations, or whether the same result is obtained so that multiplication of rational numbers may be said to be associative. Consider the two possible "associations" as follows:

$$\left(\frac{a}{b} \times \frac{c}{d}\right) \times \frac{e}{f} = \frac{ac}{bd} \times \frac{e}{f}$$

$$= \frac{(ac)e}{(bd)f}$$

$$\frac{a}{b} \times \left(\frac{c}{d} \times \frac{e}{f}\right) = \frac{a}{b} \times \frac{ce}{df}$$

$$= \frac{a(ce)}{b(df)}$$

However, multiplication of cardinal numbers is associative, so that

$$(ac)e = a(ce) \quad \text{and} \quad (bd)f = b(df);$$

and we may conclude that the two results above are equal.

Hence, we formulate the following property:

If $\frac{a}{b}$, $\frac{c}{d}$, *and* $\frac{e}{f}$ *are rational numbers, then*

$$\left(\frac{a}{b} \times \frac{c}{d}\right) \times \frac{e}{f} = \frac{a}{b} \times \left(\frac{c}{d} \times \frac{e}{f}\right). \qquad \text{ASSOCIATIVITY OF} \times \text{FOR } Q$$

Next, consider the rational number

$$\frac{1}{1} = \left\{\frac{1}{1}, \frac{2}{2}, \frac{3}{3}, \ldots, \frac{k}{k}, \ldots\right\}$$

and the product of this number and any other rational number:

$$\frac{1}{1} \times \frac{a}{b} = \frac{1 \times a}{1 \times b} = \frac{a}{b}$$

$$\frac{a}{b} \times \frac{1}{1} = \frac{a \times 1}{b \times 1} = \frac{a}{b}$$

These results point clearly to the fact that the rational number $\frac{1}{1}$ functions as an *identity element* for multiplication of rational numbers, a property stated formally in the following way:

If $\frac{a}{b}$ *is a rational number, then*

$$\frac{a}{b} \times \frac{1}{1} = \frac{1}{1} \times \frac{a}{b} = \frac{a}{b}. \qquad \text{IDENTITY PRINCIPLE OF} \times \text{FOR } Q$$

We emphasize again that the above is a property of the *rational number* $\frac{1}{1}$; and, in actual practice, it makes no difference which fraction is selected from the equivalence class defining $\frac{1}{1}$. For example,

$$\frac{5}{3} \times \frac{2}{2} = \frac{10}{6} = \frac{5}{3}.$$

The rational number $\frac{2}{2}$ is the same as the rational number $\frac{1}{1}$; it is the identity element for multiplication. Also,

$$\frac{4}{4} \times \frac{1}{2} = \frac{4}{8} = \frac{1}{2}.$$

The rational number $\frac{4}{4}$ is also the same as the rational number $\frac{1}{1}$.

Because of the definition of exponent which was presented earlier (Chapter 4), we may write

$$\left(\frac{3}{4}\right)^2 = \frac{3}{4} \times \frac{3}{4},$$

indicating that the rational number $\frac{3}{4}$ is to be used as a factor two times. But, by the definition of multiplication of rational numbers, we know

$$\frac{3}{4} \times \frac{3}{4} = \frac{3 \times 3}{4 \times 4} = \frac{3^2}{4^2}.$$

Finally, then, we may write

$$\left(\frac{3}{4}\right)^2 = \frac{3^2}{4^2}.$$

In fact, if $\frac{a}{b}$ represents any rational number,

$$\left(\frac{a}{b}\right)^2 = \frac{a}{b} \times \frac{a}{b} = \frac{a^2}{b^2}.$$

The above discussion concerning the square—or the "second power"—of a rational number is easily extended to cover any whole number power of a rational number. As examples, consider the following:

$$\left(\frac{a}{b}\right)^3 = \left(\frac{a}{b} \times \frac{a}{b}\right) \times \frac{a}{b}$$

$$= \frac{a^2}{b^2} \times \frac{a}{b}$$

$$= \frac{a^3}{b^3}$$

$$\left(\frac{a}{b}\right)^4 = \frac{a^3}{b^3} \times \frac{a}{b}$$

$$= \frac{a^4}{b^4}$$

Intuitively, this extension is easily made. So, although we present no rigorous proof of the statement, we note the following:

If $\frac{a}{b}$ is a rational number, and n is a whole number greater than zero,

$$\left(\frac{a}{b}\right)^n = \frac{a^n}{b^n}.$$

13.6 EXERCISES

1. (a) Draw a representation of a segment U.
   (b) Show how U is transformed when operated upon by the fraction $\frac{3}{2}$.
   (c) Show the transformation effected when the fraction $\frac{1}{4}$ operates on the result in (b).
   (d) Show that the final result obtained in (c) is the same as that obtained when the fraction $\frac{3}{8}$ operates on the original segment U.
2. If U is a segment, and $\frac{5}{2}$ and $\frac{2}{3}$ are considered as operators, show that
$$\left(\frac{5}{2} \times \frac{2}{3}\right) U = \frac{10}{6} U.$$
(Recall that the notation "$\frac{5}{2} \times \frac{2}{3}$" means that $\frac{5}{2}$ is to operate first, followed by $\frac{2}{3}$ operating on the result.)
3. What single operator may be used to produce the same transformation of a segment U as that obtained by using operator $\frac{12}{5}$ followed by $\frac{3}{4}$?
4. Using the definition of multiplication of fractions, show that the product $\frac{6}{8} \times \frac{5}{2}$ is equivalent to the product $\frac{3}{4} \times \frac{15}{6}$.
5. $\left\{\frac{1}{2}, \frac{2}{4}, \frac{3}{6}, \frac{4}{8}, \ldots\right\}$ and $\left\{\frac{2}{3}, \frac{4}{6}, \frac{6}{9}, \frac{8}{12}, \ldots\right\}$
are two rational numbers. One way to indicate the product of these numbers is $\frac{1}{2} \times \frac{2}{3}$. List at least five other ways of indicating their product.
6. Determine the following products of rational numbers:
(Express the product by means of the simplest appropriate fraction.)

   (a) $\frac{5}{6} \times \frac{3}{4}$ (b) $\frac{6}{6} \times \frac{2}{3}$ (c) $\frac{0}{2} \times \frac{4}{5}$

   (d) $\left(\frac{3}{4}\right)^2$ (e) $\frac{3}{8} \times \frac{4}{4}$ (f) $\frac{3}{7} \times \frac{0}{7}$

   (g) $\frac{21}{10} \times \frac{7}{2}$ (h) $\frac{25}{25} \times \frac{3}{3}$ (i) $\frac{4}{4} \times \frac{0}{5}$

   (j) $\left(\frac{2}{3}\right)^3$ (k) $\frac{2^3}{3}$ (l) $\left(\frac{a}{b}\right)^{10}$
7. Verify the following instances of the associative property for multiplication of rational numbers:

   (a) $\left(\frac{2}{3} \times \frac{5}{2}\right) \times \frac{3}{4} = \frac{2}{3} \times \left(\frac{5}{2} \times \frac{3}{4}\right)$

   (b) $\left(\frac{10}{9} \times \frac{3}{5}\right) \times \frac{5}{2} = \frac{10}{9} \times \left(\frac{3}{5} \times \frac{5}{2}\right)$

   (c) $\frac{16}{3} \times \left(\frac{2}{5} \times \frac{10}{4}\right) = \left(\frac{16}{3} \times \frac{2}{5}\right) \times \frac{10}{4}$

8. (a) What is the identity element for multiplication of rational numbers? Express this element as an equivalence class of fractions.
   (b) Determine the following products:

   $$\frac{3}{3} \times \frac{2}{5}, \quad \frac{7}{7} \times \frac{2}{5}, \quad \frac{124}{124} \times \frac{2}{5}, \quad \frac{a}{a} \times \frac{2}{5} \quad (a \neq 0)$$

   (c) One sometimes sees the following "rule" in arithmetic texts:

   The numerator and denominator of a fraction may be multiplied by the same number (not zero) without changing the value of the fraction.

   How may such a rule be justified?

9. Determine the following products of cardinal numbers or of rational numbers, as the case may be:

   (a) $\frac{3}{1} \times \frac{2}{1}$ (b) 3×2 (c) $\frac{5}{1} \times \frac{9}{1}$ (d) 5×9

   (e) $\frac{25}{1} \times \frac{4}{100}$ (f) 24×4 (g) $\frac{33}{1} \times \frac{7}{1}$ (h) 33×7

10. (a) Why are the fractions $\frac{2}{3}$ and $\frac{4}{6}$ equivalent?
    (b) Why are the rational numbers $\frac{2}{3}$ and $\frac{4}{6}$ equal?

★11. Use the properties of multiplication of rational numbers to prove

$$\frac{a}{b} \times \frac{c}{d} \times \frac{e}{f} = \frac{e}{f} \times \frac{c}{d} \times \frac{a}{b},$$

where $\frac{a}{b}$, $\frac{c}{d}$, and $\frac{e}{f}$ are rational numbers.

★12. Does the set of rational numbers constitute a commutative group under the operation of multiplication? Explain.

13.7 MULTIPLICATION OF RATIONAL NUMBERS; INVERSE ELEMENTS

The product of the rational number

$$\left\{\frac{2}{3}, \frac{4}{6}, \frac{6}{9}, \ldots, \frac{2k}{3k}, \ldots\right\}$$

and the rational number

$$\left\{\frac{3}{2}, \frac{6}{4}, \frac{9}{6}, \ldots, \frac{3k}{2k}, \ldots\right\}$$

may be determined as follows:

$$\frac{2}{3} \times \frac{3}{2} = \frac{2 \times 3}{3 \times 2} = \frac{6}{6} \qquad \frac{3}{2} \times \frac{2}{3} = \frac{3 \times 2}{2 \times 3} = \frac{6}{6}$$

Thus, the product of the rational numbers $\frac{2}{3}$ and $\frac{3}{2}$ is the rational number $\frac{6}{6}$. However, as established in section 13.4, the rational number $\frac{6}{6}$ is the identity element for multiplication of rational numbers. Recalling the discussion of inverse element in section 7.10, we therefore, have

$\frac{3}{2}$ as the multiplicative inverse of $\frac{2}{3}$

and

$\frac{2}{3}$ as the multiplicative inverse of $\frac{3}{2}$

since their product is the identity element of multiplication.

DEFINITION: *Two rational numbers are* multiplicative inverses *of each other if and only if their product is the multiplicative identity element* $\frac{1}{1}$.

The inverse relationship between $\frac{2}{3}$ and $\frac{3}{2}$ exists in general for rational numbers $\frac{a}{b}$ and $\frac{b}{a}$ $(a \neq 0, b \neq 0)$. Thus

$$\frac{a}{b} \times \frac{b}{a} = \frac{ab}{ba}.$$

But, $ab = ba$ since multiplication of cardinal numbers is commutative. So,

$$\frac{a}{b} \times \frac{b}{a} = \frac{b}{a} \times \frac{a}{b} = \frac{1}{1},$$

and $\frac{a}{b}$ and $\frac{b}{a}$ are inverse elements under multiplication since their product is $\frac{1}{1}$.

If we now ask the question, "What is *the* multiplicative inverse of the number $\frac{a}{b}$?" we can at least say that $\frac{b}{a}$ is *an* inverse. But before we can justifiably label it as "*the* inverse," we must show that $\frac{a}{b}$ has no other inverse. If a number $\frac{c}{d}$ is to be a multiplicative inverse of $\frac{a}{b}$, then the following must hold:

$$\frac{a}{b} \times \frac{c}{d} = \frac{ac}{bd} = \frac{1}{1}.$$

But to say $\frac{ac}{bd} = \frac{1}{1}$ is to say

$$ac = bd,$$

or

$$\frac{b}{a} = \frac{c}{d}.$$

Hence, *any* rational number $\frac{c}{d}$ which is a multiplicative inverse of $\frac{a}{b}$ is the same as the rational number $\frac{b}{a}$; more simply, $\frac{b}{a}$ is the *only* inverse of $\frac{a}{b}$. We are entitled then to state the following property of rational numbers:

If $\frac{a}{b}$ is a rational number, $a \neq 0$, then $\frac{b}{a}$ is the multiplicative inverse of $\frac{a}{b}$ since

$$\frac{a}{b} \times \frac{b}{a} = \frac{1}{1} = \frac{b}{a} \times \frac{a}{b}.$$

MULTIPLICATIVE INVERSE FOR Q

It is easy to see also that $\frac{a}{b}$ is the inverse of $\frac{b}{a}$; therefore, $\frac{a}{b}$ and $\frac{b}{a}$ are inverses of each other. The word *reciprocal* is often used in the same sense as *multiplicative inverse* so that we may also state that the numbers $\frac{a}{b}$ and $\frac{b}{a}$ are reciprocals of each other.

EXAMPLE 2. What is the reciprocal of the rational number

$$\left\{\frac{3}{4}, \frac{6}{8}, \frac{9}{12}, \ldots, \frac{3k}{4k}, \ldots\right\}?$$

Solution: This question may be asked more simply as follows: What is the reciprocal of $\frac{3}{4}$? The reciprocal is $\frac{4}{3}$ since $\frac{3}{4} \times \frac{4}{3} = \frac{1}{1}$.
To answer the original question, we might say then that the reciprocal is

$$\left\{\frac{4}{3}, \frac{8}{6}, \frac{12}{9}, \ldots, \frac{4k}{3k}, \ldots\right\}.$$

EXAMPLE 3. What is the reciprocal of $\frac{9}{12}$?

Solution: The reciprocal is $\frac{12}{9}$.
(Note: Why is this example really the same as Example 1?)

EXAMPLE 4. What is the reciprocal of $\frac{97}{21}$?

Solution: The reciprocal is $\frac{21}{97}$.

EXAMPLE 5. What is the reciprocal of $\frac{0}{5}$?

Solution: This number *has no reciprocal.* Why not?

13.8 DIVISION OF RATIONAL NUMBERS

In order to develop a definition for division of rational numbers, let us consider briefly division of cardinal numbers. We say, for instance

$$12 \div 4 = 3$$

since

$$4 \cdot 3 = 12.$$

In other words, if $12 \div 4 = n$, then $4 \cdot n = 12$; thus division of cardinal numbers may be defined in terms of multiplication. We demand that the same sort of definition hold for division of rational numbers. If $\frac{a}{b}$ and $\frac{c}{d}$ $(c \neq 0)$ are rational numbers, we may consider the quotient $\frac{a}{b} \div \frac{c}{d}$, arbitrarily calling this quotient $\frac{x}{y}$. By analogy with the case for division of cardinal numbers, then, we demand the following:

If

$$\frac{a}{b} \div \frac{c}{d} = \frac{x}{y},$$

then

$$\frac{c}{d} \cdot \frac{x}{y} = \frac{a}{b}.$$

But

$$\frac{c}{d} \cdot \frac{x}{y} = \frac{cx}{dy}$$

by the definition of multiplication of rational numbers. So, by transitivity of equality,

$$\frac{cx}{dy} = \frac{a}{b}.$$

But, if the rational numbers $\frac{cx}{dy}$ and $\frac{a}{b}$ are equal, then

$$(cx)b = (dy)a,$$

which, by associativity and commutativity of multiplication of cardinal numbers, yields

$$(bc)x = (ad)y,$$

or

$$\frac{x}{y} = \frac{ad}{bc}.$$

Recall now that $\frac{x}{y}$ represents the quotient $\frac{a}{b} \div \frac{c}{d}$. In effect, the steps above show that this quotient must be $\frac{ad}{bc}$ if the quotient is to behave in the way we demand. Thus,

$$\frac{a}{b} \div \frac{c}{d} = \frac{ad}{bc}.$$

Furthermore, since $\frac{ad}{bc}$ is the product of the numbers $\frac{a}{b}$ and $\frac{d}{c}$, we arrive at the following definition for *division of rational numbers:*

DEFINITION: *If* $\frac{a}{b}$ *and* $\frac{c}{d}$ *are rational numbers* $\left(\frac{c}{d} \neq \frac{0}{1}\right)$,

$$\frac{a}{b} \div \frac{c}{d} = \frac{a}{b} \times \frac{d}{c}.$$

The effect of the above definition is to allow us to consider each quotient as the product of the dividend and the reciprocal of the divisor.

EXAMPLE 6. Divide $\frac{2}{3}$ by $\frac{3}{4}$.

Solution:

$$\frac{2}{3} \div \frac{3}{4} = \frac{2}{3} \times \frac{4}{3}$$
$$= \frac{8}{9}$$

Because we defined division as we did, we know of course $\frac{3}{4} \times \frac{8}{9} = \frac{2}{3}$, and this is easily verified.

EXAMPLE 7. Divide $\frac{0}{6}$ by $\frac{5}{7}$.

Solution:

$$\frac{0}{6} \div \frac{5}{7} = \frac{0}{6} \times \frac{7}{5}$$
$$= \frac{0}{30}$$

Of course, $\frac{0}{6} = \frac{0}{30} = \frac{0}{1}$. This problem could also have been written $\frac{0}{1} \div \frac{5}{7} = \frac{0}{1}$.

13.9 DIVISION OF FRACTIONS

Division of rational numbers was defined without reference to fractions from whence the notion of rational numbers arose. Such an approach was possible because of the fact that division was defined in terms of multiplication, and multiplication of rational numbers had already been defined. It is possible, however, to speak of the quotient $\frac{a}{b} \div \frac{c}{d}$, where $\frac{a}{b}$ and $\frac{c}{d}$ are interpreted as operators, i.e. fractions. In fact, the definition is analogous to that for division of rational numbers, for the obvious reason that the definition of multiplication of fractions is analogous to that of multiplication of rational numbers. We agree then that the following definition of *division of fractions* may be used when needed:

DEFINITION: *If* $\frac{a}{b}$ *and* $\frac{c}{d}$ *are fractions,* $c \neq 0$,

$$\frac{a}{b} \div \frac{c}{d} \sim \frac{a}{b} \times \frac{d}{c}.$$

13.10 A FRACTION AS A QUOTIENT

A fraction may be considered as the quotient of two whole numbers by virtue of the following argument.

Let x represent the quotient $2 \div 3$, that is, let

$$2 \div 3 = x. \qquad \text{(I)}$$

Just as $20 \div 4 = 5$ implies $4 \cdot 5 = 20$, we demand that equation (I) convey the following meaning:

$$3 \cdot x = 2 \qquad \text{(II)}$$

We saw in the previous chapter, however, that the fraction $\frac{3}{1}$ and the whole number 3 are in effect the same operator; likewise, $\frac{2}{1}$ and 2 are the same as operators. Therefore, we write equation (II) as

$$\frac{3}{1} \cdot x = \frac{2}{1}. \qquad \text{(III)}$$

Because of the relationship between multiplication and division, equation (III) is equivalent to the following:

$$x = \frac{2}{1} \div \frac{3}{1}$$

We have already defined division of fractions, however; hence we have:

$$x = \frac{2}{1} \cdot \frac{1}{3} = \frac{2 \cdot 1}{1 \cdot 3}$$

$$x = \frac{2}{3}$$

Thus, x, which at the outset represented the quotient $2 \div 3$, has been shown also to be the fraction $\frac{2}{3}$.

13.11 INEQUALITIES; MULTIPLICATION AND DIVISION

Let $\frac{a}{b}$ and $\frac{c}{d}$ be two rational numbers such that

$$\frac{a}{b} < \frac{c}{d}.$$

What shall we mean by such a relation between two rational numbers? We have already defined inequality of fractions (Chapter 12). Therefore, we shall say that the relation

$$\frac{a}{b} < \frac{c}{d}$$

holds for the *rational numbers* $\frac{a}{b}$ and $\frac{c}{d}$ if and only if it holds for the fractions $\frac{a}{b}$ and $\frac{c}{d}$—that is, if and only if

$$ad < bc.$$

(It may be verified that this relation is independent of the particular fractions selected to represent the rational numbers.)

EXAMPLE 8. Compare the rational numbers $\frac{15}{26}$ and $\frac{4}{7}$.

Solution: $\frac{4}{7} < \frac{15}{26}$ since $4 \cdot 26 < 7 \cdot 15$.

Suppose now that $\frac{a}{b} < \frac{c}{d}$, where $\frac{a}{b}$ and $\frac{c}{d}$ are rational numbers, and that the following inequality is formed by multiplying each of the numbers by the number $\frac{x}{y}$:

$$\frac{a}{b} \cdot \frac{x}{y} < \frac{c}{d} \cdot \frac{x}{y} \tag{IV}$$

May we conclude that this inequality is indeed valid? The inequality (IV) may be rewritten as

$$\frac{ax}{by} < \frac{cx}{dy},$$

and this is true if and only if

$$(ax)(dy) < (by)(cx). \tag{V}$$

Properties of cardinal numbers may be invoked to rewrite (V) as

$$(xy)(ad) < (xy)(bc). \tag{VI}$$

By the cancellation law for cardinal numbers, (VI) is equivalent to

$$ad < bc. \tag{VII}$$

We know (VII) is true, however, since we started by stating $\frac{a}{b} < \frac{c}{d}$. Retracing our steps, then, we have established the following:

If $\frac{a}{b} < \frac{c}{d}$, *then* $\frac{a}{b} \cdot \frac{x}{y} < \frac{c}{d} \cdot \frac{x}{y}$,

where $\frac{a}{b}$, $\frac{c}{d}$, *and* $\frac{x}{y}$ *are rational numbers* $(x \neq 0)$.

The converse of this statement is also valid, as the following steps make clear:

If $\frac{a}{b} \cdot \frac{x}{y} < \frac{c}{d} \cdot \frac{x}{y}$,

then $\left(\frac{a}{b} \cdot \frac{x}{y}\right) \cdot \left(\frac{y}{x}\right) < \left(\frac{c}{d} \cdot \frac{x}{y}\right) \cdot \frac{y}{x}$, (Why?)

and $\frac{a}{b} \cdot \left(\frac{x}{y} \cdot \frac{y}{x}\right) < \frac{c}{d} \cdot \left(\frac{x}{y} \cdot \frac{y}{x}\right)$, (Why?)

and $\frac{a}{b} \cdot \frac{1}{1} < \frac{c}{d} \cdot \frac{1}{1}$, (Why?)

and $\frac{a}{b} < \frac{c}{d}$.

In effect, then, we have a cancellation law which may be stated as follows:

If $\frac{a}{b} \cdot \frac{x}{y} < \frac{c}{d} \cdot \frac{x}{y}$, *then* $\frac{a}{b} < \frac{c}{d}$,

where $\frac{a}{b}$, $\frac{c}{d}$, *and* $\frac{x}{y}$ *are rational numbers* $(x \neq 0)$.

The validity of the following statement is also easily established by use of previous definitions and properties.

$$\frac{a}{b} = \frac{c}{d} \Leftrightarrow \frac{a}{b} \cdot \frac{x}{y} = \frac{c}{d} \cdot \frac{x}{y},$$

where $\frac{a}{b}$, $\frac{c}{d}$, *and* $\frac{x}{y}$ *are rational numbers,* $x \neq 0$.

The proof is left to the reader. (See also Problem 8 of section 13.12.)

13.12 EXERCISES

1. (a) Determine the following products:

$$\frac{3}{5} \times \frac{5}{3}, \quad \frac{2}{9} \times \frac{9}{2}, \quad \frac{6}{1} \times \frac{1}{6}, \quad \frac{a}{b} \times \frac{b}{a} \quad (a \neq 0,\ b \neq 0)$$

(b) Give the reciprocal (multiplicative inverse) of each of the following rational numbers:

$$\frac{3}{5}, \quad \frac{9}{2}, \quad \frac{6}{1}, \quad \frac{23}{31}, \quad \frac{98}{47}, \quad \frac{a}{b} \quad (a \neq 0,\ b \neq 0)$$

(c) Explain why the rational number $\frac{0}{1}$ has no reciprocal.

(d) Why is it incorrect to say that the reciprocal of *any* rational number $\frac{a}{b}$ is $\frac{b}{a}$?

2. Determine what rational number $\frac{x}{y}$ must be in order to make each of the following sentences true:

(a) $\frac{7}{3} \cdot \frac{x}{y} = \frac{14}{6}$ (b) $\frac{7}{3} \cdot \frac{x}{y} = \frac{21}{21}$ (c) $\frac{7}{3} \cdot \frac{x}{y} = \frac{1}{1}$

(d) $\frac{7}{3} \cdot \frac{x}{y} = \frac{6}{6}$ (e) $\frac{3}{8} \cdot \frac{8}{3} = \frac{x}{y}$ (f) $\frac{3}{8} \cdot \frac{40}{15} = \frac{x}{y}$

(g) $\frac{2}{5} \cdot \frac{x}{y} = \frac{0}{1}$ (h) $\frac{0}{1} \cdot \frac{x}{y} = \frac{2}{5}$

3. Determine the following quotients:

(a) $\frac{2}{3} \div \frac{2}{3}$ (b) $\frac{2}{3} \div \frac{3}{2}$ (c) $\frac{8}{7} \div \frac{4}{14}$

(d) $\frac{5}{9} \div \frac{15}{27}$ (e) $\frac{0}{3} \div \frac{1}{5}$ (f) $\frac{0}{3} \div \frac{47}{92}$

(g) $\frac{24}{1} \div \frac{3}{1}$ (h) $24 \div 3$ (i) $\frac{45}{1} \div \frac{9}{1}$

(j) $45 \div 9$ (k) $\frac{e}{f} \div \frac{r}{s}$ $(r \neq 0)$

4. What conclusion can be drawn from each of the following:

(a) $\frac{r}{s} \cdot \frac{2}{3} < \frac{x}{y} \cdot \frac{2}{3}$ (b) $\frac{0}{2} \cdot \frac{x}{y} < \frac{3}{4} \cdot \frac{x}{y}$

5. Use the definition of division of rational numbers to prove the following:

If $\frac{a}{b} < \frac{c}{d}$, then $\frac{a}{b} \div \frac{e}{f} < \frac{c}{d} \div \frac{e}{f}$ $(e \neq 0)$.

6. In defining the quotient $\frac{a}{b} \div \frac{c}{d}$, why is it necessary to state "$c \neq 0$"?

7. For each of the following pairs of rational numbers, determine whether the numbers are equal or unequal; in the latter case, determine which is smaller:

(a) $\frac{3}{4}, \frac{2}{3}$ (b) $\frac{19}{37}, \frac{11}{23}$ (c) $\frac{0}{5}, \frac{4}{5}$ (d) $\frac{18}{36}, \frac{27}{54}$

(e) $\frac{8}{33}, \frac{11}{48}$ (f) $\frac{101}{200}, \frac{201}{400}$ (g) $\frac{15}{7}, \frac{17}{9}$ *(h) $\frac{x+1}{y}, \frac{x}{y}$

★8. Consider the statement

"$\frac{a}{b} = \frac{c}{d} \Leftrightarrow \frac{a}{b} \cdot \frac{x}{y} = \frac{c}{d} \cdot \frac{x}{y}$, $x \neq 0$"

of section 13.11.

(a) What *two* statements are contained in this single statement?
(b) Why is it necessary to stipulate "$x \neq 0$"?

Returning to the basic notion of fractions as operators, we let $\frac{a}{b}$ be a fraction which transforms segment U into segment V. Then

$$\frac{a}{b}U = V,$$

$$aU = bV. \qquad \text{(VIII)}$$

Also, let $\frac{c}{d}$ be a fraction which transforms the segment U into segment W. Then

$$\frac{c}{d}U = W,$$

$$cU = dW. \qquad \text{(IX)}$$

Multiplying both members of equation (VIII) by d, and multiplying both members of equation (IX) by b, the following equations may be derived:

$$adU = bdV,$$

$$bcU = bdW$$

Thus, $$adU + bcU = bdV + bdW,$$

and by distributivity,

$$(ad + bc)U = bd(V + W). \qquad \text{(X)}$$

Equation (X) is equivalent to the following:

$$\frac{ad + bc}{bd} U = V + W.$$

Therefore, we see that the single fraction $\frac{ad + bc}{bd}$ operates on U to produce a segment $V + W$, which is the *sum* of segment $V\left(\text{produced by } \frac{a}{b} \text{ operating on } U\right)$ and segment $W\left(\text{produced by } \frac{c}{d} \text{ operating on } U\right)$. This development suggests the following definition for *addition of fractions:*

DEFINITION: *If* $\frac{a}{b}$ *and* $\frac{c}{d}$ *are fractions,*

$$\frac{a}{b} + \frac{c}{d} \sim \frac{ad + bc}{bd}.$$

EXAMPLE 9. Find a fraction equivalent to $\frac{1}{2} + \frac{2}{3}$.

Solution:

$$\frac{1}{2} + \frac{2}{3} \sim \frac{1 \cdot 3 + 2 \cdot 2}{2 \cdot 3} \sim \frac{3 + 4}{6} \sim \frac{7}{6}$$

In terms of transformations of segments, this means the segment produced by $\frac{7}{6}$ operating on a segment U is the same as the *sum* of two other segments—the one produced by $\frac{1}{2}$ operating on U, and the one produced by $\frac{2}{3}$ operating on U.

13.14 ADDITION OF RATIONAL NUMBERS; DEFINITION

Consider now the problem of determining the sum of the two *rational numbers* $\frac{a}{b}$ and $\frac{c}{d}$. Each of them is an equivalence class of fractions; the fraction $\frac{a}{b}$ is in the class defining the number $\frac{a}{b}$, and the fraction $\frac{c}{d}$ is in the class defining the number $\frac{c}{d}$. We might then add the *fractions* $\frac{a}{b}$ and $\frac{c}{d}$ in accordance with the definition of the preceding section, obtaining

$$\frac{a}{b} + \frac{c}{d} \sim \frac{ad + bc}{bd}.$$

The sum of two fractions is a fraction; so $\frac{ad + bc}{bd}$ is a fraction. However, because of the way in which it was obtained, it might seem natural to define the *rational number* $\frac{ad + bc}{bd}$ to be the sum of the rational numbers $\frac{a}{b}$ and $\frac{c}{d}$.

Before making such a definition, however, we must be certain that the sum so obtained is independent of the fractions chosen to represent the numbers $\frac{a}{b}$ and $\frac{c}{d}$. Suppose, therefore, that $\frac{a'}{b'}$ is any other fraction equivalent to $\frac{a}{b}$:

$$\frac{a}{b} \sim \frac{a'}{b'}$$

$$ab' = ba'$$

Suppose also that $\frac{c'}{d'}$ is any other fraction equivalent to $\frac{c}{d}$:

$$\frac{c}{d} \sim \frac{c'}{d'}$$

$$cd' = dc'$$

Now, if the fractions $\frac{a'}{b'}$ and $\frac{c'}{d'}$, rather than the fractions $\frac{a}{b}$ and $\frac{c}{d}$, are added, the following fraction is obtained:

$$\frac{a'd' + b'c'}{b'd'}$$

Is this fraction equivalent to $\frac{ad + bc}{bd}$? To show this, we must show

$$(a'd' + b'c')bd = b'd'(ad + bc)$$

which, by distributivity, commutativity, and associativity, is equivalent to

$$(a'b)dd' + (c'd)bb' = (b'a)dd' + (d'c)bb'.$$

However, this last statement is true since $a'b = b'a$ and $c'd = d'c$. Therefore, the preceding steps may be retraced, establishing the following:

$$\frac{ad + bc}{bd} \sim \frac{a'd' + b'c'}{b'd'}$$

Thus, the same rational number is determined regardless of the fractions chosen to represent the rational numbers being added. With this in mind, we make the following definition:

DEFINITION: *If* $\frac{a}{b}$ *and* $\frac{c}{d}$ *are rational numbers,*

$$\frac{a}{b} + \frac{c}{d} = \frac{ad + bc}{bd}.$$

EXAMPLE 10. What is the sum of the rational numbers $\frac{2}{3}$ and $\frac{3}{4}$?

Solution: $$\frac{2}{3} + \frac{3}{4} = \frac{2 \cdot 4 + 3 \cdot 3}{3 \cdot 4} = \frac{8 + 9}{12} = \frac{17}{12}$$

EXAMPLE 11. What is the sum of the rational numbers $\frac{4}{6}$ and $\frac{6}{8}$?

Solution: $$\frac{4}{6} + \frac{6}{8} = \frac{4 \cdot 8 + 6 \cdot 6}{6 \cdot 8} = \frac{32 + 36}{48} = \frac{68}{48}$$

Why is this example really the same as Example 10?

Is addition of rational numbers commutative? Consider the sum $\frac{a}{b} + \frac{c}{d}$:

$$\frac{a}{b} + \frac{c}{d} = \frac{ad + bc}{bd}$$

Consider also the sum $\frac{c}{d} + \frac{a}{b}$:

$$\frac{c}{d} + \frac{a}{b} = \frac{cb + da}{db}$$

However, since a, b, c, and d are whole numbers, we know $ad + bc = cb + da$, and $bd = db$. Therefore, the two sums above are equal, leading to the formulation of the following property:

If $\frac{a}{b}$ *and* $\frac{c}{d}$ *are rational numbers,*

$$\frac{a}{b} + \frac{c}{d} = \frac{c}{d} + \frac{a}{b}.$$ COMMUTATIVITY OF + FOR Q

Consider next the following sum in which the first two rational numbers are associated:

$$\left(\frac{a}{b} + \frac{c}{d}\right) + \frac{e}{f} = \frac{ad + bc}{bd} + \frac{e}{f}$$

$$= \frac{(ad + bc)f + (bd)e}{(bd)f}$$

$$= \frac{adf + bcf + bde}{bdf}$$

Using the same three rational numbers, but associating now the last two, we have:

$$\frac{a}{b} + \left(\frac{c}{d} + \frac{e}{f}\right) = \frac{a}{b} + \frac{cf + de}{df}$$

$$= \frac{a(df) + b(cf + de)}{b(df)}$$

$$= \frac{adf + bcf + bde}{bdf}$$

In simplifying the above expressions, previously established properties of whole numbers were utilized; the final results indicate that the sums are the same for the two different associations.

We conclude the following:

If $\frac{a}{b}, \frac{c}{d}$, *and* $\frac{e}{f}$ *are rational numbers,*

$$\left(\frac{a}{b} + \frac{c}{d}\right) + \frac{e}{f} = \frac{a}{b} + \left(\frac{c}{d} + \frac{e}{f}\right).$$

ASSOCIATIVITY OF + FOR Q

The rational number

$$\left\{\frac{0}{1}, \frac{0}{2}, \frac{0}{3}, \frac{0}{4}, \ldots, \frac{0 \cdot k}{k}, \ldots\right\}$$

has a very special property so far as addition is concerned. Let $\frac{a}{b}$ be any rational number. Then

$$\frac{a}{b} + \frac{0}{1} = \frac{a \cdot 1 + b \cdot 0}{b \cdot 1} = \frac{a + 0}{b} = \frac{a}{b}.$$

Also,

$$\frac{0}{1} + \frac{a}{b} = \frac{0 \cdot b + 1 \cdot a}{1 \cdot b} = \frac{0 + a}{b} = \frac{a}{b}.$$

Hence, we see that the rational number $\frac{0}{1}$ functions as an identity element for addition of rational numbers, a fact expressed by the following property:

If $\frac{a}{b}$ *is a rational number, then*

$$\frac{a}{b} + \frac{0}{1} = \frac{0}{1} + \frac{a}{b} = \frac{a}{b}.$$

IDENTITY PRINCIPLE OF + FOR Q

Furthermore, there can be no other identity element of addition. For, suppose it is known that

$$\frac{a}{b} + \frac{c}{d} = \frac{a}{b}.$$

Then

$$\frac{ad + bc}{bd} = \frac{a}{b},$$

which implies $adb + b^2c = adb$,

or $b^2c = 0$.

We know, however, $b \neq 0$ (why?). Hence, if $b^2c = 0$, c must be zero. In other words, if a rational number $\frac{c}{d}$ functions as an identity element of addition, it must be the case that $c = 0$. But if $c = 0$, $\frac{c}{d}$ is precisely the rational number $\frac{0}{1}$, and so we are entitled to speak of $\frac{0}{1}$ as *the* identity element of addition of rational numbers.

EXAMPLE 12. $\frac{0}{1} + \frac{7}{8} = \frac{7}{8}$

EXAMPLE 13. $\frac{15}{23} + \frac{0}{6} = \frac{15}{23}$. Note that the rational number $\frac{0}{6}$ is the same as the rational number $\frac{0}{1}$.

13.16 ADDING WITH COMMON DENOMINATORS

The fractions $\frac{a}{b}$ and $\frac{c}{b}$ are often said to have the same denominator, or the "common denominator" b (see section 12.6). In practice, this language may be applied also to rational numbers if we remember that a rational number is defined as an equivalence class of fractions. From the definition the sum of the rational numbers $\frac{a}{b}$ and $\frac{c}{b}$ is determined as

$$\frac{a}{b} + \frac{c}{b} = \frac{ab + bc}{b \cdot b}.$$

The sum might be left as above. However, we also consider

$$\frac{ab + bc}{b \cdot b} = \frac{a + c}{b}$$

since $(ab + bc)b = b \cdot b(a + c)$ by properties of whole numbers. Therefore, we have

$$\frac{a}{b} + \frac{c}{b} = \frac{a + c}{b},$$

corresponding to the sum of any two fractions with the same denominator. Also we may discover from the definition of addition of fractions (section 13.13) that

$$\frac{a}{b} + \frac{c}{b} \sim \frac{a + c}{b}.$$

EXAMPLE 14. $\frac{3}{7} + \frac{2}{7} = \frac{3 + 2}{7} = \frac{5}{7}$

Show that the same sum is found by adding the rational numbers $\frac{3}{7}$ and $\frac{2}{7}$ according to the definition of section 13.14. Also compare the addition of the fractions, $\frac{3}{7}$ and $\frac{2}{7}$, with that of the rational numbers above.

In practice then we add the rational numbers by treating them as fractions of the equivalence class that defines the given rational number. We have seen that determining the sum of two fractions with a common denominator is especially simple, and any sum of fractions may be so expressed. In order to express an indicated sum such as $\frac{2}{5} + \frac{3}{10}$ with a common denominator, we replace each of the fractions with an equivalent fraction which has the least common denominator. To do this, we must find the least common multiple of the denominators of the given fractions. Recalling the method explained in sections 10.6 and 10.7, we find LCM(5, 10) = 10. Thus:

EXAMPLE 15. $\frac{2}{5} + \frac{3}{10} = \frac{4}{10} + \frac{3}{10} = \frac{7}{10}$. Why is $\frac{2}{5} = \frac{4}{10}$?

EXAMPLE 16. $\frac{5}{12} + \frac{2}{9} = \frac{15}{36} + \frac{8}{36} = \frac{23}{36}$

36 is said to be the least common denominator of the fractions $\frac{5}{12}$ and $\frac{2}{9}$. In effect, it is the least common multiple of 12 and 9.

13.17 DISTRIBUTIVE PROPERTY FOR RATIONAL NUMBERS

In the set of whole numbers, we saw that the operations of multiplication and addition were related by means of the Distributive Property. It seems natural then to question whether or not this property is also valid in the set of rational numbers. First, let us look at the expression

$$\frac{a}{b}\left(\frac{c}{d} + \frac{e}{f}\right),$$

which may be simplified as follows:

$$\begin{aligned}\frac{a}{b}\left(\frac{c}{d} + \frac{e}{f}\right) &= \frac{a}{b}\left(\frac{cf + de}{df}\right)\\ &= \frac{a(cf + de)}{b(df)}\\ &= \frac{acf + ade}{bdf}\end{aligned}$$

Again we have made use—without specific mention—of various properties of the whole numbers in this simplification. Next, let us look at the expression

$$\left(\frac{a}{b}\right)\left(\frac{c}{d}\right) + \left(\frac{a}{b}\right)\left(\frac{e}{f}\right)$$

which may be simplified in this way:

$$\left(\frac{a}{b}\right)\left(\frac{c}{d}\right) + \left(\frac{a}{b}\right)\left(\frac{e}{f}\right) = \frac{ac}{bd} + \frac{ae}{bf}$$
$$= \frac{(ac)(bf) + (bd)(ae)}{(bd)(bf)}$$
$$= \frac{acfb + adeb}{b^2df}$$

However, it may be verified that

$$\frac{acfb + adeb}{b^2df} = \frac{acf + ade}{bdf}$$

by the definition of equal rational numbers. Thus, the preceding results lead to the following property:

If $\frac{a}{b}, \frac{c}{d}$, *and* $\frac{e}{f}$ *are rational numbers,*

$$\frac{a}{b}\left(\frac{c}{d} + \frac{e}{f}\right) = \frac{ac}{bd} + \frac{ae}{bf}.$$ DISTRIBUTIVITY OF $\times$ OVER $+$ FOR Q

13.18 EXERCISES

1. (a) What is the sum of the fractions $\frac{3}{4}$ and $\frac{1}{2}$?
   (b) Using a segment U, show that the segment obtained by $\frac{5}{4}$ operating on U is the sum of two segments—the segment obtained by $\frac{3}{4}$ operating on U, and the segment obtained by $\frac{1}{2}$ operating on U.
2. Determine the following sums:

   (a) $\frac{2}{3} + \frac{4}{3}$ (b) $\frac{2}{7} + \frac{3}{7}$ (c) $\frac{5}{6} + \frac{2}{3}$ (d) $\frac{1}{3} + \frac{3}{4}$

   (e) $\frac{5}{8} + \frac{5}{6}$ (f) $\frac{4}{9} + \frac{5}{12}$ (g) $\frac{4}{1} + \frac{3}{1}$ (h) $4 + 3$

   (i) $\frac{7}{1} + \frac{8}{1}$ (j) $7 + 8$ (k) $\frac{47}{1} + \frac{23}{1}$ (l) $47 + 23$

   (m) $\frac{29}{37} + \frac{15}{41}$ (n) $\frac{r}{s} + \frac{t}{w}$
3. Use the definition of addition of rational numbers to verify the following instance of the associative property of addition:

$$\left(\frac{2}{3} + \frac{1}{4}\right) + \frac{3}{2} = \frac{2}{3} + \left(\frac{1}{4} + \frac{3}{2}\right)$$

4. (a) Determine the following sums:

$$\frac{5}{6} + \frac{0}{1}, \quad \frac{5}{6} + \frac{0}{7}, \quad \frac{3}{8} + \frac{0}{1}, \quad \frac{12}{29} + \frac{0}{2}, \quad \frac{x}{y} + \frac{0}{1}$$

(b) What rational number serves as the identity element for addition? Express this rational number as an equivalence class of fractions.

(c) If $\frac{a}{b} + \frac{x}{y} = \frac{a}{b}$, what conclusion can be drawn?

5. Use the definitions of addition and multiplication of rational numbers to verify the following instance of the distributive property:

$$\frac{2}{3}\left(\frac{1}{2} + \frac{3}{4}\right) = \left(\frac{2}{3} \cdot \frac{1}{2}\right) + \left(\frac{2}{3} \cdot \frac{3}{4}\right)$$

6. Use the definition of addition of rational numbers to verify the following instance of the commutative property of addition:

$$\frac{2}{3} + \frac{5}{7} = \frac{5}{7} + \frac{2}{3}$$

13.19 SUBTRACTION OF RATIONAL NUMBERS

Having defined addition of rational numbers, it seems natural to consider next subtraction, using the definition of addition to formulate a definition for subtraction (in much the same way we used multiplication to suggest a definition for division). In the arithmetic of whole numbers, we say, for example,

$$8 - 5 = 3$$

is equivalent to saying

$$3 + 5 = 8.$$

Making use of this relationship between addition and subtraction, we consider the sentence

$$\frac{a}{b} - \frac{c}{d} = \frac{x}{y},$$

where $\frac{a}{b}$, $\frac{c}{d}$, and $\frac{x}{y}$ are rational numbers, and $\frac{x}{y}$ is the result of subtracting $\frac{c}{d}$ from $\frac{a}{b}$. The sentence is equivalent to the sentence

$$\frac{x}{y} + \frac{c}{d} = \frac{a}{b}.$$

We shall then use this sentence (since it involves the already defined operation of addition) to characterize the number $\frac{x}{y}\left(\text{i.e., } \frac{a}{b} - \frac{c}{d}\right)$.

If

$$\frac{x}{y} + \frac{c}{d} = \frac{a}{b},$$

then

$$\frac{xd + yc}{yd} = \frac{a}{b}$$

and

$$b(xd + yc) = (yd)a.$$

We now have a sentence involving whole numbers, and it is equivalent to the following:

$$(bd)x + (bc)y = (ad)y$$

Now, if $ad \geq bc$, we obtain

$$(bd)x = (ad - bc)y$$

which implies $\frac{x}{y} = \frac{ad - bc}{bd}$.

Remembering that $\frac{x}{y}$ is the rational number which we want to call the *difference* $\frac{a}{b} - \frac{c}{d}$, we are led to the following definition:

DEFINITION: *If* $\frac{a}{b}$ *and* $\frac{c}{d}$ *are rational numbers, and* $\frac{a}{b} \geq \frac{c}{d}$,

$$\frac{a}{b} - \frac{c}{d} = \frac{ad - bc}{bd}.$$

Note the condition "$\frac{a}{b} \geq \frac{c}{d}$" in the definition. This condition is equivalent to the condition "$ad \geq bc$" and it is apparent that this latter condition must hold in order for the difference $ad - bc$ (which appears in the definition) to be defined.

EXAMPLE 17. $\frac{3}{4} - \frac{2}{3} = \frac{3 \cdot 3 - 4 \cdot 2}{4 \cdot 3} = \frac{9 - 8}{12} = \frac{1}{12}$

Let $\frac{a}{d}$ and $\frac{b}{d}$ be two rational numbers such that

$$\frac{a}{d} < \frac{b}{d}. \tag{XI}$$

There is no loss in generality by using the same "denominator" for both fractions since it has been established (section 13.16) that any two rational numbers may be so expressed. Proceeding from inequality (XI) above, we have

$$ad < db. \tag{XII}$$

Let c be any whole number; then, from (XII) we obtain

$$ad + cd < cd + bd, \tag{XIII}$$

by previously established properties of whole numbers. Again, (XIII) yields

$$(a + c)d < d(b + c),$$

which implies

$$\frac{a + c}{d} < \frac{b + c}{d}. \tag{XIV}$$

Finally, from the discussion in section 13.16, we know that (XIV) may be written

$$\frac{a}{d} + \frac{c}{d} < \frac{b}{d} + \frac{c}{d}.$$

We have then established the following:

If $\frac{a}{d} < \frac{b}{d}$, *then*

$$\frac{a}{d} + \frac{c}{d} < \frac{b}{d} + \frac{c}{d},$$

where $\frac{a}{d}, \frac{b}{d}$, *and* $\frac{c}{d}$ *are rational numbers.*

Furthermore, we may argue "in the opposite direction," or conversely. Suppose

$$\frac{a}{d} + \frac{c}{d} < \frac{b}{d} + \frac{c}{d}.$$

Then:

$$\frac{a + c}{d} < \frac{b + c}{d}$$

$$(a + c)d < d(b + c)$$

$$ad + cd < db + dc$$

Then, by properties of whole numbers,

$$ad < db,$$

which implies

$$\frac{a}{d} < \frac{b}{d}.$$

This latter argument may be summarized in the following way:

If $\frac{a}{d} + \frac{c}{d} < \frac{b}{d} + \frac{c}{d}$, *then*

$$\frac{a}{d} < \frac{b}{d},$$

where $\frac{a}{d}$, $\frac{b}{d}$, *and* $\frac{c}{d}$ *are rational numbers.*

The two statements proved thus far in this section involve the inequality relation "<"; analogous statements for the equality relation "=" may also be established. Let $\frac{a}{d}$ and $\frac{b}{d}$ be two rational numbers, such that

$$\frac{a}{d} = \frac{b}{d}.$$

Then:

$$ad = db$$

$$ad + cd = cd + db$$

$$(a + c)d = d(b + c)$$

$$\frac{a + c}{d} = \frac{b + c}{d}$$

$$\frac{a}{d} + \frac{c}{d} = \frac{b}{d} + \frac{c}{d}$$

This latter argument is summarized as follows:

If $\frac{a}{d} = \frac{b}{d}$, *then*

$$\frac{a}{d} + \frac{c}{d} = \frac{b}{d} + \frac{c}{d},$$

where $\frac{a}{d}$, $\frac{b}{d}$, *and* $\frac{c}{d}$ *are rational numbers.*

The following statement may also be proved in the manner established for the previous theorems of this section. (Details of the proof are left to the reader.)

If $\frac{a}{d} + \frac{c}{d} = \frac{b}{d} + \frac{c}{d}$, *then*

$$\frac{a}{d} = \frac{b}{d},$$

where $\frac{a}{d}$, $\frac{b}{d}$, *and* $\frac{c}{d}$ *are rational numbers.*

13.21 WHOLE NUMBERS AND RATIONAL NUMBERS; ISOMORPHISM

Consider the rational number

$$\left\{\frac{3}{1}, \frac{6}{2}, \frac{9}{3}, \frac{12}{4}, \ldots, \frac{3k}{k}, \ldots\right\}$$

which, as we have seen, may be variously named as "the rational number $\frac{3}{1}$," "the rational number $\frac{6}{2}$," etc. The point of interest here is that this rational number may be given a name, $\frac{3}{1}$, in which the "denominator" is 1. (Contrast this with the rational number $\frac{2}{3}$, for example, whose equivalence class of fractions contains no fraction with denominator 1.)

We turn our attention then to a subset of the rational numbers—the subset containing all those rational numbers, and only those rational numbers, which may be named in such a way as to have a denominator of 1. This subset of the rational numbers may be denoted as:

$$\left\{\frac{0}{1}, \frac{1}{1}, \frac{2}{1}, \frac{3}{1}, \frac{4}{1}, \ldots, \frac{k}{1}, \ldots\right\}$$

(Please note that this is *not* an equivalence class; the elements are distinct rational numbers.) In brief, then, we may say that we are dealing here with the subset of rational numbers of the form $\frac{k}{1}$. There exists a significant relationship between this subset of the rational numbers and the set of whole numbers.

In order to establish this relationship, let us set up a one-to-one correspondence between the two sets, as follows:

Let the correspondent of the rational number $\frac{k}{1}$ *be the whole number k; conversely, let the correspondent of the whole number k be the rational number* $\frac{k}{1}$.

Thus, under this correspondence, the rational number $\frac{2}{1}$ and the whole number 2 are made to correspond; similarly for $\frac{3}{1}$ and 3, $\frac{4}{1}$ and 4, $\frac{5}{1}$ and 5, $\frac{6}{1}$ and 6, etc. The correspondence between the two sets may be presented schematically as follows:

$$\begin{array}{c}
\{0,\ 1,\ 2,\ 3,\ 4,\ 5,\ 6,\ 7,\ \ldots,\ k,\ \ldots\} \\
\updownarrow\ \updownarrow\ \updownarrow\ \updownarrow\ \updownarrow\ \updownarrow\ \updownarrow\ \updownarrow\ \qquad \updownarrow \\
\left\{\frac{0}{1}, \frac{1}{1}, \frac{2}{1}, \frac{3}{1}, \frac{4}{1}, \frac{5}{1}, \frac{6}{1}, \frac{7}{1}, \ldots, \frac{k}{1}, \ldots\right\}
\end{array}$$

Within each of these two sets, the operations of addition and multiplication have been defined. For example, the whole numbers 2 and 3, under the operation of addition, yield the sum 5; i.e., $2 + 3 = 5$. If we now select the correspondents of 2 and 3, $\frac{2}{1}$ and $\frac{3}{1}$, they may be added to yield the sum $\frac{5}{1}$, which is the correspondent of 5. Schematically, this situation may be represented as follows:

$$\begin{array}{c}
\{\ldots,\ 2,\ 3,\ \ldots,\ 2+3,\ \ldots\} \\
\updownarrow\ \updownarrow \qquad \updownarrow \\
\left\{\ldots, \frac{2}{1}, \frac{3}{1}, \ldots, \frac{2+3}{1}, \ldots\right\}
\end{array}$$

From the way in which addition has been defined for the two sets under consideration, it is not difficult to see that the sum $a + b$ of any two whole numbers a and b corresponds to the sum $\frac{a+b}{1}$ of the rational numbers $\frac{a}{1}$ and $\frac{b}{1}$, which are the correspondents of a and b, respectively, under the correspondence scheme we have introduced. Thus, the sum of two numbers corresponds to the sum of their correspondents—a fact often expressed by stating that *sums are preserved* under the correspondence between the sets.

Not only are sums preserved, but also products are preserved. The product ab of two whole numbers a and b corresponds to $\frac{ab}{1}$, which is the product of $\frac{a}{1}$ and $\frac{b}{1}$, the correspondents of a and b, respectively. (The validity of this statement is easily appreciated by selecting any two whole numbers, and testing the relationship stated. The proof in general, of course, depends simply upon the definitions we have made earlier for multiplication of whole numbers and of rational numbers.)

The following diagram illustrates what we have established concerning preservation of sums and products under the correspondence between our two sets:

$$\{0,\ 1,\ 2,\ \ldots,\ a,\ \ldots,\ b,\ \ldots,\ a+b,\ \ldots,\ ab,\ \ldots\}$$
$$\updownarrow \quad \updownarrow \quad \updownarrow \qquad \updownarrow \qquad \updownarrow \qquad \updownarrow \qquad \updownarrow$$
$$\left\{\frac{0}{1}, \frac{1}{1}, \frac{2}{1}, \ldots, \frac{a}{1}, \ldots, \frac{b}{1}, \ldots, \frac{a+b}{1}, \ldots, \frac{ab}{1}, \ldots\right\}$$

We have here an instance of *isomorphism* between sets, and we say:

> *The set of whole numbers* is isomorphic to *the set of rational numbers of form* $\frac{k}{1}\cdot$

The significance of an isomorphism between sets is that *structurally* the sets are the same. In our case, for instance, we can look at the statement

$$2 + 3 = 5$$

and think "the sum of the rational numbers $\frac{2}{1}$ and $\frac{3}{1}$ is $\frac{5}{1}$." Although 2, 3, and 5 are whole numbers, we know that their correspondents behave in precisely the way they do so far as the operations of addition and multiplication are concerned.

13.22 PROPERTIES OF RATIONAL NUMBERS; SUMMARY

In section 3.10, a partial list of properties was presented—partial, because two of the properties were left blank since they do not apply to the set of cardinal numbers, which were being considered at that time. We now present the list again, because all the properties applicable to cardinal numbers are applicable also to the rational numbers; additionally, we are able to fill in one of the properties (P_{10}) which was left blank for the cardinals. In the following list, then, it is to be understood that x, y, and z represent *rational numbers*.

P_1	$\forall_x \forall_y\ x + y = y + x$	COMMUTATIVITY OF +
P_2	$\forall_x \forall_y \forall_z\ x + (y + z) = (x + y) + z$	ASSOCIATIVITY OF +
P_3	$(\exists_0) : (\forall_x)\ x + 0 = 0 + x = x$	IDENTITY PRINCIPLE FOR +
P_4	. . . .	. . . .
P_5	$\forall_x \forall_y\ x \cdot y = y \cdot x$	COMMUTATIVITY OF ·
P_6	$\forall_x \forall_y \forall_z\ x \cdot (y \cdot z) = (x \cdot y) \cdot z$	ASSOCIATIVITY OF ·
P_7	$(\exists_1) : (\forall_x)\ x \cdot 1 = 1 \cdot x = x$	IDENTITY PRINCIPLE FOR ·
P_8	$\forall_x \forall_y \forall_z\ x(y + z) = x \cdot y + x \cdot z$	DISTRIBUTIVITY FOR · OVER +
P_9	$x \cdot y = 0 \Rightarrow x = 0$ or $y = 0$	ZERO PRODUCT PRINCIPLE ·
P_{10}	$(\forall_{x \neq 0})(\exists_y) : x \cdot y = 1$	MULTIPLICATIVE INVERSE

We emphasize again that in this list the variables x, y, and z represent rational numbers. P_3, for example, is concerned with the identity element of addition which, as we have seen, is the rational number $\frac{0}{1}$. A specific instance of P_3 would be "$\frac{2}{3} + \frac{0}{1} = \frac{0}{1} + \frac{2}{3} = \frac{2}{3}$". The set of rational numbers then is characterized by properties P_1–P_{10} (with P_4 still omitted).

13.23 **EXERCISES**

1. Determine the following differences (where possible):

   (a) $\frac{2}{3} - \frac{1}{2}$ (b) $\frac{10}{7} - \frac{4}{5}$ (c) $\frac{10}{7} - \frac{5}{4}$ (d) $\frac{5}{4} - \frac{10}{7}$

   (e) $\frac{5}{6} - \frac{0}{1}$ (f) $\frac{0}{1} - \frac{5}{6}$ (g) $\frac{5}{8} - \frac{2}{3}$ (h) $\frac{10}{16} - \frac{4}{6}$

   (i) $\frac{5n}{8n} - \frac{2n}{3n}$ $(n \neq 0)$ (j) $\frac{r}{s} - \frac{0}{1}$ $(s \neq 0)$

   (k) $\frac{r}{s} - \frac{t}{s}$ $(s \neq 0)$, $(r > t)$

2. If $\frac{m}{n} - \frac{c}{d} = \frac{x}{y}$, then $\frac{x}{y} + \frac{c}{d} =$ ____________.

3. Use the numbers 5 and 3 to illustrate what is meant by the following:

   Sums and products are preserved under the correspondence

   $k \leftrightarrow \frac{k}{1}$

   between the set of whole numbers and the set of rational numbers of form $\frac{k}{1}$.

★4. Consider set $A = \{0, 1, 2, 3, 4, \ldots, k, \ldots\}$, the set of whole numbers, and the set $B = \{0, 2, 4, 6, 8, \ldots, 2k, \ldots\}$, the set of even whole numbers. Set up a one-to-one correspondence in which each element of A corresponds to its double in set B.

   (a) Are sets A and B isomorphic under the operation of addition?
   (b) Are sets A and B isomorphic under the operation of multiplication?

5. If $\frac{a}{b}$ and $\frac{c}{d}$ are rational numbers such that $\frac{a}{b} \cdot \frac{c}{d} = \frac{0}{1}$, what conclusion can be drawn?

6. What property of the rational numbers is not shared by the cardinal numbers? Give three numerical instances of this property.

★7. The following statement

$$\frac{a}{b} \leq \frac{c}{d} \Leftrightarrow \frac{a}{b} + \frac{x}{y} \leq \frac{c}{d} + \frac{x}{y}$$

actually contains four separate statements. Identify them, and give a numerical instance of each.

★8. Prove property P_9 for the rationals.

9. Find the solution sets of the following open sentences (equations and inequalities) where the domain is the set of rational numbers:

(a) $3x = 17$ (b) $2x + 1 = 8$ (c) $3x - 5 = 13$
(d) $2x + 1 > 6$ (e) $5x - 2 < 7$ (f) $\frac{2}{3}x = \frac{17}{5}$
(g) $\frac{4}{7}x + \frac{2}{3} < \frac{47}{21}$

13.24 REFERENCE QUESTIONS

1. How are the notions of fraction and rational number related? For an approach to the answer to this question which is somewhat different from that presented in this chapter, see

   Van Engen, Henry. "Rate Pairs, Fractions, and Rational Numbers," *The Arithmetic Teacher*, 7: 389–398; 1960.

2. How may a rational number be constructed as a class of ordered pairs of whole numbers? For an interesting answer to this question —one adaptable to the elementary classroom—see

   Hildebrand, Francis H. and Johnson, Nellie. "An Ordered Pair Approach to Addition of Rational Numbers in Second Grade," *The Arithmetic Teacher*, 12: 106–108; 1965.

3. For still another approach to development of rational numbers, see

   National Council of Teachers of Mathematics. *Topics in Mathematics for Elementary School Teachers* (29th yearbook). Washington, D.C.: NCTM, 1964. Pp. 290–300.

14 DECIMAL REPRESENTATION AND REAL NUMBERS

THE DECIMAL SYSTEM OF NUMERATION, *or a system with any other base, used to name the cardinal numbers, can be extended to represent many rational numbers. If we permit an infinite decimal (or any other base) multiplicative-additive place system, we shall be able to represent all the rationals and an entire new set of numbers called real numbers. Finally for each real number on the ray* $\overrightarrow{OX}$ *we can create an opposite number, called a negative real number, which is associated to a point on the ray* $\overrightarrow{OX'}$ *complementary to* $\overrightarrow{OX}$ *forming line* $\overleftrightarrow{XX'}$. *We shall study this extension of numeration and number in this chapter.*

14.1 DENSITY OF THE RATIONAL NUMBERS

Every cardinal number has an immediate successor, and hence between two successive cardinals there are no other numbers. For example, there is no whole number x such that

$$2 < x < 3.$$

However, the rational numbers have no immediate successors. In fact between any two unequal rational numbers, there are an infinite number of other rational numbers. That there is no next rational number for a given rational number has important geometrical implications. For example, to the point assigned to $\frac{3}{4}$ on the calibrated ray, there can be no next point having an assigned rational number. In fact, as we shall see, there is *no next point* on the number line.

We shall prove that between two unequal rational numbers, no matter how small their difference, there are other rational numbers. As an example, the rational numbers $\frac{1}{100{,}000}$ and $\frac{2}{100{,}000}$ differ by only $\frac{1}{100{,}000}$, but between these two rationals one can find at least the rationals $\frac{11}{1{,}000{,}000}, \frac{12}{1{,}000{,}000}, \ldots, \frac{19}{1{,}000{,}000}\cdot$ (Note that frequently we use the word "rational" as synonymous to "rational number.")

THEOREM: *Let $\frac{a}{b}$ and $\frac{c}{d}$ be two rationals with $\frac{a}{b} < \frac{c}{d}$. Then $\frac{a + c}{b + d}$ is greater than $\frac{a}{b}$ but less than $\frac{c}{d}$.*

Proof:

$$\frac{a}{b} < \frac{c}{d} \Rightarrow ad < bc \tag{I}$$

Adding ab to each member of this inequality, we get

$$ab + ad < ab + bc,$$

or by the distributive law,

$$a(b + d) < b(a + c).$$

Then by the definition of inequality

$$\frac{a}{b} < \frac{a + c}{b + d}\cdot$$

Similarly, adding cd to each member of (I), we have

$$ad + cd < bc + cd$$

or

$$d(a + c) < c(b + d),$$

that is

$$\frac{a + c}{b + d} < \frac{c}{d}.$$

This proves the theorem.

Here the difference between $\frac{a}{b}$ and $\frac{c}{d}$ may be made as small as desired. But no matter how small the difference, the theorem says that another rational may be found between the given rationals. Therefore, between two rational numbers, no matter how close, there are an infinite number of other rational numbers. Thus, the set of rational numbers is said to be *dense*.

Any fraction $\frac{p}{q}$ is the representation of a rational number. Certain special fractions are those for which q is a power of ten. For example

$$\frac{4}{1}, \frac{3}{10}, \frac{57}{10^3}, \frac{268}{10}, \frac{54}{10^5}$$

are illustrations of these special rational numbers. We shall prove later that

$$\frac{2}{3}, \frac{5}{7}, \frac{23}{30}, \frac{2}{99}, \text{ and many others,}$$

are rational numbers which cannot be represented by a fraction in which the denominator is a power of ten. Formally, we have:

DEFINITION: A decimal rational number *is one which can be represented by a fraction in which the denominator is a power of ten. The fraction is called a decimal fraction. All other rational numbers are* nondecimal *rational numbers.*

We shall first study the set of decimal rationals. For any given rational number there is always a simplest fraction which names it. By considering this simplest fraction we can decide whether or not it represents a *decimal rational number.* We consider two questions:

First, suppose $\frac{a}{b}$ is the simplest fraction for some decimal rational number. What is the nature of the number b?

Since $\frac{a}{b}$ represents a decimal rational, there exists some number f which, multiplying numerator and denominator of $\frac{a}{b}$, will transform it into a decimal fraction. Then

$$\frac{a \cdot f}{b \cdot f} = \frac{c}{10^n}$$

where $a \cdot f = c$ and $b \cdot f = 10^n$. Since $10^n = (2 \cdot 5)^n = 2^n \cdot 5^n$, we have

$$b \cdot f = 2^n \cdot 5^n,$$

and hence b divides $2^n \cdot 5^n$. Thus b can have only the prime factors 2 or 5, and each to a power less than or equal to n. (Why could b not have 5 as a factor more times than n?) We thus have

$$b = 2^x \cdot 5^y \quad \text{where} \quad x \leq n \text{ and } y \leq n.$$

The denominator b cannot contain prime factors other than 2 or 5. For example, $\frac{7}{80}$ is a decimal rational because $80 = 2^4 \cdot 5$ but $\frac{7}{30}$ is not a decimal rational because $30 = (2 \cdot 5) \cdot 3$ and the denominator has other factors than 2 or 5.

Secondly, suppose $\frac{a}{b}$ is a simplest fraction for a decimal rational number. What is the decimal fraction representation?

From the previous discussion we know that $b = 2^x \cdot 5^y$. This may be transformed into a power of 10 as follows:

(a) If $x < y$, then $y - x$ is a whole number. We multiply numerator and denominator of $\frac{a}{b}$ by 2^{y-x}, obtaining

$$\frac{a}{b} = \frac{a}{2^x \cdot 5^y} = \frac{a \cdot 2^{y-x}}{2^x \cdot 5^y \cdot 2^{y-x}} = \frac{a \cdot 2^{y-x}}{2^{x+(y-x)} \cdot 5^y}$$

$$= \frac{a \cdot 2^{y-x}}{2^y \cdot 5^y} = \frac{a \cdot 2^{y-x}}{(2 \cdot 5)^y} \quad \text{or} \quad \frac{a \cdot 2^{y-x}}{10^y}.$$

(b) If $x = y$, then $2^x \cdot 5^y = 2^x \cdot 5^x = (2 \cdot 5)^x = 10^x$, and the fraction is already a decimal fraction.

(c) If $x > y$, then $x - y$ is a whole number. We multiply numerator and denominator by 5^{x-y} as follows:

$$\frac{a}{b} = \frac{a}{2^x \cdot 5^y} = \frac{a \cdot 5^{x-y}}{(2^x \cdot 5^y)5^{x-y}} = \frac{a \cdot 5^{x-y}}{2^x \cdot 5^{y+(x-y)}}$$

$$= \frac{a \cdot 5^{x-y}}{2^x \cdot 5^x} = \frac{a \cdot 5^{x-y}}{(2 \cdot 5)^x} \quad \text{or} \quad \frac{a \cdot 5^{x-y}}{10^x}.$$

For example,

$$\frac{7}{40} = \frac{7}{2^3 \cdot 5} = \frac{7 \cdot 5^2}{(2^3 \cdot 5)5^2} = \frac{7 \cdot 25}{2^3 \cdot 5^3} = \frac{175}{10^3} = \frac{175}{1000}$$

and

$$\frac{17}{250} = \frac{17}{2 \cdot 125} = \frac{17}{2 \cdot 5^3} = \frac{17 \cdot 2^2}{(2 \cdot 5^3)2^2} = \frac{68}{2^3 \cdot 5^3} = \frac{68}{10^3} = \frac{68}{1000}.$$

To test whether or not a given fraction represents a decimal rational, we first transform it to its simplest form and then apply the foregoing tests. Thus $\frac{306}{68}$ has a prime factor 17 in its denominator and appears not to be a decimal. But, if we simplify the fraction, we obtain

$$\frac{306}{68} = \frac{2 \cdot 3^2 \cdot 17}{2^2 \cdot 17} = \frac{3^2}{2} = \frac{9 \cdot 5}{2 \cdot 5} = \frac{45}{10},$$

which is a decimal fraction.

The numbers of the form

$$\frac{1}{10}, \frac{1}{10^2}, \frac{1}{10^3}, \ldots, \frac{1}{10^k} \cdots \text{ (in decreasing order. Why?)}$$

are called unit decimal rationals. Note that for any unit decimal rational, in the order given, multiplying any one of them by 10 yields the next greater unit decimal, for example, $10 \cdot \frac{1}{10^3} = \frac{1}{10^2}$. Using this property we can extend the decimal system of notation for whole numbers to include the rational numbers. For this purpose we define the expression 10^0 to have the value 1. Note also that the fraction $\frac{1}{10}$ can be written in the form 10^{-1} (section 11.6). Then the fraction

$$\frac{1}{10^2} = \frac{1}{10} \cdot \frac{1}{10} = \left(\frac{1}{10}\right)^2 = (10^{-1})^2 = 10^{-2}.$$

Similarly $\frac{1}{10^3} = 10^{-3}$, etc., so that 10^{-6} is the same as $\frac{1}{10^6}$. Thus we have a sequence of powers of ten as follows:

$$\ldots, 10^3 = 1000,\ 10^2 = 100,\ 10^1 = 10,\ 10^0 = 1,\ 10^{-1} = \frac{1}{10},$$
$$10^{-2} = \frac{1}{100},\ 10^{-3} = \frac{1}{1000}, \ldots$$

The numeral 578 means $5 \cdot 10^2 + 7 \cdot 10^1 + 8 \cdot 10^0$. Now consider the rational number $\frac{275{,}642}{1000}$. We can write this in the form

$$\frac{2 \cdot 10^5 + 7 \cdot 10^4 + 5 \cdot 10^3 + 6 \cdot 10^2 + 4 \cdot 10^1 + 2 \cdot 10^0}{10^3}.$$

Dividing each term of the numerator by 10^3, we obtain

$$2 \cdot \left(\frac{10^5}{10^3}\right) + 7 \cdot \left(\frac{10^4}{10^3}\right) + 5 \cdot \left(\frac{10^3}{10^3}\right) + 6 \cdot \left(\frac{10^2}{10^3}\right) + 4 \cdot \left(\frac{10^1}{10^3}\right)$$
$$+ 2 \cdot \left(\frac{10^0}{10^3}\right)$$

or

$$2 \cdot 10^2 + 7 \cdot 10^1 + 5 \cdot 10^0 + 6 \cdot \frac{1}{10} + 4 \cdot \frac{1}{10^2} + 2 \cdot \frac{1}{10^3}.$$

More conveniently we can write this in a form

275.642,

where the period mark—called the *decimal point*—indicates that the exponent of the place value immediately to its left is zero; that is, this place value is 10^0 or 1. This is called the decimal representation of the rational number. It is customary in this case to call the number represented by the digits to the left of the decimal point the *whole number part* of the rational, and the number represented by the digits to the right of the decimal point the *decimal fraction part* of the rational number. The places to the right of the decimal point are called *decimal places.* Thus 275 is the whole number part and $\frac{642}{1000}$ is the decimal fraction part of the rational number 275.642. There are three decimal places in the numeral. Now we can write:

$$\frac{1}{10} = 0.1, \quad \frac{1}{100} = 0.01, \quad \frac{1}{1000} = 0.001, \text{ etc.}$$

$$\frac{48}{10} = 4.8, \quad \frac{48}{100} = 0.48, \quad \frac{48}{10{,}000} = 0.0048$$

$$2.65 = \frac{265}{100}; \qquad 3.1416 = \frac{31{,}416}{10{,}000}$$

In general, there are as many decimal places in the decimal fraction part of a rational number as there are zeros in the denominator of the decimal fraction representation.

The numbers $\frac{1}{1}, \frac{2}{1}, \frac{3}{1}, \ldots$ are called *whole rational numbers.* Since $1 = \frac{10}{10}$, $2 = \frac{20}{10}$, etc., for all the rational numbers we now have the

set of whole rationals $\subset$ set of decimal rationals $\subset$ set of rationals.

14.3 EXERCISES

1. Find several rationals between $\frac{1}{2}$ and $\frac{7}{12}$.
2. Show that the *average* of $\frac{1}{2}$ and $\frac{7}{12}$ is between these two numbers.
3. Prove: If $\frac{a}{b} < \frac{c}{d}$, then $\frac{a}{b} < \dfrac{\frac{a}{b} + \frac{c}{d}}{2} < \frac{c}{d}$.
4. Which of the following are decimal rationals:

   (a) $\frac{24}{15}$ (b) $\frac{28}{25}$ (c) $\frac{25}{28}$ (d) $\frac{21}{35}$
5. Find the decimal fraction for each of the following:

   (a) $\frac{117}{260}$ (b) $\frac{94}{80}$ (c) $\frac{27}{125}$
6. Find the simplest fraction for each of the following:

   (a) 0.42 (b) 0.036 (c) 8.45
7. Transform each of the following fractions to a common denominator:

   (a) $\frac{3}{4}, \frac{2}{25}, \frac{7}{20}, \frac{11}{125}$ (b) 0.2, 6.34, 0.045
8. Explain why $\frac{1}{10^2}$ can be written as 10^{-2}. $\left(\text{Recall } 10^{-1} = \frac{1}{10}.\right)$

9. Prove that $\frac{1}{3}$ is not a decimal rational number.
10. Distinguish among the following:
    (a) rational number
    (b) fraction
    (c) decimal fraction
    (d) decimal rational
    (e) decimal representation of a rational

    Illustrate by examples.

14.4 OPERATIONS ON DECIMAL RATIONALS

Addition and subtraction of decimal rationals are carried out exactly in the same algorism as for whole numbers. It is clear that if the numbers have the same denominator, all that is necessary is to add (or subtract) the numerators, for

$$\frac{a}{10^n} + \frac{b}{10^n} = \frac{a+b}{10^n}.$$

If the denominators are not the same, we can make them the same by the fundamental principle of fractions. Thus to add

$$\frac{3}{100} + \frac{4}{10} \quad \text{or} \quad \begin{array}{r} 0.03 \\ +0.4 \\ \hline \end{array},$$

we transform it to

$$\frac{3}{100} + \frac{40}{100} = \frac{40+3}{100} \quad \text{or} \quad \begin{array}{r} 0.03 \\ +0.40 \\ \hline 0.43 \end{array}.$$

To subtract we proceed in the same manner:

$$0.4 - 0.08 \quad \text{or} \quad \begin{array}{r} 0.40 \\ -0.08 \\ \hline 0.32 \end{array} \quad \text{or} \quad \frac{4}{10} - \frac{8}{100} \quad \text{or} \quad \frac{40}{100} - \frac{8}{100}$$

Note that in the subtraction of $a - b$, it is always the case that $a \geq b$.

To multiply two decimal rationals, first consider them in decimal fraction form. For example, we can write

$$2.63 \times 0.415$$

in the form

$$\frac{263}{100} \times \frac{415}{1000}.$$

By the definition of multiplication of fractions, this becomes

$$\frac{263 \times 415}{10^2 \times 10^3} = \frac{109145}{10^5} \quad \text{or} \quad 1.09145.$$

In general, to multiply two decimal rationals, multiply in the usual manner, ignoring the decimal point, and there will be as many decimal places in the product as there are in the sum of the numbers of decimal places in the two factors.

In division of decimal rationals, generally, the quotient is not a decimal rational. In this case we proceed to an approximation of the quotient. This is discussed later in this chapter.

Given $\frac{a}{10^r}$ and $\frac{b}{10^s}$ where a and b are whole rational numbers, we have

$$\frac{a}{10^r} \div \frac{b}{10^s} = \frac{a}{10^r} \cdot \frac{10^s}{b} = \frac{a}{b} \cdot \frac{10^s}{10^r}.$$

If $s > r$, the answer can be written in the form $\frac{a}{b} \cdot 10^{s-r}$.

If $s = r$, the answer is merely $\frac{a}{b}$.

If $s < r$, the answer is $\frac{a}{b} \cdot \frac{1}{10^{r-s}}$.

In every case, the quotient will be decimal if and only if b contains only the prime factors 2 or 5.

EXAMPLE 1. Find $8.4 \div 0.512$.

Solution: $8.4 \div 0.512 \Rightarrow \frac{84}{10} \div \frac{512}{1000} = \frac{84}{10} \times \frac{1000}{512} = \frac{84 \cdot 10^2}{512}$.

But $84 = 2^2 \cdot 21$ and $512 = 2^9$. Hence

$$\frac{84}{512} \cdot 10^2 = \frac{21 \cdot 10^2}{2^7}.$$

Multiplying by 5^7, we have

$$\frac{21 \cdot 10^2 \cdot 5^7}{2^7 \cdot 5^7} = \frac{21 \cdot 5^7}{10^7} \cdot 10^2 = \frac{21 \cdot 5^7}{10^5} = \frac{1{,}640{,}625}{10^5} \quad \text{or} \quad 16.40625.$$

14.5 DECIMAL APPROXIMATIONS TO NONDECIMAL RATIONAL NUMBERS

We have already learned that every rational number which is not a whole rational number has a value between two consecutive numbers. Thus $\frac{37}{14}$ is $\frac{28 + 9}{14}$ or $2\frac{9}{14}$ and its value lies between 2 and 3. We write the double inequality

$$2 < \frac{37}{14} < 3$$

and indicate this value on the number ray by a point in the interval from 2 to 3. (See Figure 14–1(a).) To find the approximate position of this point, we note that

(1) $\frac{37}{14}$ is not a decimal fraction since the denominator has the factor 7, and

(2) $\frac{37}{14}$ lies between two successive tenths in the interval 2 to 3.

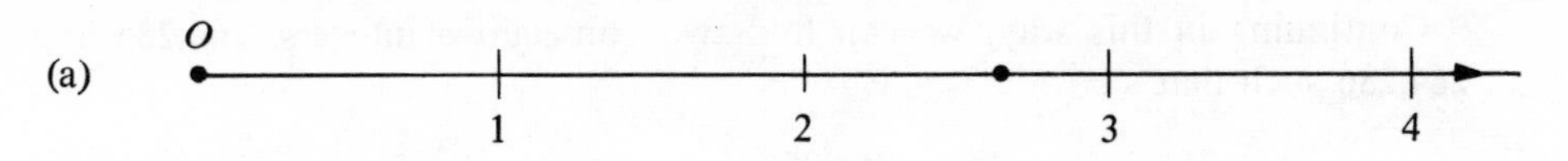

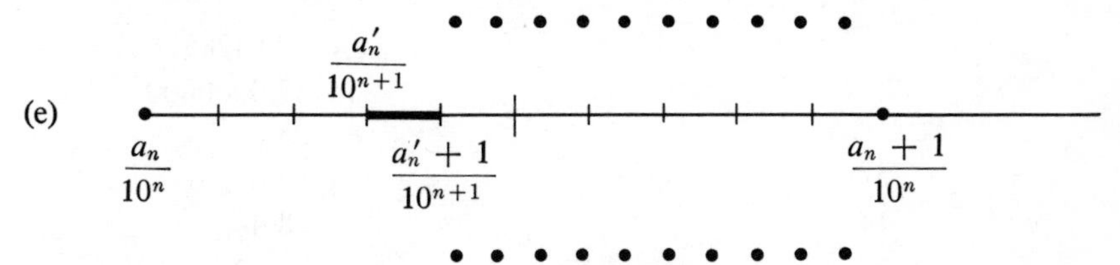

FIGURE 14–1

The second condition says, in fact, that there are two consecutive whole numbers a and $a + 1$, such that

$$\frac{a}{10} < \frac{37}{14} < \frac{a+1}{10}.$$

How do we find the number a? By the inequality relation we have

$$\frac{a}{10} < \frac{37}{14} \Rightarrow 14a < 370 \quad \text{or} \quad a < \frac{370}{14}; \qquad \text{that is,} \quad a < 26\frac{6}{14}.$$

It is easy to show similarly that $\frac{27}{10} > \frac{37}{14}$. Hence

$$\frac{26}{10} < \frac{37}{14} < \frac{27}{10}.$$

Therefore $\frac{37}{14}$ lies in the interval 2.6 to 2.7 as shown in Figure 14–1(b), where the interval from 2 to 3 has been magnified.

We shall now show that we can locate $\frac{37}{14}$ between two successive decimal fractions, for which the denominator is a power as high as we please.

Let $\frac{a'}{100} < \frac{37}{14}$. Then $14a' < 3700$ or $a' < 264\frac{4}{14}$, and hence we can write

$$\frac{264}{100} < \frac{37}{14} < \frac{265}{100}. \quad \text{(Check the second inequality.)}$$

In Figure 14–1(c) we indicate the approximate location of the value of $\frac{37}{14}$ on the interval 2.64 to 2.65. In this figure the interval of Figure 14–1(b) for 2.6 to 2.7 has been magnified ten times.

Continuing in this way, we can find two consecutive integers, 264,285 and 264,286 such that

$$\frac{264{,}285}{10^5} < \frac{37}{14} < \frac{264{,}286}{10^5} \quad \text{or} \quad 2.64285 < \frac{37}{14} < 2.64286$$

(see Figure 14–1(d)) and in general we can find two consecutive whole numbers a_n and $a_n + 1$ such that

$$\frac{a_n}{10^n} < \frac{37}{14} < \frac{a_n + 1}{10^n}$$

where n is as large as we wish. (See Figure 14–1(e).)

In practice we find the values of a_n by continued division as shown at the right. This gives the sequence of inequalities:

$$2 < \frac{37}{14} < 3$$

$$2.6 < \frac{37}{14} < 2.7 \qquad \left(\frac{1}{10}\right)$$

$$2.64 < \frac{37}{14} < 2.65 \qquad \left(\frac{1}{100}\right)$$

$$2.642 < \frac{37}{14} < 2.643 \qquad \left(\frac{1}{1000}\right)$$

. . . .

$$2.6428571 < \frac{37}{14} < 2.6428572 \qquad \left(\frac{1}{10{,}000{,}000}\right)$$

. . . .

```
        2.6428571 . . .
   14)37.0000000 . . .
      28
       9 0
       8 4
         60 ⟶
         56
          40
          28
          120
          112
            80
            70
            100
             98
              20
              14
              60 ⟶
```

In the second line of this sequence we find that $\frac{37}{14}$ is between 2.6 and 2.7. To which of these rational numbers is $\frac{37}{14}$ closer? That is, which is the smaller value

$$\frac{37}{14} - 2.6 \quad \text{or} \quad 2.7 - \frac{37}{14}\,?$$

To answer the question we go to the third line of the sequence and note

$$2.64 < \frac{37}{14} < 2.65.$$

Hence, as can be visualized in Figure 14–1(c), the rational is closer to 2.6 than it is to 2.7. Therefore we say: "To the nearest tenth, $\frac{37}{14}$ is approximately 2.6" and we write

$$\frac{37}{14} \approx 2.6 \text{ (to the nearest tenth).}$$

Similarly, looking at Figure 14–1(d), we note that the point corresponding to $\frac{37}{14}$ is in the eighth tenth interval between 2.64285 and 2.64286, and hence, to the nearest hundred-thousandth, $\frac{37}{14} \approx 2.64286$. In general, we can state the rule:

For a nondecimal rational $\frac{p}{q}$, *to find the decimal to the nearest* $\frac{1}{10^k}$, *find the value in decimal form to at least* $(k + 1)$ *decimal places. If the* $(k + 1)$*th digit is less than* 5, *the nearest value to* $\frac{1}{10^k}$ *is given by the kth digit. If the* $(k + 1)$*th digit is* 5 *or more, the nearest value to* $\frac{1}{10^k}$ *is given by the kth place digit increased by one.*

EXAMPLE 2. Find the decimal value of $\frac{29}{13}$ to the nearest thousandth.

Solution: By continued division to at least four decimal places we find

$$2.2307 < \frac{29}{13} < 2.2308.$$

Since $7 > 4$, we have, to the nearest thousandth,

$$\frac{29}{13} \approx 2.231.$$

$$\begin{array}{r} 2.2307 \\ 13\overline{)29.0000} \\ \underline{26} \\ 3\,0 \\ \underline{2\,6} \\ 4\,0 \\ \underline{3\,9} \\ 100 \\ \underline{91} \\ 9 \end{array}$$

14.6 INFINITE REPEATING DECIMALS

The two preceding sections have shown the following:

1. If a rational number has only the factors 2 and 5 in the denominator of its simplest fractional representation, it is a decimal rational. Hence there is a representation of the number in decimal form. It is a *terminating decimal* and has a final decimal place after which only zeros occur in any further places.

2. If a rational number has prime factors other than 2 or 5 in the denominator of its simplest fractional representation, it is a nondecimal rational. Hence it has no decimal fraction representation. However, it can be approximated between two consecutive decimal fractions $\frac{a}{10^k}$ and $\frac{a+1}{10^k}$, where k can be as large as desired.

Statement 2 above implies that the decimal representation of a nondecimal fraction can go on and on forever. The fraction is bound closer and closer between two terminating decimals, as the denominators of the enclosing decimal fractions get larger (that is, as the last place value to the right in the decimal representation gets smaller). However, the sequence of digits in the decimal part of the numeral sooner or later follows a pattern as we shall now see.

Let us consider the fraction $\frac{4}{11}$. Here

$$0 < \frac{4}{11} < 1.$$

We wish to bound the fraction more closely. Consider

$$\frac{x}{10} < \frac{4}{11} < \frac{x+1}{10}.$$

Using the first inequality, we find

$$11x < 40 \quad \text{or} \quad x < 3\frac{7}{11}.$$

Therefore, we can write

$$\frac{3}{10} < \frac{4}{11} < \frac{4}{10} \quad \text{and} \quad \frac{4}{11} \approx 0.4.$$

To bound the fraction still more closely, we may continue with

$$\frac{x}{100} < \frac{4}{11} < \frac{x+1}{100}.$$

It will be seen that the value of x at each stage may be found by the usual division process shown at the right. Thus,

$$\frac{36}{100} < \frac{4}{11} < \frac{37}{100} \quad \text{and} \quad \frac{4}{11} \approx 0.36.$$

$$\begin{array}{r} 0.36 \\ 11\overline{)4.000} \\ 3\,3 \\ \hline 70 \\ 66 \\ \hline 40 \end{array}$$

But at this stage the remainder is a 4 and the subsequent digits of the dividend are all zeros and hence the division process will repeat itself. Thus, without continuing, we know

$$\frac{4}{11} \approx 0.3636\overparen{36} \qquad \text{(II)}$$

where the loop over the last two digits indicates this couple will repeat itself if we carry the approximation further. A decimal numeral that repeats itself in this fashion is called a *repeating* or *periodic decimal.* The more periods that are appended to the numeral, the closer is the approximation of the value to $\frac{4}{11}$.

If the decimal numeral is allowed to repeat its period forever (that is, infinitely), we indicate this by placing dots above the digits in the last period and we say that the result is *an infinite repeating decimal* which is the same as, or another name for $\frac{4}{11}$. Thus

$$\frac{4}{11} = 0.3636\dot{3}\dot{6}. \qquad \text{(III)}$$

Note the difference between the expressions (II) and (III).

Similarly:

$$\frac{1}{3} \approx 0.3 \text{ or } 0.333$$

but $$\frac{1}{3} = 0.33\dot{3}$$

$$\frac{2}{3} \approx 0.7 \text{ or } 0.667$$

but $$\frac{2}{3} = 0.666$$

Every rational number that is not a whole or decimal rational can now be represented by an infinite repeating decimal. This follows because in the division process of transforming a fraction into a decimal either

(a) the process terminates and the fraction represents a whole or decimal rational, or

(b) if the division does not terminate, the process yields successive remainders each less than the denominator. For the fraction $\frac{a}{b}$, the only remainders one can have are $0, 1, 2, \ldots, b - 1$. Sooner or later, one of these remainders will recur and then the division process repeats itself, and hence the sequence of digits in the quotient repeats itself.

Thus every rational number is given as a terminating decimal or an infinite repeating decimal.

EXAMPLE 3. Find the infinite decimal representation of $\frac{12}{7}$.

Solution: Divide 12 by 7, using the usual algorism. The remainder 5 appears again after six partial divisions. Hence the period is 714285 and

$$\frac{12}{7} = 1.714285\dot{7}\dot{1}\dot{4}\dot{2}\dot{8}\dot{5}$$

where we write "=" because the dots above the last six digits shall now signify a repetition of the period forever. (Another way would be to write

$$\textit{Limit } 1.\dot{7}\dot{1}\dot{4}\dot{2}\dot{8}\dot{5} = \frac{12}{7}$$

but we shall not discuss limits in this book.)

$$\begin{array}{r}
1.714285 \\
7\overline{)12.000000} \\
\underline{7} \\
50 \longrightarrow \\
\underline{49} \\
10 \\
\underline{7} \\
30 \\
\underline{28} \\
20 \\
\underline{14} \\
60 \\
\underline{56} \\
40 \\
\underline{35} \\
5 \longrightarrow
\end{array}$$

Conversely, we can show that any repeating decimal must represent a rational number. For example, suppose

$$N = 0.234\dot{2}\dot{3}\dot{4}. \tag{IV}$$

Since the period is three places we multiply each side of this equation by 10^3 and obtain

$$1000N = 234.234\dot{2}\dot{3}\dot{4}. \tag{V}$$

Subtracting (IV) from (V), we have

$$999N = 234, \quad N = \frac{234}{999} = \frac{26}{111}.$$

We can now write

$$\frac{234}{1000} < \frac{26}{111} < \frac{235}{1000} \quad \text{or} \quad \frac{234234}{1{,}000{,}000} < \frac{26}{111} < \frac{234235}{1{,}000{,}000}, \text{ etc.}$$

Finally, we can now show that all terminating decimals, which are decimal rationals, may be represented as infinite repeating decimals by decreasing the value of the terminal place by one, and using a single repeating period of 9's. Thus

$$\frac{1}{2} = 0.5 = 0.49\dot{9}.$$

This appears to be reasonable, for by extending the number of places, each with the digit 9, we can approach 0.5 as close as we care to. If the 9's are extended infinitely, we shall say the infinite decimal is another name for 0.5. Similarly, $0.18 = 0.1799\dot{9}$; $0.125 = 0.12499\dot{9}$; etc. Thus:

> *A rational number may be represented by an infinite repeating decimal and any infinite repeating decimal represents a rational number. However, if the rational number is whole or decimal, it can also be represented by a finite terminating decimal numeral.*

For example,

$$\frac{12}{5},\ 346,\ 2.4,\ 5.68,\ \text{etc.},$$

are whole or decimal rationals and

$$2.49\dot{9},\ 3.6849\dot{9},\ \text{etc.},$$

are decimal rationals but

$$\frac{2}{3},\ 4\frac{3}{7},\ 5.68\dot{6}\dot{8},\ 3.66\dot{6},\ \text{etc.},$$

are nondecimal rationals.

EXAMPLE 4. Find an infinite decimal representation for $\frac{297}{111}$.

Solution: $\frac{297}{111} = 2\frac{75}{111}$. Now divide 75 by 111. After the third digit of the quotient, the remainder is 75 and the division repeats. Hence

$$\frac{75}{111} = 0.675\dot{6}\dot{7}\dot{5}$$

and

$$\frac{297}{111} = 2.675\dot{6}\dot{7}\dot{5}.$$

```
      .675
111)75.000 ⟶
    66 6
     8 40
     7 77
       630
       555
        75 ⟶
```

14.7 EXERCISES

1. (a) Find the product $\frac{2}{3} \times \frac{4}{15}$.
   (b) Find a decimal approximation of $\frac{2}{3}$ and $\frac{4}{15}$ to the nearest hundredth.
   (c) Find the product of the decimals of part (b). Compare the answer to (c) with the decimal approximation of the answer to part (a) by giving the decimal approximation to which they agree.

2. Repeat Exercise 1, for the numbers $\frac{5}{8}$ and $\frac{7}{25}$ for approximation:
   (a) to the nearest hundredth (b) to the nearest thousandth

3. (a) Change $\frac{3}{7}$ to an infinite decimal fraction.
   (b) Change $\frac{4}{7}$ to an infinite decimal fraction.
   (c) Add the resulting decimal fractions.

4. If $\frac{4}{9}$ and $\frac{5}{9}$ are transformed into infinite decimal fractions, the sum of the digits of corresponding places is always 9. Show this and explain why.

5. In dividing a by b, the quotient is a terminating decimal fraction. What do you know about the number b?

6. In the example in section 14.5 the successive approximations to $\frac{37}{14}$ were 2, 2.6, 2.64, 2.642, . . .
   (a) Using $\frac{a}{10^k} < \frac{37}{14}$, $k = 0, 1, 2, 3, \ldots$, show how these decimal fraction approximations were obtained.
   (b) From the answer to part (a), justify the continued division shown in Section 14.5.

7. Distinguish among, and give examples of the following:
   (a) whole rational number
   (b) decimal rational number
   (c) decimal fraction
   (d) nondecimal rational number
   (e) repeating decimal fraction
   (f) repeating decimal fraction ending in $\dot{9}$

8. Find the repeating decimal period for $\frac{1}{13}$.

9. Find the common fraction form for $0.418\dot{1}\dot{8}$. (Hint: Find the form for $4.18\dot{1}\dot{8}$ and divide the result by 10.)

10. Find the common fraction form for:
    (a) $0.736\dot{3}\dot{6}$ (b) $2.1374\dot{3}\dot{7}\dot{4}$

11. Using the method illustrated on page 272, bound the fraction $\frac{27}{11}$ by the nearest tenths, hundredths, and thousandths.

12. (a) Find, as a fraction in common form, the difference between 0.33 and $0.3\dot{3}$.
    (b) Will the difference between 0.33 . . . 3 to n places, n finite, and $0.3\dot{3}$ ever be zero?
    (c) As n becomes large what can you say about the difference in part (b)?

13. Represent $\frac{1}{13}$ as a repeating decimal. From the result obtain the infinite decimal representation for $\frac{2}{13}$, $\frac{5}{13}$, and $\frac{10}{13}$.

Just as we are able to locate (at least approximately) a point on the number ray that corresponds to a rational number, it would appear that if we select a point on the number ray, we could find the number assigned to it (at least approximately). For example, let P be a point selected at random on the number ray. Let n be the number to be assigned to this point. From Figure 14–2(a) we note at once that

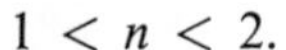

$$1 < n < 2.$$

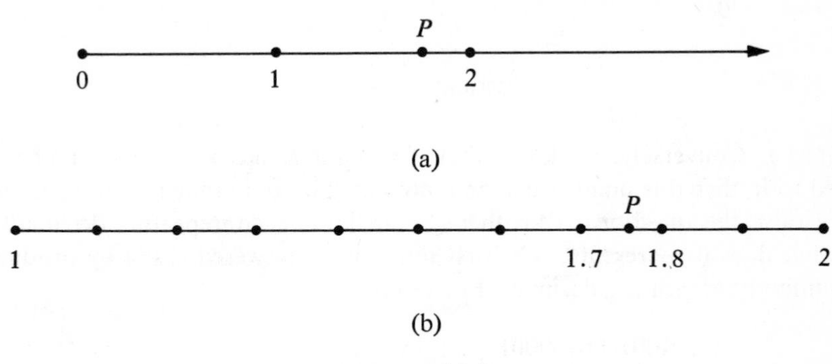

FIGURE 14–2

Now divide the segment from 1 to 2 into ten equal parts. An enlarged version of this is shown in Figure 14–2(b). From the figure we note that P is in the eighth division and hence

$$1.7 < n < 1.8.$$

We can continue this way, by dividing the segment from 1.7 to 1.8 into ten equal segments, and thus, if the point P falls in the fourth segment, we know

$$1.73 < n < 1.74.$$

In this way we get a decimal rational approximation to the number assigned to point P. Evidently, we are limited in the preciseness of such an approximation by the size of our chosen unit and the refinement of our construction instruments.

We have shown, however, that to every rational number, there is an assigned point on the number ray. We now ask a reverse question. Is it possible to assign to each point of the line a rational number? The answer is "no." There are points on the number ray that can have no rational number assigned to them. We shall see why in the next section.

We consider here only infinite decimal numerals of the type

$$0.\overline{a_1a_2a_3 \ldots a_n \ldots},$$

that is, numerals for values between 0 and 1. If this decimal is a repeating one, it represents a rational number and this number is assigned to a point P on the number ray, which is between O and U (or the points to which 0 and 1 are

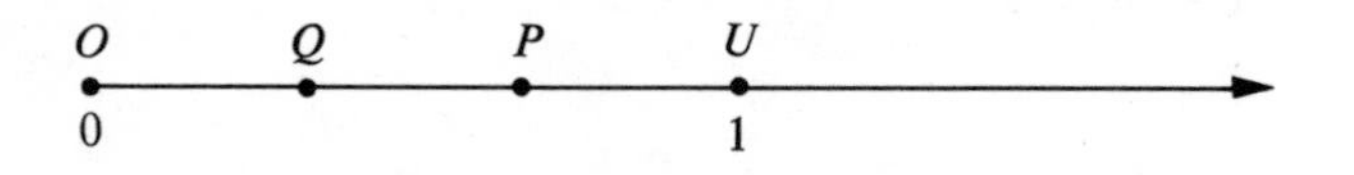

FIGURE 14–3

assigned.) Conversely, we know that if a point Q has a rational number assigned to it, then this number can be represented by an infinite repeating decimal.

We raise the questions: Can there be an infinite nonrepeating decimal? If so, what does it represent? The first question is answered easily by producing an infinite nonrepeating decimal. For example,

$$0.101001000100001\ldots,$$

where the number of "0's" occurring between each successive "1" increases by one each time (going to the right), will be nonrepeating. It has no period. Thus there are infinite nonrepeating decimals.

To see what these nonrepeating decimals represent, let us return to a repeating decimal, for example,

$$\frac{4}{11} = 0.36363\dot{6}.$$

If we terminate this decimal after each succeeding digit, we get a sequence of values:

$$0.00, \quad 0.36, \quad 0.3636, \quad 0.363636, \quad 0.36363636, \quad \ldots$$

In this sequence

(1) each term is a rational number.
(2) each succeeding term grows larger in numerical value and we say the sequence is *monotonic increasing*.
(3) there exists a *least upper bound*, namely $\frac{4}{11}$.

This third statement needs amplification. An *upper bound* of a monotonic increasing sequence can be any number for which all terms of the infinite sequence are smaller in value. Thus the numbers $\frac{5}{11}, \frac{6}{11}, \ldots, 1, 100$ are also upper bounds to the sequence. But of all these upper bounds $\frac{4}{11}$ is the least because *there is no rational number less than* $\frac{4}{11}$ *that bounds the sequence.*

For example, $\frac{3635}{10{,}000} < \frac{4}{11}$, but the term 0.3636 is already greater than 0.3635. In fact, for any stated rational number less than $\frac{4}{11}$, there is a term of the sequence greater than this rational number. This is illustrated in Figure 14–4 where the vertical bar represents $\frac{4}{11}$ as the least upper bound.

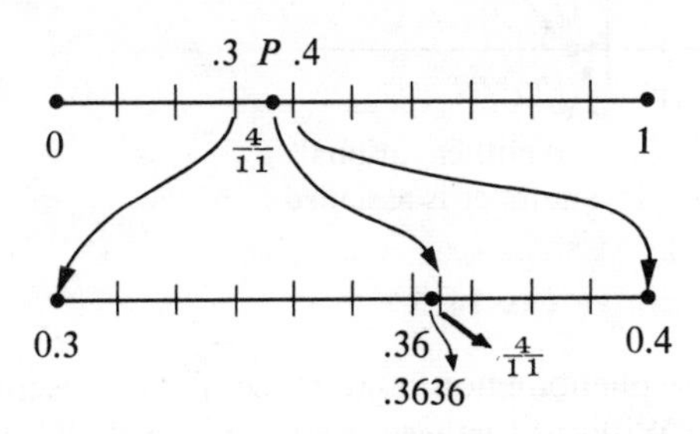

FIGURE 14–4

Every monotonic increasing sequence of rational numbers represented by the successively increasing number of periods of an infinite repeating decimal has a least upper bound. The infinite decimal is another name for this least upper bound.

Thus $0.363\dot{6}\dot{3}$ is the least upper bound of the given sequence and is another name for $\frac{4}{11}$.

Now consider the nonrepeating infinite decimal

0.101001000100001 . . .

which we can also represent as a monotonic increasing sequence of rationals, for example,

0.1, 0.101, 0.101001, 0.1010010001, . . .

In this sequence

(1) each term is a rational number.
(2) each succeeding term grows larger in numerical value and the sequence is monotonic increasing,

but

(3) there exists *no least rational upper bound.*

This last statement needs amplification. In the case of an infinite repeating decimal there was a rational number as the least upper bound. In fact, this rational least upper bound was the limit of the sequence. However, for the nonrepeating decimal, the points corresponding to the sequence approach a point P on the ray, but this point does not represent a rational number. While we shall not prove it here, it is true that for any rational number assigned to a corresponding point Q, having a value greater than that of point P, we can always find rational values assigned to points between P and Q, and this no matter how close

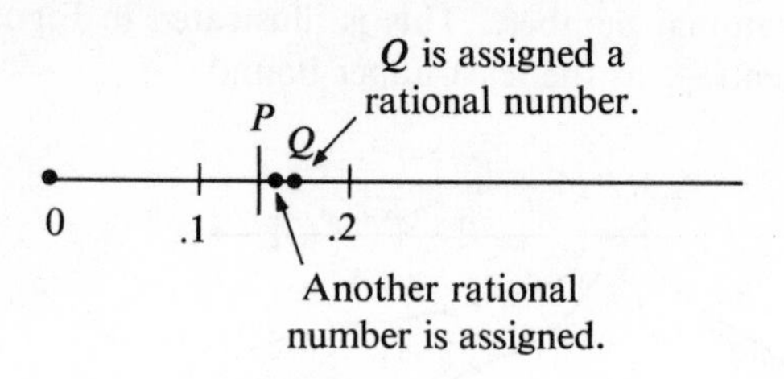

FIGURE 14–5

Q is to P. This is a strange phenomenon, and hence if P represents a number, it is a nonrational number. Without further discussion, we shall admit that

(a) there is a number which can be assigned to P and it will be called *irrational.*
(b) irrational numbers are named by infinite nonrepeating decimals.

The question can well arise "Are there other numbers than the rational and irrational numbers which can be assigned to the points on the number ray?" The answer is "no." Every point on the number ray represents either

(1) a rational number named by an infinite repeating decimal

or

(2) an irrational number named by an infinite nonrepeating decimal.

14.10 SQUARE ROOT OF A NUMBER

In section 9.2 we informally introduced *square root.* Now we formally give the following definition:

DEFINITION: *The* square root *of a number, if it exists, is one of the two equal factors whose product is the number. The* square root *of n is designated by* $\sqrt{n}$.

Thus $\sqrt{4} = 2$, because $2 \cdot 2 = 4$. $\sqrt{25} = 5$ because $5 \cdot 5 = 25$. However, $\sqrt{3}$ is not a *whole* number, for $1 \cdot 1 = 1$ and $2 \cdot 2 = 4$, and there is no whole number x for which $x \cdot x = 3$. Is there a rational number which is $\sqrt{3}$, that is, some number between 1 and 2? We shall prove that $\sqrt{3}$ is not a rational number.

Notice that $\sqrt{\frac{4}{25}} = \frac{2}{5}$ because $\frac{2}{5} \cdot \frac{2}{5} = \frac{4}{25}$, and $\sqrt{0.81} = 0.9$ because

$$0.9 \cdot 0.9 = 0.81.$$

Suppose $\sqrt{3} = \frac{p}{q}$ where $\frac{p}{q}$ is the simplest form of a rational. Then

p and q can have no common factor.

If $\sqrt{3} = \frac{p}{q}$, then $\frac{p}{q} \cdot \frac{p}{q} = 3$ or

$$p^2 = 3q^2. \tag{VI}$$

This says p^2 and $3q^2$ are the same number. Now $3q^2$ has the prime factor 3, so p^2 also has the prime factor 3. Since $p^2 = p \cdot p$, p must have the prime factor 3, so that p^2 has the prime factor 3 twice. In other words

$$p = 3k \quad \text{and} \quad p \cdot p = 3 \cdot k \cdot 3 \cdot k = 3 \cdot 3 \cdot k \cdot k = 9k^2.$$

Then replacing p^2 by $9k^2$ in (VI), we have

$$9k^2 = 3q^2 \quad \text{or} \quad 3k^2 = q^2. \tag{VII}$$

Now, repeating the same argument for (VII) as we used for (VI), we are forced to admit q has the factor 3. Now we find both p and q have the factor 3. But this is impossible since $\frac{p}{q}$ is a fraction in its simplest form and hence p and q have no common factor.

How did we arrive at this contradiction? By assuming that $\sqrt{3}$ was a rational number. Hence this assumption is false and we must admit that $\sqrt{3}$ is not a rational number.

$\sqrt{3}$ is an irrational number.

The reader should restudy this argument until he understands it completely.

But we can approximate $\sqrt{3}$ by rational numbers. For by actual multiplication the reader can verify the following inequalities:

$$1 < \sqrt{3} < 2$$
$$1.7 < \sqrt{3} < 1.8$$
$$1.73 < \sqrt{3} < 1.74$$
$$1.732 < \sqrt{3} < 1.733$$
$$1.7321 < \sqrt{3} < 1.7322$$
$$\cdots\cdots\cdots$$

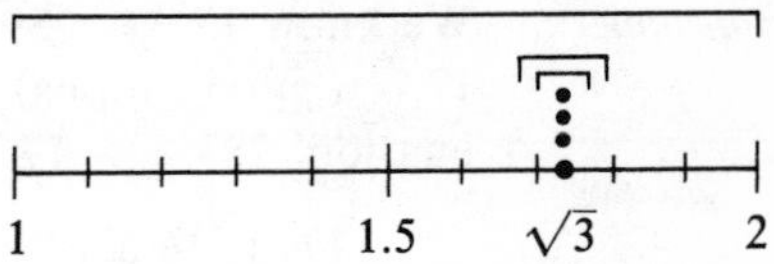

FIGURE 14–6

Now we can square 1.73210 and 1.73211, and find

$$1.732105 < \sqrt{3} < 1.732106,$$

and so on. Continuing in this way, we can find an approximate value as close to $\sqrt{3}$ as we wish, either from below or from above. However, as we continue this approximation from below by rational approximations, we can never find a rational number as a least upper bound for the sequence on the left, for if we did $\sqrt{3}$ would be rational, which it is not. Hence the infinite decimal representing $\sqrt{3}$ must be nonrepeating.

There is an easy way to approximate the square root of a number. Suppose we desire to find $\sqrt{36}$ and do not use the obvious answer 6. We know that $5^2 = 25$ and hence 5 is too small a value. But dividing 36 by 5, the approximate quotient is 7, which is too large a value. However, the average of the divisor and quotient, $\dfrac{5+7}{2}$ is 6 and this is the square root of 36. This suggests a procedure.

(1) Find an approximate value to the square root by estimating. It may be too large or too small an estimate.
(2) Using the estimate as a divisor, divide the number to find the quotient.
(3) Average the divisor and quotient. The result is a closer approximation.

Let us try this with $\sqrt{2}$. We know that $(1.4)^2 = 1.96$ and $(1.5)^2 = 2.25$; hence 1.4 is a good estimate for $\sqrt{2}$. Dividing 2.00 by 1.4, we find that the quotient is 1.428.

$$\begin{array}{r} 1.428 \\ 1.4\overline{)2.00} \\ \underline{1\ 4} \\ 60 \\ \underline{56} \\ 40 \\ \underline{28} \\ 120 \\ \underline{112} \end{array}$$

The average of the divisor and the quotient is

$$\frac{1.400 + 1.428}{2} = 1.414$$

and this is a much better approximation. Now we can divide 2.00000000 by 1.414 to seven decimal places and obtain the closer rational approximation 1.4142136. In general, if the quotient and dividend agree in the first k digits from left to right, the quotient may be carried to $2k$ digits and the average will be a rational approximation of $2k$ digits.

EXAMPLE 5. Find $\sqrt{283.4}$ correct to six digits.

Solution: We know $17^2 = 289$ so that 17 is a good rational approximation. $283.4 \div 17 = 16.6$.

$$\begin{array}{r} 16.6 \\ 17\overline{)283.4} \\ \underline{17} \\ 113 \\ \underline{102} \\ 11\ 4 \\ \underline{10\ 2} \\ 1\ 20 \end{array}$$

Then $\dfrac{17 + 16.6}{2} = 16.8$.

Try 16.8 as a divisor.

$283.4 \div 16.8 = 16.8690.$

$$\begin{array}{r} 16.8690 \\ 16.8\overline{)283.4} \\ \underline{168} \\ 115\ 4 \\ \underline{100\ 8} \\ 14\ 60 \\ \underline{13\ 44} \\ 1\ 160 \\ \underline{1\ 008} \\ 1520 \\ \underline{1512} \\ 80 \end{array}$$

Then

$$\frac{16.8 + 16.8690}{2} = 16.8345$$

is a square root correct to six digits.

The symbol $\sqrt{a}$, where a is a rational number, sometimes represents a rational number and hence can be written as an infinite repeating decimal. For example,

$$\sqrt{9} = 3 = 2.\dot{9}, \sqrt{\tfrac{4}{9}} = \tfrac{2}{3} = 0.66\dot{6}, \text{etc.}$$

But sometimes $\sqrt{a}$ represents an irrational number, for example,

$$\sqrt{2} = 1.414\ldots, \sqrt{3} = 1.732\ldots,$$

$$\sqrt{\tfrac{2}{3}} = \sqrt{0.66\dot{6}} = 0.816496\ldots, \text{etc.}$$

How can we tell when the symbol $\sqrt{a}$ is rational or irrational, if a is a rational number? If the division process in finding the average terminates by being exact and giving the same quotient as the divisor, then the square root is rational; otherwise it is irrational.

EXAMPLE 6. Find $\sqrt{580644}$ and tell whether it is rational or irrational.

Solution: 750 is an approximation, since $750^2 = 562500$.

$580644 \div 750 \approx 770$. Hence $\frac{1}{2}(750 + 770) = 760$ is a better approximation.

$580644 \div 760 = 764$. Hence $\frac{1}{2}(760 + 764) = 762$ is a better approximation.

$580644 \div 762 = 762$ (Exactly). Hence $\sqrt{580644} = 762$; it is rational.

Another way to tell whether $\sqrt{a}$ is rational or irrational is to use the factored form of the number. If all the factors occur an even number of times, the square root is a rational; otherwise it is not. This follows from the fact that any number expressed in prime factor form, when squared, repeats each of its factors. Thus if

$$n = 2^2 \cdot 3^2 \cdot 5 \cdot 7,$$

then

$$n^2 = (2^2 \cdot 3^2 \cdot 5 \cdot 7)(2^2 \cdot 3^2 \cdot 5 \cdot 7) = 2^4 \cdot 3^4 \cdot 5^2 \cdot 7^2.$$

EXAMPLE 7. Find $\sqrt{392.04}$.

Solution: Write the symbol in the form $\sqrt{\dfrac{39204}{100}}$.

$$\text{Factor } 39204 = 2^2 \cdot 9801 = 2^2 \cdot 3^2 \cdot 1089$$
$$= 2^2 \cdot 3^2 \cdot 3^2 \cdot 121 = 2^2 \cdot 3^4 \cdot 11^2.$$

Hence

$$\sqrt{\frac{39204}{100}} = \frac{\sqrt{2^2 \cdot 3^4 \cdot 11^2}}{\sqrt{10^2}} = \frac{2 \cdot 3^2 \cdot 11}{10} = \frac{198}{10} = 19.8;$$

it is rational.

14.11 EXERCISES

1. Find the least upper bound of each of the following sequences:

   (a) 0.9, 0.99, 0.999, 0.9999, ...

   (b) 0.00, 0.45, 0.4545, 0.454545, ...

   (c) 0.234, 0.234234, 0.234234234, ...

2. Represent, where possible, each of the following as an infinite repeating decimal.

   (a) 2 (b) $\frac{1234}{9999}$ (c) $\sqrt{3}$ (d) $\sqrt{0.5625}$ (e) $\frac{1}{13}$

3. Which of the following decimals, if continued, have a pattern that indicates a possible repeating decimal?

   (a) 0.123412341234 . . . (b) 0.1020304050 . . .

   (c) 0.101010101 . . . (d) 0.21324354 . . .

   (e) 3.14159261 . . . (f) 1.41421 . . .

   (g) 0.131331333133331 . . .

4. For each of the following rational sequences give, if there exists, (1) an upper bound, and (2) a least upper bound:

   (a) 1, $1\frac{1}{2}$, $1\frac{3}{4}$, $1\frac{7}{8}$, $1\frac{15}{16}$, ...

   (b) 2.0, 2.1, 2.2, 2.3, 2.4, 2.5, ...

   (c) 2.0, 2.2, 2.23, 2.234, 2.2345, 2.23456, ...

   (d) 0.44, 0.444, 0.4444, ...

   (e) 1, $1\frac{1}{3}$, $1\frac{4}{9}$, $1\frac{13}{27}$, $1\frac{40}{81}$, ...

5. Find each of the following correct to the nearest ten-thousandth.

   (a) $\sqrt{5}$ (b) $\sqrt{11}$ (c) $\sqrt{21843}$

   (d) $\sqrt{3.1416}$ (Hint: $(1.7)^2 = 2.89$)

6. (a) If $\sqrt{n}$ is a rational number, find several values for n.

   (b) If $\sqrt{n}$ is an irrational number, find several values for n.

   (c) Justify your answers to (a) and (b).

7. Prove $\sqrt{5}$ is not a rational number. (See section 14.10.)

8. (a) Show that $\frac{17}{12} > \sqrt{2}$.

   (b) Show that $\frac{577}{408} > \sqrt{2}$.

   (c) Show that $\frac{17}{12} > \frac{577}{408}$.

   (d) Is $\frac{17}{12}$ a least upper bound for $\sqrt{2}$? Is $\frac{577}{408}$ a least upper bound?

9. If $a < \sqrt{N} < b$, where $N = a \cdot b$, show that $a < \frac{a+b}{2} < b$, and hence $\frac{a+b}{2}$ is closer to $\sqrt{N}$ than a or b is.

10. Show that:

(a) $\sqrt{27.3} = \frac{1}{10}\sqrt{2730}$ (b) $\sqrt{679} = \frac{\sqrt{6790}}{\sqrt{10}}$

11. By factorization find:

(a) $\sqrt{23409}$ (b) $\sqrt{17.64}$ (c) $\sqrt{\frac{5184}{2401}}$

12. Construct a nonrepeating infinite decimal and locate the assigned point P approximately on a number ray.

14.12 PROPERTIES OF REAL ARITHMETIC NUMBERS OF THE NUMBER RAY

To all the points on the number ray, we now have assigned a number, either rational or irrational, and all possible rational and irrational numbers can be assigned to a point on the number ray. These numbers can be represented by many different symbols, but all of them can be represented by infinite decimal numerals. These numbers are the important ones in school arithmetic and we review here their main properties. We shall call them the *real arithmetic numbers.*

(a) Given any two of these numbers, we can always find a number which is their sum. For example to add $2.33\dot{3}$ and $27.044\dot{4}$ we have, by the ordinary process of addition, the sum $29.377\dot{7}$, which is a rational number. To add $\sqrt{2}$ to $\sqrt{3}$ we use the symbol $(\sqrt{2} + \sqrt{3})$ as the sum, and approximate it by using rational approximations to each addend. Thus $\sqrt{2} + \sqrt{3} \approx 1.4142 + 1.7321$,

$$\sqrt{2} + \sqrt{3} \approx 3.1463.$$

In this manner we note that the set of real numbers is closed to addition.

Since we may use rational approximations for all real numbers, we at once have the following properties for addition:

P_1 $\forall_x \forall_y\ x + y = y + x$ COMMUTATIVITY OF +

P_2 $\forall_x \forall_y \forall_z\ x + (y + z) = (x + y) + z$ ASSOCIATIVITY OF +

P_3 $\exists_0 : \forall_x\ x + 0 = 0 + x = x$ IDENTITY PRINCIPLE OF +

P_4 does not hold for the real numbers treated thus far and is developed in the next section.

(b) Given any two of these numbers, we can always find a number which is their product. For example, $2.3\dot{3} \cdot 5.4\dot{4}$ gives us the product $2\frac{1}{3} \cdot 5\frac{4}{9}$ or $12\frac{19}{27}$. If we multiply these numbers in approximate decimal form, we shall get only a rational approximation to the product and hence not a repeating decimal. Thus, $2.333 \cdot 5.44 = 12.700852$, while $12\frac{19}{27}$ is the repeating decimal $12.\dot{7}0\dot{3}$. The difference of the two results is due to the error in omitting the infinite parts from the approximate decimals used in the multiplication.†

---

† We shall not discuss the theory of these errors in this book.

In this manner we see that it is possible to make the agreement that the set of real numbers is closed to multiplication. Again by using rational approximations for all numbers, the following properties hold for multiplication:

P_5 $\forall_x \forall_y \; x \cdot y = y \cdot x$ COMMUTATIVITY OF ·

P_6 $\forall_x \forall_y \forall_z \; x \cdot (y \cdot z) = (x \cdot y) \cdot z$ ASSOCIATIVITY OF ·

P_7 $\exists_1 : \forall_x \; x \cdot 1 = 1 \cdot x = x$ IDENTITY PRINCIPLE OF ·

P_8 $\forall_x \forall_y \forall_z \; x(y + z) = x \cdot y + x \cdot z$ DISTRIBUTIVITY FOR · OVER +

P_9 $x \cdot y = 0 \Rightarrow x = 0 \text{ or } y = 0$ ZERO PRODUCT PRINCIPLE

(c) Given a number x, not zero, there is another number y, such that $x \cdot y = 1$. The number y is called the *inverse element* of (or *reciprocal* of) x for multiplication with respect to its identity element 1. This we found was the case for all the rational numbers, excluding zero, where $\frac{b}{a}$ was found to be the reciprocal of $\frac{a}{b}$. Nonzero irrational numbers also have reciprocals. For example, to find the reciprocal of $\sqrt{2}$, we say

$$\sqrt{2} \cdot x = 1$$

or

$$x = 1 \div \sqrt{2}.$$

But a quotient may be regarded as a fraction (as in section 13.9), and we write

$$\frac{1}{\sqrt{2}},$$

where here *we extend our definition of fraction to be an ordered pair of numbers not restricted to cardinal numbers.* We apply the same rules of operation to our newly defined fractions as we did to the earlier ones. We can also verify this property by using rational approximations. We first multiply numerator and denominator of $\frac{1}{\sqrt{2}}$ by $\sqrt{2}$ and get

$$\frac{1}{\sqrt{2}} = \frac{1 \cdot \sqrt{2}}{\sqrt{2} \cdot \sqrt{2}} = \frac{\sqrt{2}}{\sqrt{4}} = \frac{\sqrt{2}}{2}.$$

Using $\sqrt{2} \approx 1.414$

and $\frac{1}{\sqrt{2}} = \frac{\sqrt{2}}{2} \approx 0.707,$

we get $(1.414) \cdot (0.707) = 0.999698.$

However, we wished to show

$$\sqrt{2} \cdot \frac{1}{\sqrt{2}} = 1 = 0.99999\dot{9}.$$

The difference in the two products is the error in the rational approximation to the irrational numbers.

It is easy to see that if x is not zero, we can write its reciprocal, or inverse element for multiplication, in the form $\frac{1}{x}$, or as in the case of fractions as x^{-1}. We then have the important property

P_{10} $\forall_{x \neq 0} \exists_{x^{-1}} : x \cdot x^{-1} = 1$ MULTIPLICATIVE INVERSE

Because of the existence of the *multiplicative inverse*, or *reciprocal*, we can always divide any number x by another number y (not zero) and find the quotient as one of our numbers. To do this, we merely write the division of $x \div y$ in the form $\frac{x}{y} = x \cdot \frac{1}{y} = x \cdot y^{-1}$. To divide x by y, multiply x by the reciprocal of y.

The set of numbers, excluding zero as a divisor, is closed to division.

14.13 NEGATIVE NUMBERS; REAL NUMBERS

For the real arithmetic numbers, the 9 properties given in the previous section are the important ones. Of course there are many other useful properties they possess which were listed in the study of the rational numbers. However, there is one property that they do not possess. There is no inverse element for the

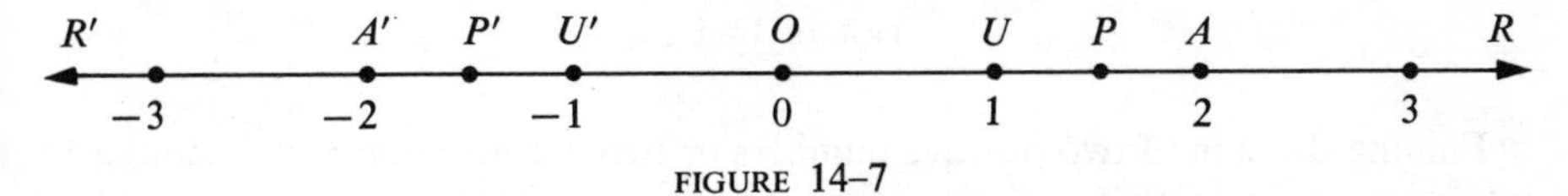

FIGURE 14–7

operation of addition with respect to its identity element 0. Thus if x is not zero, there is no number y to add to x so that $x + y = 0$. (Except for 0 itself, which is trivial.) We shall now *create* a whole new set of numbers for which an inverse element for addition will exist for every number.

For this purpose, first consider the arithmetic real number ray. Now extend this ray to the left to form the line $\overleftrightarrow{RR'}$. We shall call $\overrightarrow{OR'}$ the *opposite ray* for the present. To each point on $\overrightarrow{OR}$ there is a corresponding point on $\overrightarrow{OR'}$ which is symmetric to it with respect to the origin O. Thus P' is symmetric to P because $\overline{OP} \cong \overline{OP'}$. To each point on $\overrightarrow{OR'}$ we assign a number, called the *opposite of the number* assigned to the symmetric point on $\overrightarrow{OR}$. The numeral assigned to the point on $\overrightarrow{OR'}$ shall be the same as that assigned to the symmetric point on $\overrightarrow{OR}$ with the exception that it shall be preceded by the symbol "−" called the "opposite" or "negative."

Thus to U, we have the symmetric U' to which we assign the number -1, called "the opposite of one" or "negative one." Similarly, to the number 2 there is an opposite, named "−2," and generally to any point P on $\overrightarrow{OR}$ with number n, there is a symmetric point P' on $\overrightarrow{OR'}$ with number $-n$. To avoid ambiguity we shall call the arithmetic numbers on $\overrightarrow{OR}$ the positive real numbers. The set of all these numbers and the number zero assigned to the origin is called the set of *real numbers*, and the line formed by the two rays is called the *real line* or *real number line*.

From the manner in which the negative numbers were constructed, that is, by assigning them to points on the ray $\overrightarrow{OR'}$, it would seem natural to call them the opposite of the positive numbers. Thus the opposite of 3 is negative three which we write -3; the opposite of $2.33\dot{3}$ is -2.333, and the opposite of $\sqrt{2}$ is $-\sqrt{2}$, and so on. But we can also consider the positive numbers as being the opposite of the negative numbers. Thus the opposite of -3, which can be written as $-(-3)$, is 3; the opposite of $-\sqrt{3}$ is $-(-\sqrt{3})$, or $\sqrt{3}$. In general, the opposite of a real number may be a negative or positive number, depending on which real number is given.

We may also speak of the real numbers as *directed numbers* since the positive numbers are directed one way on a ray of a line and the negative numbers are directed the opposite way on the complementary ray of the line. Now to every real number we can assign a segment, $\overline{OP}$. We say $\overline{OP}$ is a directed segment since if P is on $\overrightarrow{OR}$, it has one direction (positive) and if Q is on $\overrightarrow{OR'}$, it has the opposite direction (negative). Using these segments, we can derive a rule for adding the positive and negative real numbers.

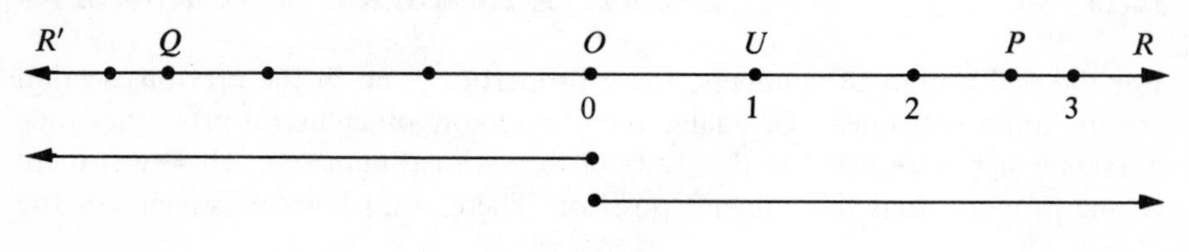

FIGURE 14–8

Finding the sum of two positive numbers or two negative numbers is similar to adding rational numbers. For example, let us add 2 to 3. At the end of segment $\overline{OA}$, where A is the point to which 2 is assigned, we adjoin a segment $\overline{AC}$ congruent to $\overline{OB}$ (B is assigned point 3). On the ray, the point C corresponds to 5, which is

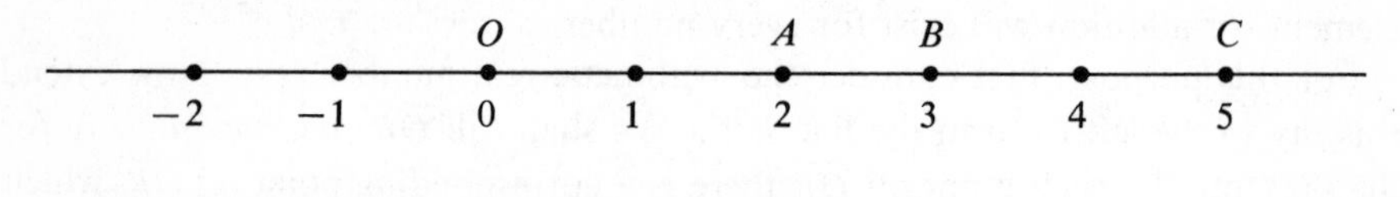

FIGURE 14–9

the sum. Similarly, to find the sum of $(-2) + (-3)$, to segment $\overline{OA'}$ where A' is assigned the number (-2) we adjoin the directed segment $\overline{A'C'}$ which is congruent to OB', and the point C' corresponds to -5, which is the sum.

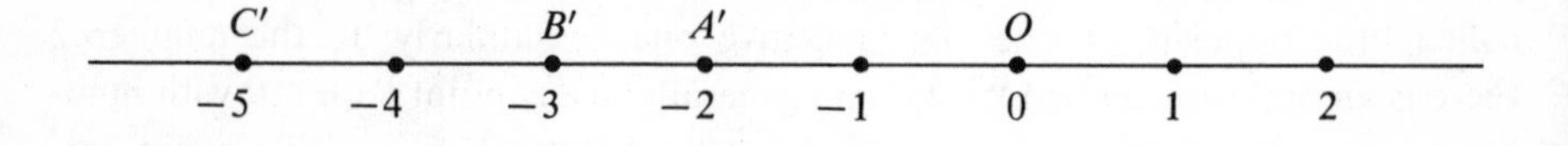

FIGURE 14–10

If the two numbers whose sum is required are one negative, one positive, we shall use the commutative law and place the positive segment first. Thus to find $2 + (-3)$, we adjoin to $\overline{OA}$ the directed segment $\overline{AD'}$ which is congruent to $\overline{OB'}$. The point D' falls at the number (-1), which is the sum. Thus,

$$2 + (-3) = -1.$$

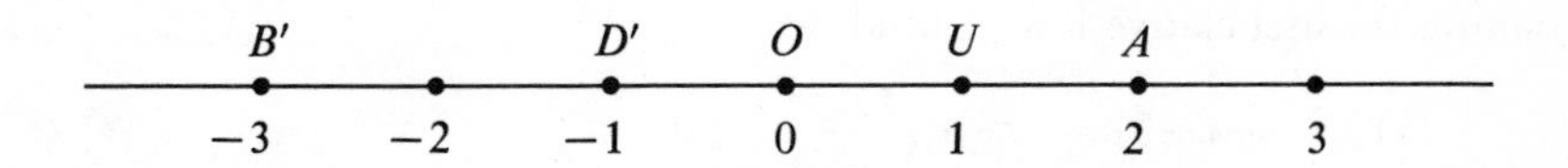

FIGURE 14–11

If we add 3 to -2 we shall find in a similar way that the terminal point is 1, and hence

$$3 + (-2) = 1.$$

From this discussion it is easy to see that for the real numbers addition is always possible and that properties P_1 to P_3 of section 14.12 hold for all real numbers. However, we are now in a position to determine two additional properties that hold for all real numbers, but do not hold for the set of real arithmetic numbers or the positive real numbers.

For any given real number, positive or negative, we can now find the opposite of that number, and by the method described above, the sum of these two numbers will always be zero. Then $3 + (-3) = 0$, $(-2) + 2 = 0$, $\sqrt{2} + (-\sqrt{2}) = 0$, and in general,

$$n + (-n) = 0.$$

This is true because the segment $\overline{OP}$ of a number is always congruent to the segment $\overline{OP'}$ of its opposite, and hence the terminal point of the sum is the origin, to which is assigned the number zero. We state this as a general property

P_4 $\forall_x \exists_{-x} : x + (-x) = 0$ ADDITIVE INVERSE

The number $(-x)$ is called the *additive inverse* of x. We thus have an additive inverse element with respect to addition, also called the *opposite of a number*, just as for multiplication we had an inverse element, also called the reciprocal.

For the arithmetic numbers, subtraction was not always possible; for example, $2 - 8$ was not possible because there is no arithmetic number which added to 8 will yield the sum 2. However, for the real numbers, we now shall show that subtraction is always possible. Our definition of subtraction is

$$a - b = c \text{ if and only if } a = c + b.$$

Thus $5 - 2$ is possible and is 3, because $5 = 3 + 2$.

For the real numbers, $2 - 5$ is also possible because

$$(1) \quad 2 - 5 = x \text{ if and only if } 2 = x + 5.$$

Now add -5 to each side and

$$(2) \quad 2 + (-5) = (x + 5) + (-5).$$

Assuming the associative law to hold, we have

$$(3) \quad 2 + (-5) = x + [5 + (-5)].$$

The expression in brackets is zero, by P_4; so

$$(4) \quad 2 + (-5) = x + 0 = x,$$

because of the addition property of zero.

From statements (1) and (4), we have

$$(5) \quad 2 - 5 = 2 + (-5)$$

and since addition is always possible and we know $2 + (-5) = (-3)$, we know

$$2 - 5 = -3.$$

(Two minus five equals negative three.)

Generally, let a and b be any two real numbers. Then

$$(1) \quad a - b = x \Rightarrow a = x + b$$
$$(2) \quad a + (-b) = (x + b) + (-b)$$
$$(3) \quad a + (-b) = x + [b + (-b)]$$
$$(4) \quad b + (-b) = 0,\ x + 0 = x,\ a + (-b) = x$$
$$(5) \quad a - b = a + (-b).$$

The reader should supply the reasons for each of these steps. Statement (5) gives us a rule for subtraction of the real numbers, namely:

To subtract b from a, add the opposite of b to a.

Thus every subtraction can be transformed into an equivalent addition and we know that:

The set of real numbers is closed to subtraction.

So, with the real numbers we can always add, subtract, multiply, and divide (except by zero). With these numbers we have a real number line to every point of which is assigned a real number, and conversely. The ten properties listed in sections 14.12 to 14.13 hold for all the real numbers. For two different real numbers, it is always the case that the one is either greater than or less than the other, so that these real numbers are *ordered*, and the way they are assigned to the points of a line orders all the points of the line.

By the *arithmetic value* or *absolute value* of a real number we shall mean the following:

1. The absolute value of a positive real number is the number itself.
2. The absolute value of zero is zero.
3. The absolute value of a negative real number is its opposite.

To designate the absolute value of a real number, we place the numeral between vertical bars. Thus

$$|5| = 5, \quad |0| = 0, \quad |-3| = 3.$$

To multiply two real numbers, the following rules are applied:

I. If both numbers are positive, or both are negative, the product is equal to the product of their absolute values.

For example:

$$(2)(6) = |2| \cdot |6| = 2 \cdot 6 = 12$$
$$(-2)(-6) = |-2| \cdot |-6| = 2 \cdot 6 = 12$$

II. If the numbers are one positive, the other negative, the product is equal to the opposite of the product of the absolute values.

For example:

$$(2)(-6) = -(|2| \cdot |-6|) = -(2 \cdot 6) = -12$$
$$(-5)(3) = -(|-5| \cdot |3|) = -(5 \cdot 3) = -15$$

As a consequence of these definitions, every positive number has two real square roots, one positive, the other negative.

Since $(-3)(-3) = 9$ and $(3)(3) = 9$, we write $\sqrt{9} = 3$ and $-\sqrt{9} = -3$. Note that *we do not write* $\sqrt{9} = \pm 3$, for then the symbol $\sqrt{9}$ would be ambiguous. Also note that $\sqrt{-9}$ cannot be a real number. Why?

14.14 EXERCISES

1. (a) Find the sum and the product of $1\frac{6}{11}$ and $2\frac{2}{5}$.
   (b) Find the sum and product of 1.5454 and 2.3999.
   (c) Find the sum and product of $1.54\dot{5}\dot{4}$ and $2.399\dot{9}$.
   (d) Explain the differences between the answers to part (b) and those to (a) and (c).
2. (a) Find $\sqrt{2}$ and $\sqrt{3}$ each correct to four decimal places.
   (b) Find a rational approximation to $\sqrt{2} + \sqrt{3}$ and $\sqrt{2} \cdot \sqrt{3}$, using the results of part (a).
   (c) Find $\sqrt{6}$ correct to four decimal places and check it with the result of $\sqrt{2} \cdot \sqrt{3}$, in part (b).
   (d) Show that $\sqrt{2} \cdot \sqrt{3} = \sqrt{2 \cdot 3}$ but $\sqrt{2} + \sqrt{3} \neq \sqrt{2 + 3}$.

3. Give the opposite of each of the following real numbers:

   (a) 5 (b) -6 (c) $2.3\dot{3}$
   (d) $-4.44\dot{4}$ (e) $-(-3)$ (f) -3
   (g) $-(-(-2))$ (h) $-\sqrt{3}$ (i) -14.421

4. Give the number which is the sum of each of the following, illustrating on a number line:

   (a) $2 + 5$ (b) $2 + (-5)$ (c) $-2 + 5$
   (d) $-2 + (-5)$ (e) $-\sqrt{2} + 3$ (f) $-\sqrt{2} + \sqrt{3}$
   (g) $-2 + (-\sqrt{3})$

5. Using the numbers 2, $-1\frac{1}{2}$, and $\sqrt{2}$ and any numbers to be associated with them, illustrate all the listed 10 properties of real numbers.

6. Find the multiplicative and additive inverse of each of the following:

   (a) 2 (b) -3 (c) $2.36\dot{3}\dot{6}$ (d) $-4.63\dot{6}\dot{3}$ (e) $\sqrt{2}$

7. Find the answer to each of the following:

   (a) $8 - (-2)$ (b) $6 - 12$
   (c) $\sqrt{2} - (-5\sqrt{2})$ (d) $0.22\dot{2} - 0.33\dot{3}$

8. By using rational approximations, place the following in monotonic increasing order: $\sqrt{3}$, $1\frac{8}{11}$; $1.722\dot{2}$; $1.7\dot{3}$; 1.7321; $1.72\dot{9}\dot{9}$.

9. Is $3 + \sqrt{3}$ a real number? If so, give a rational approximation to it.

10. (a) Represent $\frac{1}{101}$ as an infinite repeating decimal.
    (b) By inserting zeros in the representation of (a), form an infinite nonrepeating decimal.
    (c) Which result in (a) and (b) is the greater? Why?

14.15 REFERENCE QUESTIONS

1. Is every rational number associated with a periodic decimal? Is every periodic decimal associated with a rational number? For a simple method of expressing any periodic decimal in the form a/b, see

   Niven, Ivan. *Numbers: Rational and Irrational.* New York: Random House, 1961. pp. 30–31.

2. How is a nonrational number defined with reference to its decimal numeral? Often, the notion of "nested intervals" is used in defining irrational numbers. For a discussion of this, see

   National Council of Teachers of Mathematics. *The Growth of Mathematical Ideas, K–12* (24th yearbook). Washington, D.C.: NCTM, 1959. Pp. 52–57.

   In this connection, see also

   Adler, Irving. *The New Mathematics.* New York: John Day Co., 1958. Pp. 98–115.

15 MEASUREMENT OF GEOMETRIC FIGURES

IN THIS CHAPTER, *we return to a consideration of sets of points, or geometric figures. Such sets were discussed in Chapter 6, but at that time numbers were almost totally absent from the discussion; a rereading of Chapter 6 will reveal that the properties of geometric figures introduced at that time were independent of number concepts. It is the purpose of this chapter to inject numbers into a study of sets of points, thus enhancing our understanding of common geometric figures.*

15.1 MEASURING DISCRETE SETS

Consideration has been given earlier to sets and to the "size" of a set. This notion of size of a set is sometimes referred to as the "power" or the "manyness" of a set. In Figure 15–1, a set A is represented; furthermore, the elements of this set have

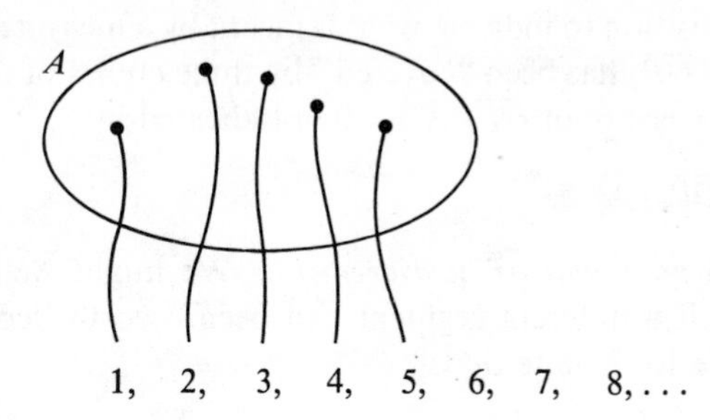

FIGURE 15–1

been placed into one-to-one correspondence with the ordered set of cardinal numbers. Since the last number in the set of counting numbers to be matched is the number 5, the size of the set A (or the "power" of the set) is said to be 5. What has been illustrated here, of course, is the familiar process of *counting* the elements of a set.

A set, such as set A of Figure 15–1, whose elements can be counted (regardless of whether the number of elements is finite or infinite) is called a *discrete set*. The cardinal number of such a set (which may be determined by counting) is a measure of the size of the set. For the set A of Figure 15–1, for example, we may write

$$m(A) = 5$$

to indicate that the measure of this discrete set is 5. This is equivalent to the more familiar statement that there are 5 elements in the set; we are here simply introducing the notion of measure of a set.

Not all sets are discrete sets. Consider, for example, a segment, which is a set of points. One cannot count the points of a segment as he counts the elements of a discrete set; between any two points of a segment is another point, and so the points cannot be matched with a subset of the cardinal numbers. A set (such as a segment) whose elements cannot be counted is called a *continuous set;* the measurement of such sets is the concern of the following sections.

15.2 MEASUREMENT OF SEGMENTS; CONGRUENCE

In Figure 15–2, two points, O and I, are indicated on the line l; and these two points of course determine a segment $\overline{OI}$ (see Chapter 6 for discussion of seg-

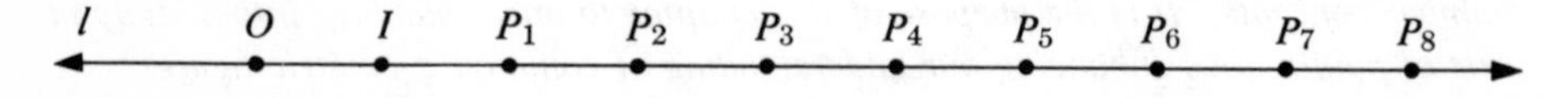

FIGURE 15–2

ments). Let us use this segment $\overline{OI}$ to "calibrate" the ray $\overrightarrow{OI}$ in the following manner. Lay off segment $\overline{IP_1}$ so that $\overline{IP_1}$ is a copy of $\overline{OI}$, and the intersection of segments $\overline{OI}$ and $\overline{IP_1}$ consists of precisely one point, in this case point I. Next, lay off a segment $\overline{P_1P_2}$ so that it too is a copy of $\overline{OI}$ and so that $\overline{IP_1} \cap \overline{P_1P_2} = P_1$. We are now in a position to indicate what is meant by a measure of a segment such as $\overline{OP_2}$. Note that $\overline{OP_2}$ has been "covered" by three copies of $\overline{OI}$. We may therefore say that the measure of $\overline{OP_2}$ is 3, often indicated by

$$m(\overline{OP_2}) = 3,$$

where $\overline{OI}$ is used as a *unit of measurement*. We might well have obtained a different measure if a different segment had been used to "cover" $\overline{OP_2}$. Again referring to Figure 15–2, note that:

$$m(\overline{OP_1}) = 2$$
$$m(\overline{P_1P_3}) = 2$$

That is, $\overline{OP_1}$ and $\overline{P_1P_3}$ have the *same measure*. We therefore say that $\overline{OP_1}$ and $\overline{P_1P_3}$ are *congruent segments*, indicated briefly as follows:

$$\overline{OP_1} \cong \overline{P_1P_3}$$

Generalizing upon the example of the congruent segments $\overline{OP_1}$ and $\overline{P_1P_3}$, we make the following definition.

DEFINITION: *Two* segments *are* congruent *if they have the same measure.*

From the preceding discussion, we see that a segment may be measured by means of another segment selected as a unit of measurement; in a sense, we may say that a segment is measured by "comparing" it to another segment. Furthermore, this notion of measuring segments has been used to define congruent segments.

Figure 15–3 is essentially the same as Figure 15–2. $\overline{OI}$ is again taken as the unit

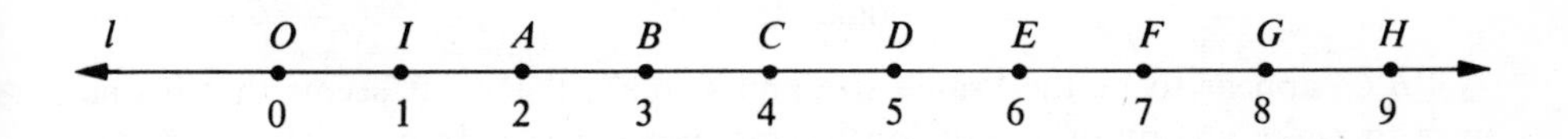

FIGURE 15–3

segment. The following observations should be checked against the figure:

$$m(\overline{OI}) = 1$$
$$m(\overline{OD}) = 5$$
$$m(\overline{AC}) = 2$$
$$m(\overline{CF}) = 3$$
$$\overline{AC} \cup \overline{CF} = \overline{AF}$$
$$\overline{AC} \cap \overline{CF} = \{C\}$$
$$m(\overline{AF}) = m(\overline{AC}) + m(\overline{CF}) = 2 + 3 = 5$$

From the last five of the preceding sentences, we make the following generalization:

> If a segment $\overline{RS}$ is the union of two segments $\overline{RX}$ and $\overline{XS}$, and $\overline{RX} \cap \overline{XS} = \{X\}$, then
>
> $$m(\overline{RS}) = m(\overline{RX}) + m(\overline{XS}).$$
>
> (Note that the wording of the statement assures us that $\overline{RX}$ and $\overline{XS}$ intersect in exactly one point, X.)

DEFINITION: *The measure of a segment $\overline{AF}$ is also called the* distance AF.

Note that the symbol AF (without any super bar) represents a number, the measure of the segment:

$$m(\overline{AF}) = AF$$

Having established a definition of congruent segments, we now turn to the problem of defining congruence in general. Let us make the initial approach by means of a specific example. In Figure 15–4, the two triangles, $\triangle ABC$ and

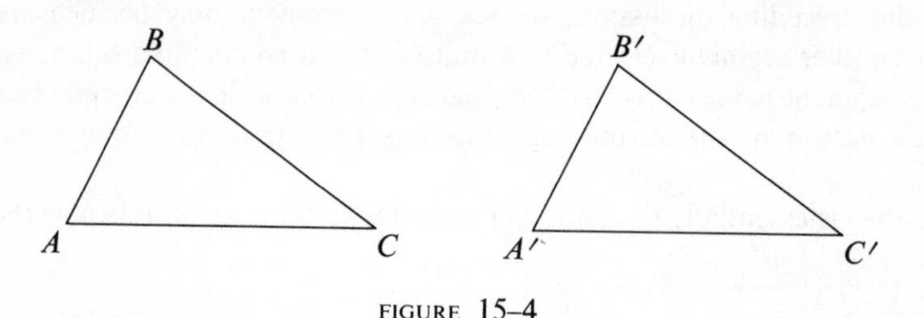

FIGURE 15–4

$\triangle A'B'C'$ appear to be the "same size and shape"; that is, it seems that if one were to make a copy of $\triangle ABC$ on tracing paper, he could make the copy "fit exactly" on $\triangle A'B'C'$. Such a process gives us a good intuitive feeling of what we want to mean by stating the two triangles under discussion are congruent. Let us now see if we can channel this intuition into a mathematical definition of congruence.

First, let us establish a one-to-one correspondence between the points of $\triangle ABC$ and the points of $\triangle A'B'C'$. Parts of this correspondence are suggested by Figure 15–5. Thus, points A and A' are made to correspond to each other, and this may

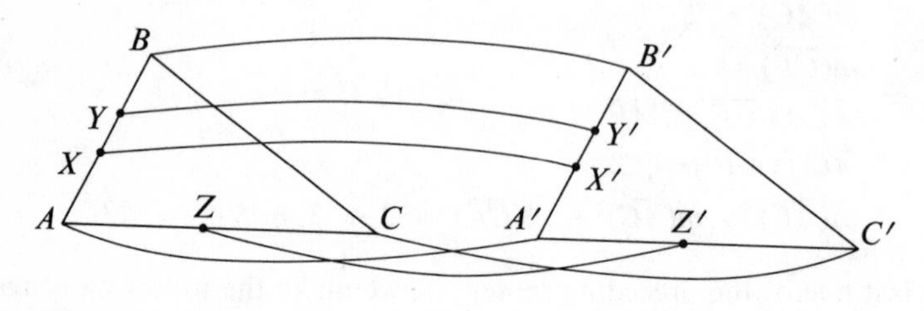

FIGURE 15–5

be indicated by writing "$A \leftrightarrow A'$." Using the same notation, we have:

$$B \leftrightarrow B'$$
$$C \leftrightarrow C'$$
$$X \leftrightarrow X'$$
$$Y \leftrightarrow Y'$$
$$Z \leftrightarrow Z'$$

Now, the points A and B of $\triangle ABC$ determine $\overline{AB}$. Their correspondents, A' and B' of $\triangle A'B'C'$ determine $\overline{A'B'}$. Therefore, we demand that the segments $\overline{AB}$ and $\overline{A'B'}$ be congruent. In fact, we make the same demand for all pairs of segments determined by pairs of corresponding points. Thus, we require that $\overline{XZ}$ be congruent to $\overline{X'Z'}$ since $X \leftrightarrow X'$ and $Z \leftrightarrow Z'$. (Note here that the segments are themselves not parts of the triangles.) In fact, this demand furnishes us with a definition of congruent triangles:

DEFINITION: *If a one-to-one correspondence can be set up between the points of one triangle and the points of another triangle so that the segment determined by any two points of one triangle is congruent to the segment determined by the corresponding points of the other triangle, then the* triangles *are said to be* congruent.

Thus, congruence for triangles is defined in terms of congruence for segments.

Why is it not enough to say simply that two triangles are congruent if a one-to-one correspondence can be established between the points of one and the points of the other? In order to answer this question, consider first the two segments $\overline{AB}$ and $\overline{CD}$ represented in Figure 15–6. The figure illustrates that a one-to-one

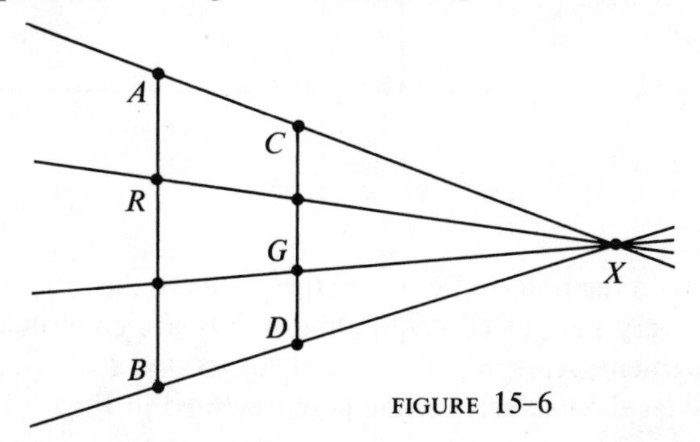

FIGURE 15–6

correspondence may be established between the points of the two segments. In the figure, X is the intersection of lines $\overleftrightarrow{AC}$ and $\overleftrightarrow{BD}$. To find the correspondent of R, determine the intersection of $\overleftrightarrow{RX}$ and $\overline{CD}$; thus, for any point of $\overline{AB}$, there is a matching point on $\overline{CD}$. To find the correspondent of G, determine the intersection of $\overleftrightarrow{GX}$ and $\overline{AB}$; thus, for any point on $\overline{CD}$, there is a matching point of $\overline{AB}$. However, $\overline{AB}$ and $\overline{CD}$ are not congruent segments; at least they need not be in order to establish a one-to-one correspondence. So we see that the notion of congruence involves something more than a one-to-one matching of points. Consider next the triangles $\triangle ABC$ and $\triangle DEF$ in Figure 15–7. We can certainly

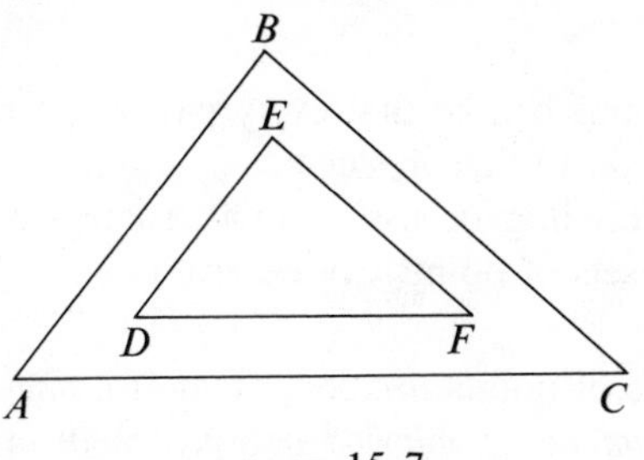

FIGURE 15–7

match the points of $\overline{AB}$ and $\overline{DE}$, the points of $\overline{BC}$ and $\overline{EF}$, and the points of $\overline{AC}$ and $\overline{DF}$ since such a matching can be established for any two segments; in this way, we can effect a one-to-one correspondence between the points of $\triangle ABC$ and the points of $\triangle DEF$. However, the triangles are not (at least need not be) congruent, and this is the reason that our definition of congruent triangles included something other than merely the notion of one-to-one correspondence.

The definition formulated for congruent triangles can be extended to include congruence of any two sets of points. The squares $ABCD$ and $A'B'C'D'$ (see Figure 15–8) will be said to be congruent if a one-to-one correspondence can be

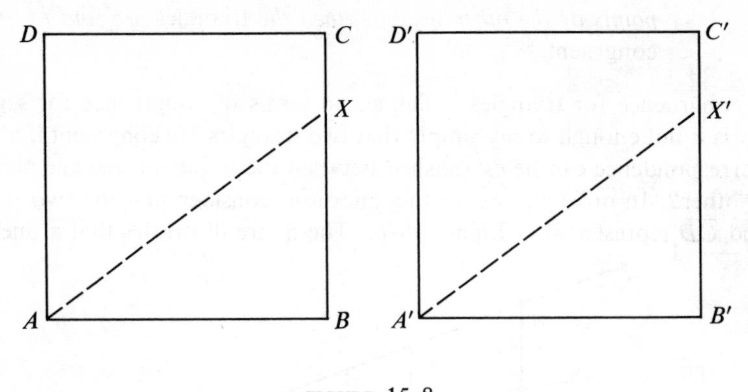

FIGURE 15–8

established between the points of one and the points of the other so that segments determined by every pair of corresponding points are congruent. Thus, if the squares are congruent, $A \leftrightarrow A'$, $X \leftrightarrow X'$, then $\overline{AX} \cong \overline{A'X'}$, etc.

Finally, consider the two sets of points represented in Figure 15–9. If the two

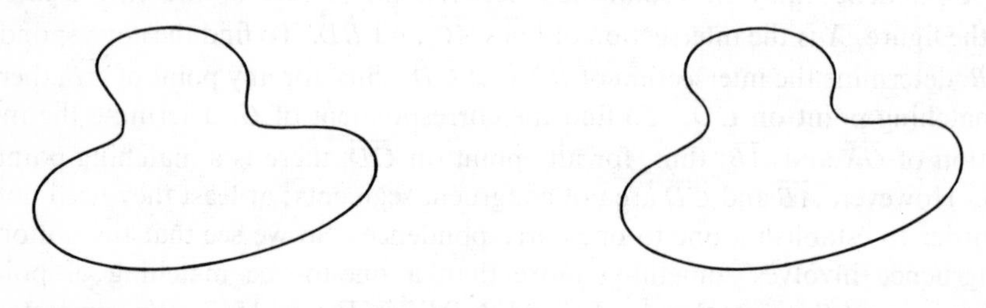

FIGURE 15–9

sets of points can be matched so that every pair of corresponding segments are congruent, the set is said to be congruent.

As a result of the preceding discussion an alternate way of stating the definition of congruence of two sets of points can be given:

DEFINITION: *Two* sets of points *are* congruent *if a one-to-one correspondence can be established between them in such a way that distances are preserved.*

Consideration of a number of examples should convince you that the definition of congruence formulated in this section is completely consistent with our intuitive notion that two congruent figures are essentially replicas of each other.

As we have seen, a segment may be measured by arbitrary selection of another segment as a unit of measurement. However, a statement such as "$m(\overline{AB}) = 3$" is virtually useless (from a utilitarian point of view) unless the unit of measurement is known. For this reason, certain units of measurement for the measurement of segments have been adopted as *standard units*. A familiar standard unit of this kind is the *inch*, and in Figure 15–10 this unit of measurement is shown. That is,

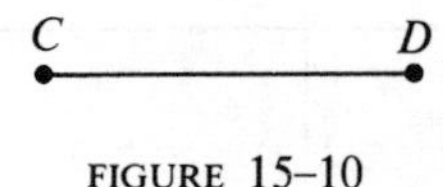

FIGURE 15–10

$m(\overline{CD}) = 1$, using an inch as the unit of measurement, or $\overline{CD}$ is a one-inch segment. Such a segment may be used then to find the measure of any segment "in inches" by using the process described in section 15.2. Other standard units are defined as follows:

> A segment with measurement of 12 inches has a measurement of 1 *foot*.
>
> A segment with measurement of 3 feet has a measurement of 1 *yard*.

The measurement of a segment is called *length*. To summarize the ideas concerning length, we consider the segment represented in Figure 15–11. In this case,

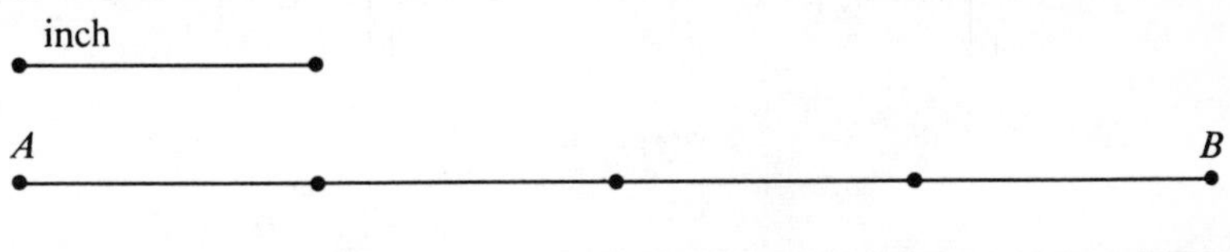

FIGURE 15–11

the unit of measurement, or the unit of length, is the inch. We see that the "coverage" is 4. That is, it takes 4 inch segments to "cover" $\overline{AB}$, and therefore the measure of $\overline{AB}$ is 4. (Note that a *measure* is a number.) On the other hand, "4 inches" is the *measurement* of $\overline{AB}$.

There are other standard units of length besides the inch, foot, and yard. For example, the mile is commonly used. And in the *metric system*, the *centimeter* is a standard unit of length; a centimeter segment is represented in Figure 15–12.

R S

FIGURE 15–12

Other units used in the metric system are defined as follows:

> A segment with a measurement of 10 centimeters has a measurement of 1 *decimeter*.
>
> A segment with a measurement of 10 decimeters has a measurement of 1 *meter*.

In building an intuitive notion of the theory of measure, we have written such sentences as "$m(\overline{AB}) = 4$." So far as the practical process of physical measurement is concerned, however, it is not possible to draw a physical representation of a segment that is exactly 4 inches long, for instance. In order to lend substance to this statement, consider the segment $\overline{CD}$ represented in Figure 15–13. In Figure

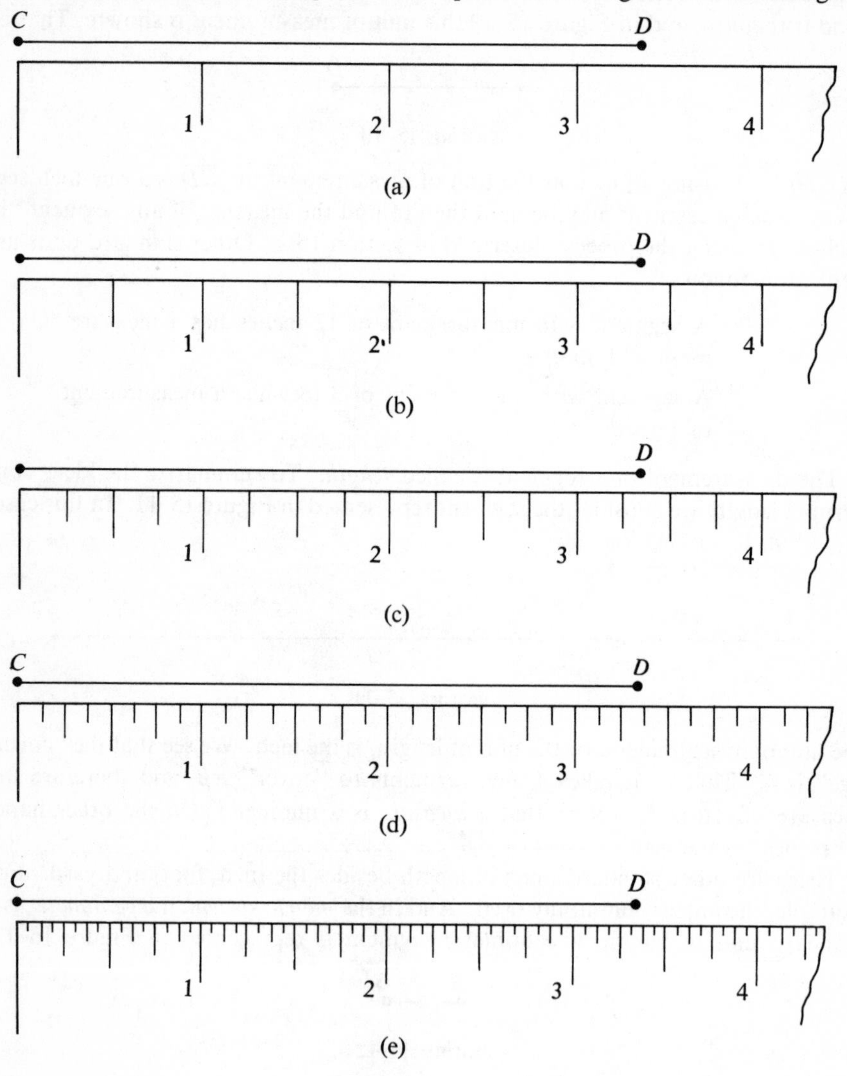

FIGURE 15–13

15–13(a), a "ruler" marked only in inches has been laid alongside $\overline{CD}$, and we see that the measurement of $\overline{CD}$ is 3 inches, to the nearest inch. In Figure 15–13(b), the ruler has been made more precise by marking every $\frac{1}{2}$ inch; this makes it visually clear that the measurement of $\overline{CD}$ is $3\frac{1}{2}$ inches, to the nearest half-inch.

Similarly, Figures 15–13(c), (d), and (e) show successive refinements of the ruler to show fourths of an inch, eighths of an inch, and sixteenths of an inch. From Figure 15–13(c), the measurement of $\overline{CD}$ is $3\frac{1}{4}$ inches, to the nearest fourth-inch. From Figure 15–13(d), the measurement of $\overline{CD}$ is $3\frac{3}{8}$ inches, to the nearest eighth-inch. And from Figure 15–13(e) the measurement of $\overline{CD}$ is $3\frac{5}{16}$ inches, to the nearest sixteenth inch.

To the naked eye, it may appear that $\overline{CD}$ is "exactly $3\frac{5}{16}$ inches in length." One is forced to admit, however, that the naked eye is not able to detect a difference of $\frac{1}{1,000,000}$ of an inch, for example. Therefore, to say that the length of a physical object is *exactly* $3\frac{5}{16}$ in. is not warranted. What we mean to say is simply that the measurement is $3\frac{5}{16}$ in. *to the nearest sixteenth inch.* If we could continue the refinement of the ruler, we would expect to get closer and closer approximations to the length of $\overline{CD}$, just as we did in Figures 15–13(a) through (e).

The preceding paragraph conveys, by means of a single instance, the meaning of the statement that "measurement is approximate, not exact." And certainly the way in which we use measurement in the everyday world corroborates this statement. For example, when one gives the distance between two towns as 10 miles, he certainly does not rule out the fact that the distance might be closer to 10 miles, 1 foot; he means that 10 is an approximate measure, correct to the nearest mile.

Here again the distinction between a geometric figure and its physical representation must be recalled. Mathematically, one may certainly conceive of a segment the measure of whose length is 4, exactly 4. In the practical art of drawing a physical representation, however, it must be conceded that we must settle for a representation whose length is *approximately* 4 inches.

15.6 PERIMETER AND CIRCUMFERENCE

The polygon represented in Figure 15–14 is the union of four segments (recall the definition of polygon in Chapter 6), and these segments are often referred to as "sides" of the polygon. Suppose the measurements of the sides $\overline{AB}$, $\overline{BC}$, $\overline{CD}$,

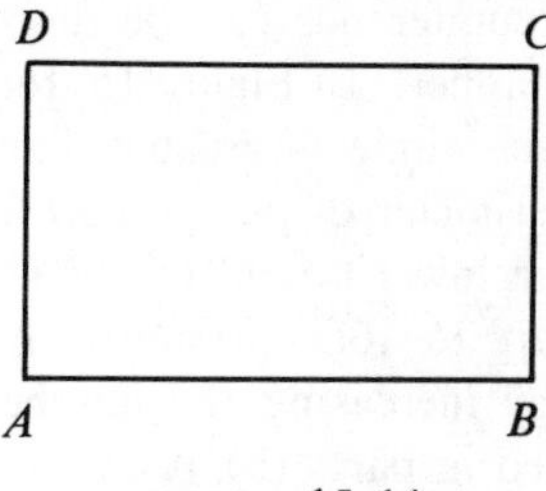

FIGURE 15–14

and $\overline{DA}$ are 5 inches, 3 inches, 5 inches, and 3 inches, respectively. The sum of the numbers 5, 3, 5, and 3 is 16; and 16 is said to be the measure of the *perimeter* of the polygon $ABCD$. That is, the measure of the perimeter of polygon $ABCD$ is

$$m(AB) + m(BC) + m(CD) + m(DA) = 5 + 3 + 5 + 3 = 16.$$

While 16 is the measure of the perimeter, the measurement is 16 inches. (Note that the perimeter is found by adding *numbers*, not "inches.") In general, the measure of the perimeter of a polygon is found by adding the measures of the segments whose union the polygon is. Thus, as another instance, the measure of the perimeter of the polygon represented in Figure 15–15 is 30, where the unit of measurement is one foot; the measurement of the perimeter is 30 feet.

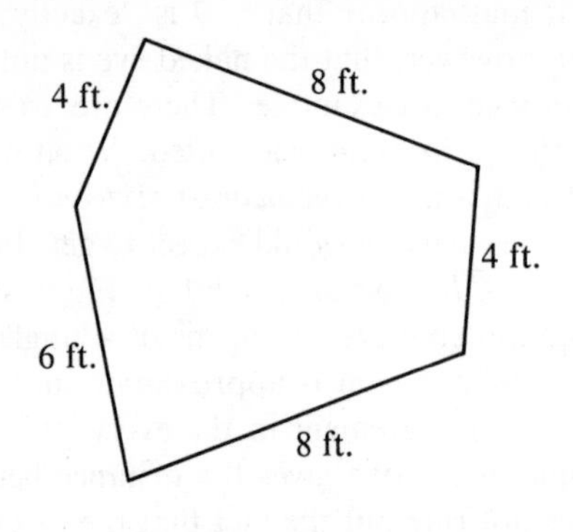

FIGURE 15–15

In general, if $a, b, c, \ldots$ represent the measures of the sides of a polygon, we may write a *formula* for the perimeter P as:

Perimeter of a polygon

$$P = a + b + c + \cdots$$

The concept of perimeter, as discussed in the preceding paragraph, is of course not applicable to every simple closed curve. In the case of a circle, for instance, one cannot add the measures of the "sides" since a circle is not the union of segments. Certainly, however, it should be possible to determine the "distance around" a circle; with a physical representation of a circle, a tape measure might be used to obtain an approximation to the desired number, called the *circumference* of the circle. (The word "perimeter" is reserved for polygons.) Mathematically, the notion of circumference can be more closely related to that of perimeter in the following manner. In Figure 15–16(a), it seems intuitively clear that the circumference of the circle is greater than the perimeter of polygon $ABCD$, and less than the perimeter of polygon $EFGH$; thus perimeters may be used to place an upper and a lower bound on the circumference of a circle. Of course, the polygons in Figure 15–16(a) do not seem to "fit" the circle closely; a closer fit can be obtained by increasing the number of sides of the polygons. Such an increase is illustrated in parts (b), (c), and (d) of Figure 15–16. Thus, Figure 15–16(d) suggests the possibility of two numbers, differing by a "small amount," between which the circumference must lie; in this way an approximation to the circumference can be made. The "small amount" by which the two perimeters differ can be made as small as desired by increasing sufficiently the number of the sides of the polygons. (The two polygons, incidentally, are said to be "inscribed in" the circle and "circumscribed about" the circle.)

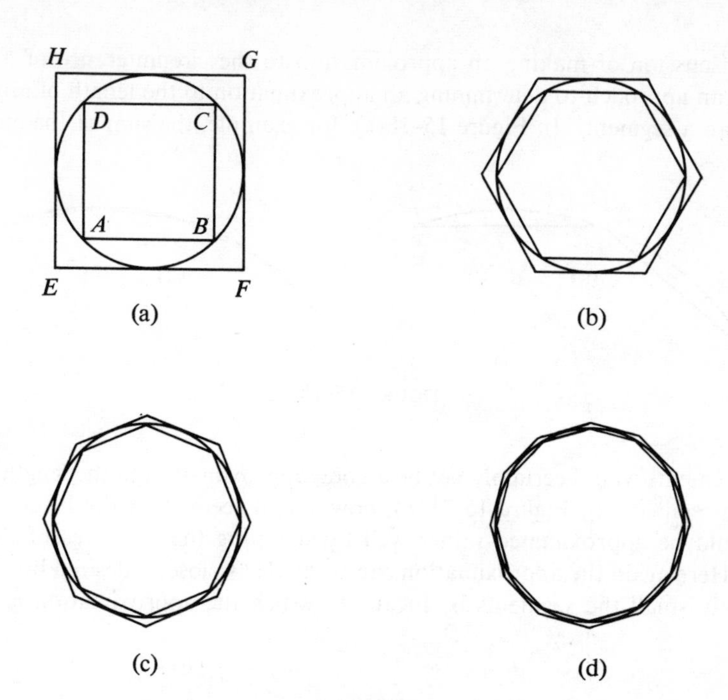

FIGURE 15–16

It can be proved that the circumference C of a circle is equal to the product $2\pi r$, or πd, where r is the measure of the *radius* of the circle and d is the measure of the *diameter* of the circle, that is, $d = 2r$ (see Figure 15–17) and π represents

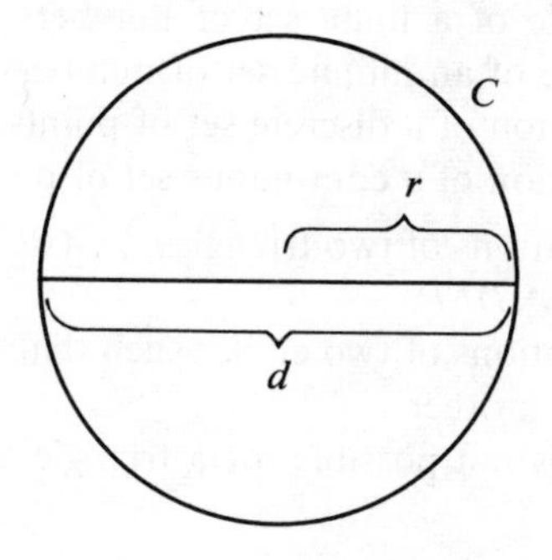

FIGURE 15–17

an infinite nonrepeating decimal 3.14159 . . . . Usually, it is sufficient to use $\pi \approx 3.14$. Thus:

Circumference of a circle
$C = 2\pi r = \pi d$

(See section 16.1.)

The discussion of making an approximation to the circumference of a circle suggests an approach to determining an approximation to the length of any path other than a segment. In Figure 15–18(a), for example, the sum of the measure

FIGURE 15–18

of the segments would certainly not be a good approximation to the length of the path represented. In Figure 15–18(b), however, it seems that the length of the path could be approximated rather well by summing the measures of the segments. Here again the approximation can be made as close as desired by making sufficiently small the segments by means of which the approximation is made.

15.7 EXERCISES

1. (a) How is a discrete set measured?
   (b) Is the measure of a discrete set exact?
   (c) Give an example of a finite set of numbers which is discrete.
   (d) Give an example of an infinite set of numbers which is discrete.
   (e) Give an illustration of a discrete set of points.
   (f) Give an illustration of a continuous set of points.
2. (a) Draw representations of two triangles, $\triangle ABC$ and $\triangle DEF$, such that $\triangle ABC \cong \triangle DEF$.
   (b) Draw representations of two circles such that the two circles are congruent to each other.
   (c) Explain why it is not possible for a triangle to be congruent to a circle.
3. 

   (a) Determine $m(\overline{AB})$ if segment U is used as the unit measurement.
   (b) Determine $m(\overline{AB})$ if segment V is used as the unit measurement.
   (c) Use an ordinary ruler to determine the length of $\overline{AB}$ to the nearest inch.

(d) Determine the length of $\overline{AB}$ to the nearest half-inch.
(e) Determine the length of $\overline{AB}$ to the nearest sixteenth-inch.

4. (a) In order to measure a segment, what kind of geometric figure is used as a unit of measurement?
   (b) Explain why a point cannot be used as a unit of measurement in measuring a segment.

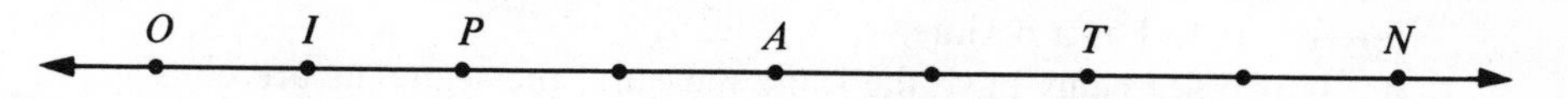

5. In the representation of line $\overleftrightarrow{ON}$ above, if $\overline{OI}$ is used as the unit of measurement,
   (a) $m(\overline{OA})$ =
   (b) $m(\overline{OI})$ =
   (c) $m(\overline{OP})$ =
   (d) $m(\overline{OT})$ =
   (e) $m(ON)$ =
   (f) determine a point X such that $m(\overline{OX}) = 1.5$.
   (g) determine a point Y such that $m(\overline{OY}) = 2.25$.

6. Explain briefly why it is not possible to draw a physical representation of a segment exactly one inch in length.

7. (a) If the measurement of $\overline{CD}$ is 24 inches, determine its measurement in feet, in yards, and in centimeters. 1 inch $\approx$ 2.54 cm.
   (b) If the measurement of $\overline{RS}$ is 3 meters, determine its measurement in decimeters, and in centimeters.
   (c) Noting that a kilometer is 1000 meters, what is the relationship between a kilometer and a mile?

8. (a) If a polygon has four sides, each of which has a measurement of $7\frac{1}{2}$ feet, what is the perimeter of the polygon?
   (b) If the perimeter of a square is 15 inches, what is the measurement of any one side of the square?
   (c) If a rectangle has two sides each measuring 10 feet, and two sides each measuring 5 feet, what is the perimeter of the rectangle?
   (d) The formula "$p = 2a + 2b$" is often given for finding the perimeter of a rectangle. Explain the meaning of this formula.
   (e) Criticize the following "definition": The perimeter of a polygon is the sum of the sides of the polygon.

9. Draw a circle; then, by inscribing a square in the circle, and circumscribing a square about the circle, determine a lower and upper bound for the circumference of the circle.

10. Using the fact that π is approximately 3.14,
    (a) determine the circumference of the circle in problem 9.
    (b) determine the circumference of a circle with radius 10 inches.
    (c) determine the circumference of a circle with diameter 10 inches.

11. Determine whether each of the following statements is true or false.
   (a) If two segments are congruent, then they have the same measure (for any specified unit of measurement).
   (b) If $\overline{AB} \cong \overline{AC}$, then B and C must name the same point.
   (c) To determine the length of a segment, any other segment may be selected as the unit of measurement.
   (d) A measure is a number.
   (e) Any path has a perimeter.
   (f) If two segments have the same measure, the segments are congruent.

15.8 MEASUREMENT OF ANGLES

In measuring a segment, another segment—called the unit of measurement—was selected, and the number of units needed to "cover" the segment was determined. Much the same sort of procedure is followed in measuring an angle, the unit of measurement itself being an angle in this case. To illustrate the process, consider the angle $\angle ABC$ represented in Figure 15–19. $\angle CBD$ is a copy of $\angle ABC$, and

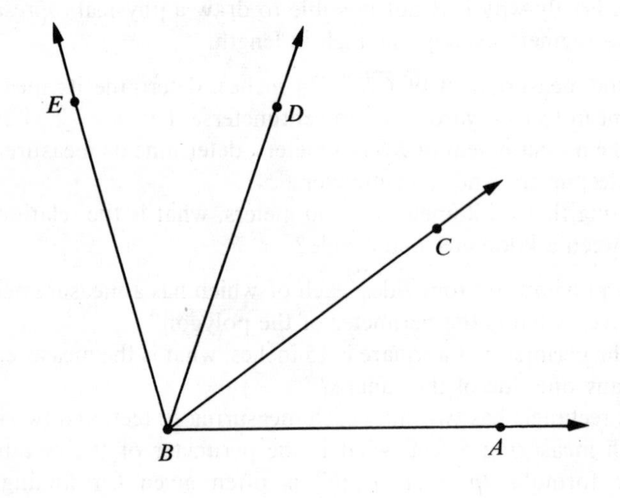

FIGURE 15–19

the intersection of the two angles is $\overrightarrow{BC}$. Likewise, $\angle DBE$ is a copy of $\angle ABC$, and $\angle CBD \cap \angle DBE = \overrightarrow{BD}$. In this way, we may think of $\angle ABE$ and its interior as being "covered" by the 3 copies of $\angle ABC$ and their interiors, when the angles are placed in a specified way. Therefore, we may say

$$m(\angle ABE) = 3$$

when $\angle ABC$ is used as the *unit of measurement*. The similarity between this process and that of measuring a segment is immediately apparent. Continuing with $\angle ABC$ as the unit of measurement, we note the following:

$$m(\angle ABD) = 2$$
$$m(\angle CBE) = 2$$

Thus, $\angle ABD$ and $\angle CBE$ have the same measure; hence, they are said to be *congruent angles.* We have, in fact, the following definition.

DEFINITION: *Two* angles *are* congruent *if they have the same measure.*

The principle is predicated, of course, upon the assumption that the two measures are determined by the same unit of measurement.

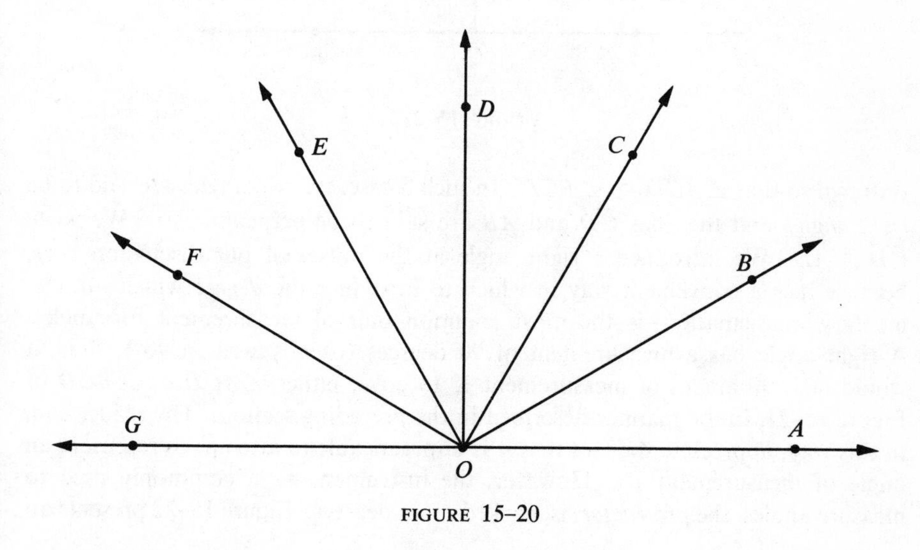

FIGURE 15–20

In Figure 15–20, if $\angle AOB$ is taken as the unit of measurement, the following observations may be made:

$$m(\angle AOC) = 2$$
$$m(\angle COF) = 3$$
$$m(\angle AOF) = 5$$
$$m(\angle AOA) = 0$$

(Note that we have here a "zero" angle; that is, the "two rays" of the angle are coincident.)

$$m(\angle AOG) = 6$$

(As a set of points, $\angle AOG$ is the same as a line; however, it may also be considered as a "straight angle.")

As in the case of measurement of length, it is desirable to have standard units for measurement of angles. Suppose C is a point on $\overleftrightarrow{AB}$ (see Figure 15–21), and $\overrightarrow{CD}$

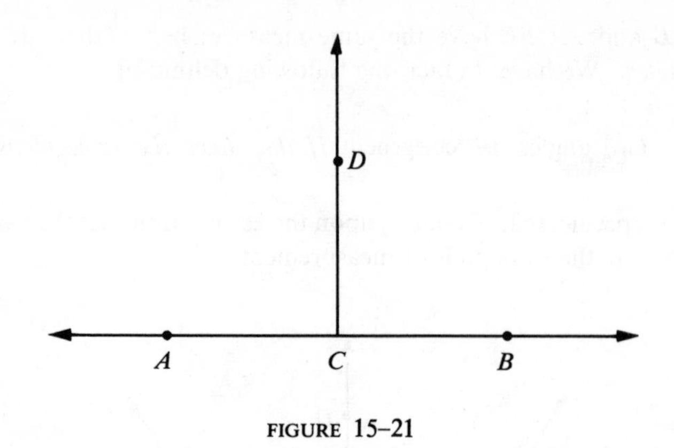

FIGURE 15–21

is drawn so that $\angle ACD \cong \angle BCD$. In such a case, the two angles are said to be *right angles* and the lines $\overleftrightarrow{CD}$ and $\overleftrightarrow{AB}$ are said to be perpendicular. We write $\overleftrightarrow{CD} \perp \overleftrightarrow{AB}$. We introduce a right angle at the outset of our discussion here, because it is a convenient way in which to introduce the *degree* which—in elementary mathematics—is the most common unit of measurement for angles. A right angle has a measurement of 90 degrees (usually written 90°); thus, it would take 90 angles of measurement 1° to cover either $\angle ACD$ or $\angle BCD$ of Figure 15–21, in the manner described in the preceding section. The reader can, in this way, appreciate the fact that it is impracticable to attempt to represent an angle of measurement 1°. However, the instrument most commonly used to measure angles, the *protractor*, is marked off in degrees. Figure 15–22 presents an

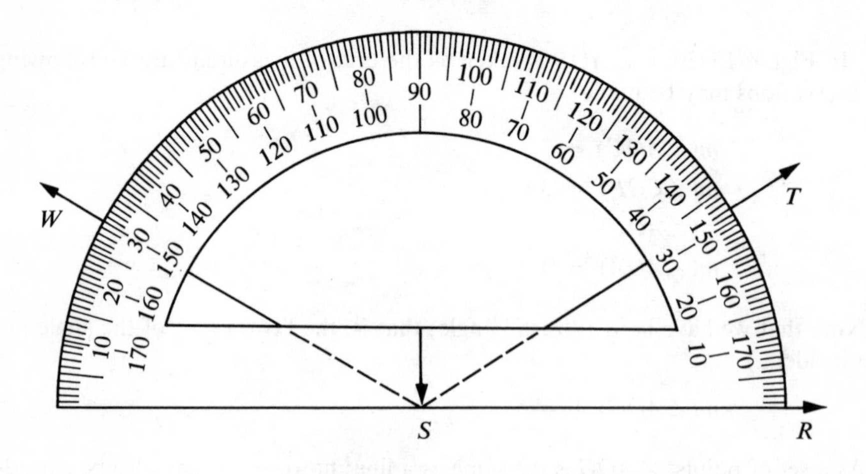

FIGURE 15–22

illustration of a protractor. According to the figure, if we read the lower scale, the following appear to be roughly true:

$$m(\angle RST) = 32$$
$$m(\angle RSW) = 150$$

The degree symbol has been omitted in the two preceding sentences since it is understood that the degree is the unit of measurement.

An angle whose degree measurement is between 0 and 90 degrees is called an *acute angle;* thus, in Figure 15–23, $\angle FGH$ is an acute angle. An angle whose

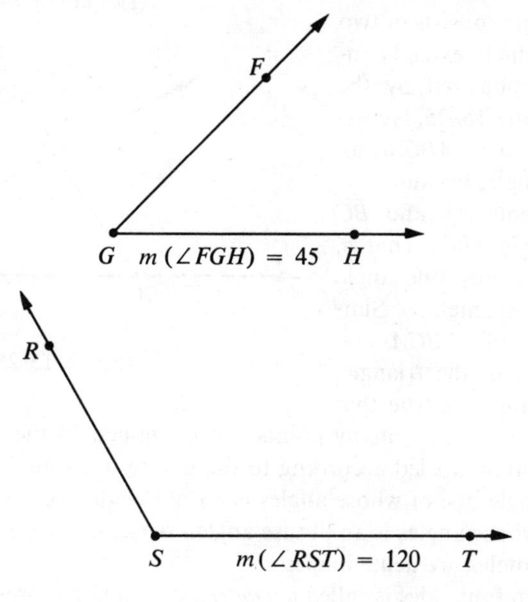

FIGURE 15–23

measurement is between 90 and 180 degrees is called an *obtuse angle;* hence in Figure 15–23, $\angle RST$ is an obtuse angle. In Chapter 6, it was noted that two opposite rays may also be considered as forming an angle; the measurement of such an angle is 180°, and it is called a *straight angle.* Furthermore, one may specify an angle of measurement 0°; in such an angle the "two" rays actually coincide.

There are other standard units of measurement for angular measurement; but the degree is the only one commonly used at the elementary level and is the only one we shall consider here. As was the case with measurement of segments (and indeed as is the case with measurement of any continuous set), measurement of an angle is approximate, not exact. Thus, to say that the measurement of an angle is 45° is to say that it is closer to 45 degrees than to any other whole number of degrees. We could not hope, for example, with our available measuring devices to distinguish between a representation of a 45° angle and a representation of a 45.0001° angle.

In Figure 15–24, a *triangle* (polygon with three sides) is represented. We often speak not only of the sides of a triangle but also of the angles of the triangle. What is meant by this? Consider the angle ABC. Triangle ABC obviously does not "contain" this angle, for the angle consists of two rays, each of which extends indefinitely, as emphasized by the extensions in Figure 15–25. Nevertheless, we speak of $\angle ABC$ as an angle of the triangle, because certainly the segments $\overline{AB}$ and $\overline{BC}$ *determine* the angle ABC. That is, there is one and only one angle containing these segments. Similarly, we speak of $\angle BCA$ and $\angle CAB$ as angles of the triangle, even though again it is true that these angles include many, many points not contained in the triangle.

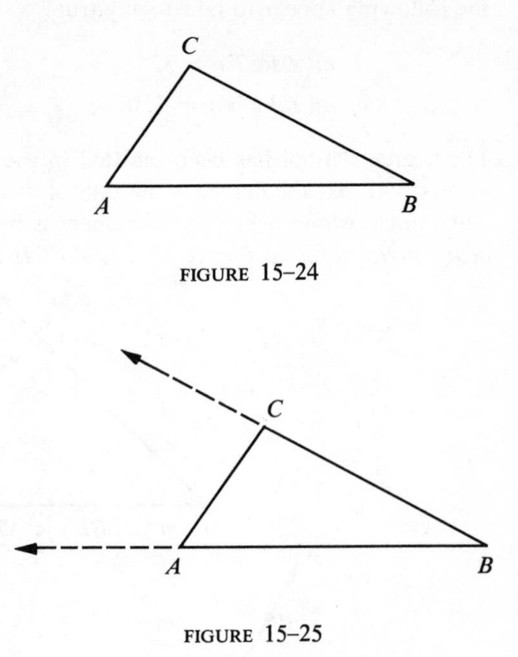

FIGURE 15–24

FIGURE 15–25

A triangle is often labeled according to the nature of its angles. Thus, a *right triangle* is a triangle one of whose angles is a right angle. An *obtuse triangle* is a triangle one of whose angles is an obtuse angle. An *acute triangle* is a triangle all three of whose angles are acute angles.

A polygon with four sides is called a *quadrilateral*, and a representation of such a polygon is shown in Figure 15–26. Here, in a manner precisely like that used in

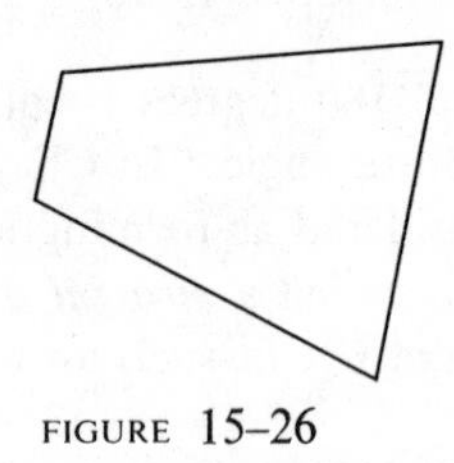

FIGURE 15–26

discussion of the triangle, we speak of the "angles of the quadrilateral," and clearly there are four of them. If the four angles of a quadrilateral are all right angles, the quadrilateral is called a *rectangle* (see Figure 15–27).

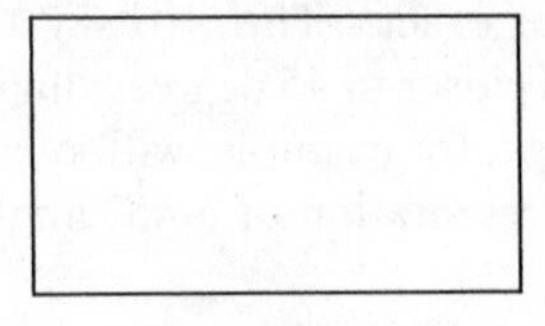

FIGURE 15–27

A *square* (see Figure 15–28) is a rectangle all of whose sides have the same measure; thus, any two sides of a square are congruent.

FIGURE 15–28

Other polygons also have special names. As examples, a polygon with five sides is a *pentagon*, a polygon with six sides is a *hexagon*, and a polygon with eight sides is an *octagon*. If the sides and angles of a polygon all have the same measure, then the polygon is called a *regular polygon*. Thus, a regular hexagon, for instance, is a polygon with six sides, any two of which are congruent and all angles of which have the same measure; that is, any two angles of a regular polygon are congruent.

15.11 MEASUREMENT OF REGIONS; AREA

It would be fruitless to attempt to cover the square region $ABCD$ of Figure 15–29 with either segments or angles. To measure such a region (and it must be emphasized that we are measuring the region, not the square) we select another region as the unit of measurement. It is most convenient to choose another square region as the unit of measurement. In Figure 15–29 then, the indication is that square region $ABCD$ can be covered by the regions of 4 squares, each of which is congruent to square $GHKL$. Thus, $m(\text{region } ABCD) = 4$ if region $GHKL$ is used as the unit of measurement. Here each of the sides of square $GHKL$ has a measurement of 1 inch, the region $GHKL$ is called a *square inch*, and we say that the surface measurement of square $ABCD$ is 4 square inches. The square inch is a standard unit for measurement of a region; one might also use a *square foot*, a *square yard*, a *square mile*, etc. The measurement of a region is called *area* of the region; thus, in the example illustrated by Figure 15–29, the area of square region $ABCD$ is 4 square inches.

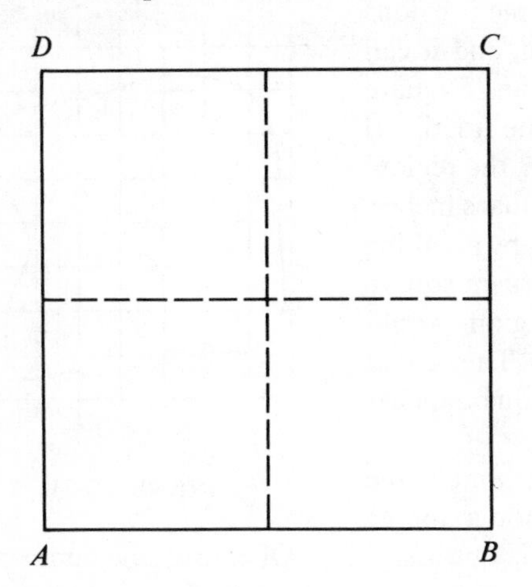

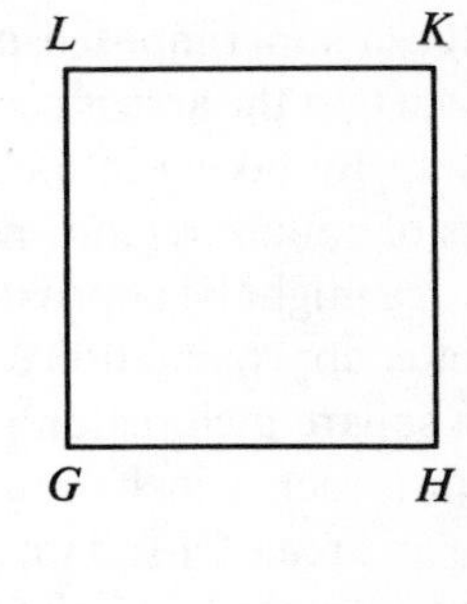

FIGURE 15–29

A definite pattern begins to emerge here. To measure a segment, another segment was chosen as the unit of measurement. To measure an angle, another angle was chosen as the unit of measurement. And now in this section in order to measure a region, another region was selected as the unit of measurement. Of course, such a pattern is cast by the very way in which we originally described the measuring process. It would, for example, be impossible to "cover a region" by use of segments just as it would be impossible to cover a segment by use of points. Although any region might be chosen as a unit of measurement in determining area, it is customary to choose a square region even if the region being measured is not itself a square. For instance, Figure 15–30 shows a rectangular region which

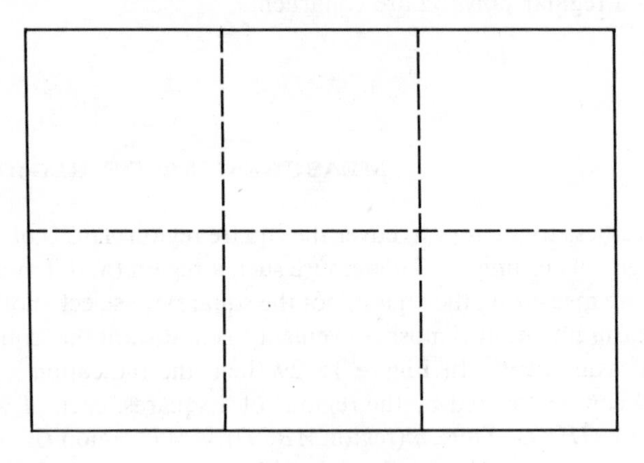

FIGURE 15–30

is covered by six square inches; that is, the area of this rectangular region is 6 square inches.

Indeed a square region may be used to measure the area of any region at all, whether or not it is polygonal. Consider the region represented in Figure 15–31. Here imagine that a "grid" of square inch regions has been superimposed over the region, and it can be seen that the area is certainly more than 25 square inches. By taking into consideration the fractional parts of square regions needed to cover the region, the area might be approximated as 36 square inches. A better approximation can be obtained by breaking each square inch region into four congruent square regions, each $\frac{1}{2}$ inch on a side. Such regions would have an area of $\frac{1}{4}$ square inch. (Why?) They could then be counted, and the number of $\frac{1}{4}$ square inches recorded.

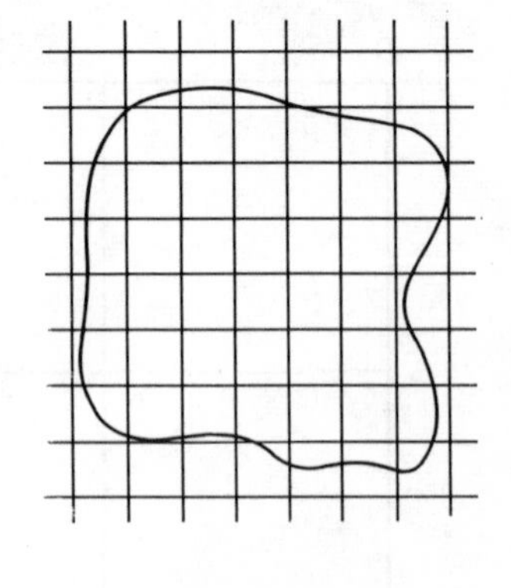

FIGURE 15–31

From the preceding discussion, we may make the basic assumption that to any plane region a unique number, called the *area* of the region, may be assigned. (Of course, the number is unique only for a specified unit of measurement; if the unit of measurement is changed, the number will not be the same as before.) Formulas are available for determining the area of common plane regions. Some of these formulas are listed below:

Area of a rectangle

$$A = bh$$

where A represents the measure of the area of a rectangle, and b and h represent the measures of two adjacent sides.

EXAMPLE 1. Determine the area of a rectangle whose sides have measurements of 5 feet, 7 feet, 5 feet, and 7 feet.

Solution: Here 5 and 7 are the measures of two adjacent sides. Hence

$$A = 5 \cdot 7 = 35.$$

Thus, the measurement of the area of the rectangle is 35 square feet.

Area of a square

$$A = s^2$$

where s represents the measure of a side of the square. (This formula is often used although there is no need for a special one since a square is indeed a rectangle.)

EXAMPLE 2. Given a square measuring 1 foot on each side (that is, a square foot), what is its area in square inches?

Solution: Here, $s = 12$ since each side has a measurement of 12 inches. Thus,

$$A = 12 \cdot 12 = 144.$$

Therefore, an area of one square foot is essentially the same as an area of 144 square inches.

Area of a triangle

$$A = \frac{1}{2}bh$$

where b represents the measure of the *base* and h represents the measure of the *altitude* (see Figure 15.32).

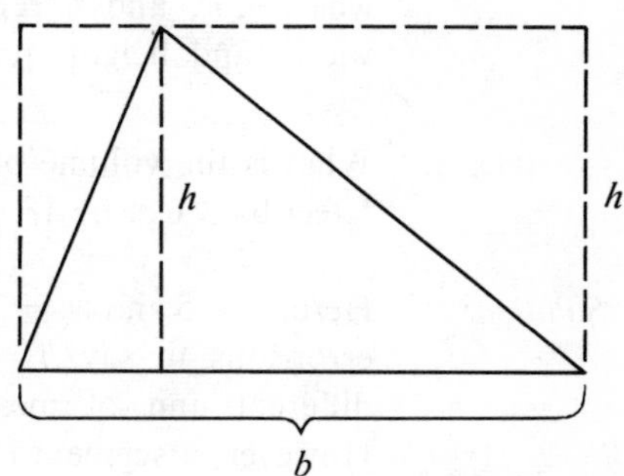

FIGURE 15–32

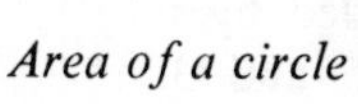

Area of a circle

$$A = \pi r^2$$

where $\pi \approx 3.14$ and r represents the measure of the radius.

Consider the problem of measuring the region enclosed by a rectangular box (see Figure 15–33(a)). Such a problem requires a new kind of unit of measurement

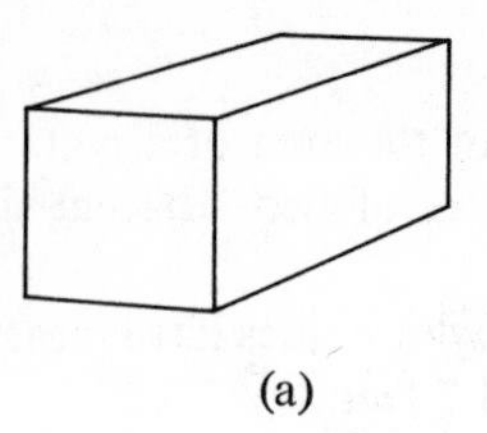

(a)

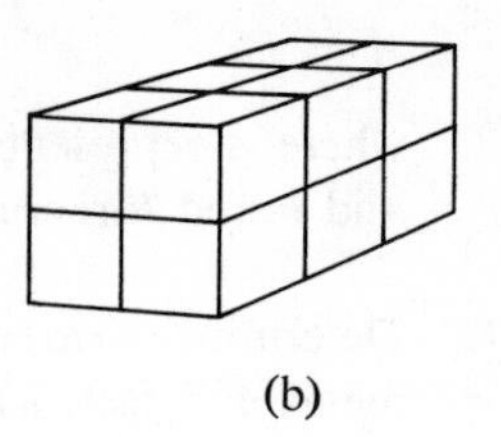

(b)

FIGURE 15–33

since it is patently impossible to "fill" a box with segments or squares. It is customary to choose a cube as a unit of measurement in this case. Such a choice is consistent with earlier choices: to measure a segment, another segment was used; to measure an angle, another angle was used; and to measure a region, another region was used. Thus, to measure a three-dimensional figure, another three-dimensional figure is used. Figure 15–33(b) illustrates what might happen if the rectangular box above were filled with cubes each of which measures one inch on every edge. From the figure it is clear that the box contains 12 cubes—2 "layers" of 6 cubes each. Thus, we say that the measurement of the *volume* of the rectangular box is 12 *cubic inches*. Obviously, if one were measuring some kind of container much larger than the one illustrated, he might use a *cubic foot*, or a *cubic yard*, or some other larger standard unit of measurement for volume.

The geometric figure of which Figures 15–33(a) and (b) are representations is frequently called a *rectangular solid*. The volume of a rectangular solid may be obtained by use of the following formula:

Volume of a rectangular solid

$$V = lwh$$

where l, w, and h represent the measures of the length, width, and height, respectively, of the rectangular solid.

EXAMPLE 3. What is the volume of a rectangular solid which measures 5 feet by 3 feet by 18 inches?

Solution: Here, $l = 5$ and $w = 3$. We note, however, that it would be erroneous to say $h = 18$ since the 18 was yielded by a different unit of measurement than were the 5 and 3. However, a segment measuring 18 inches also measures $1\frac{1}{2}$ feet. Hence, $h = 1\frac{1}{2}$.

$$V = 5 \cdot 3 \cdot 1\tfrac{1}{2} = 22\tfrac{1}{2}$$

Therefore, the volume of the rectangular solid is $22\frac{1}{2}$ cubic feet.

(Note that the volume might also have been expressed in cubic inches by expressing 5 feet as 60 inches, and 3 feet as 36 inches. Then $V = 60 \cdot 36 \cdot 18$.)

Paralleling our assumption concerning area of regions, we shall assume that to any "solid" (or three-dimensional) figure there is assigned a unique number called *volume*. We discussed above a formula for determining volume of a rectangular solid. Formulas are also available for determining volume of any common space figure. A few of these are listed below for reference:

Volume of a cube

$$V = s^3$$

where s is the measure of any one edge of the cube. (This formula is often used although there is no need for a special formula since a cube is indeed a rectangular solid.)

Volume of a sphere

$$V = \frac{4}{3}\pi r^3$$

where r is the measure of the radius of the sphere and $\pi \approx 3.14$.

Volume of a cylinder

$$V = Bh$$

where B represents the area of the base of the cylinder, and h is the measure of the height of the cylinder (see Figure 15–34).

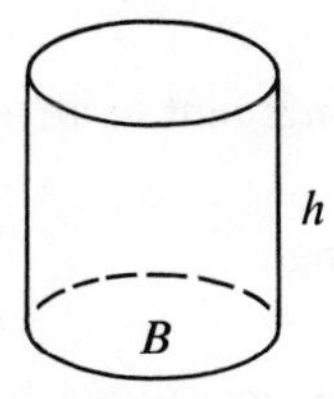

FIGURE 15–34

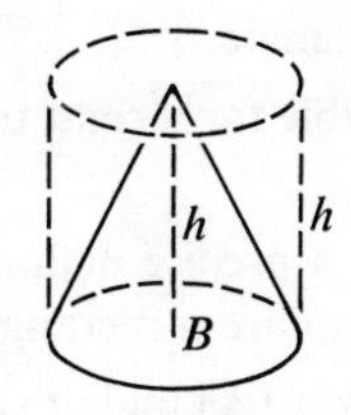

FIGURE 15–35

Volume of a cone

$$V = \frac{Bh}{3}$$

where B represents the area of the base, and h is the measure of the altitude (see Figure 15–35).

15.13 EXERCISES

1. An approximate representation of an angle of any specified measurement can be drawn by use of a protractor. Use a protractor to draw representations of the following:
   (a) $\angle ABC$ whose measurement is 30°
   (b) $\angle DEF$ whose measurement is 150°
   (c) $\angle GHK$ whose measurement is 125°
   (d) $\angle MNR$ whose measurement is 90°
   (e) $\angle TUV$ whose measurement is 5°
   (f) $\angle WXY$ whose measurement is 60°
2. Which of the angles in Problem 1 are acute? Which are obtuse? Which are right angles?
3. Would it be sensible to attempt to use a protractor to represent an angle of 45.72°? Explain.
4. If the measurement of $\angle ABC$ is 60° and the measurement of $\angle DEF$ is 60°, what is the relationship between these angles? Of what general statement is this an instance?
5. If two lines intersect in such a way as to form a right angle, the lines are said to be *perpendicular*.
   (a) If one is working in a single plane, how many lines are perpendicular to a given line at a given point of the line?
   (b) In space, how many lines are perpendicular to a given line at a given point of the line?
6. (a) Draw three noncollinear points, R, S, and T.
   (b) Draw segments $\overline{RS}$, $\overline{ST}$, and $\overline{TR}$, thus obtaining a representation of triangle RST.
   (c) Is $\angle RST$ a subset of $\triangle RST$? Explain.
7. Draw a representation of a right triangle, an acute triangle, and an obtuse triangle.
8. Is it possible for a right triangle to be congruent to an acute triangle? Explain.
9. (a) State a precise definition of a rectangle.
   (b) Is a square a rectangle? Explain.
10. (a) Draw a rectangle two of whose sides measure 6 inches and two of whose sides measure 3 inches.
    (b) How many square inches are required to "cover" the rectangular region determined by this rectangle?
    (c) A formula for the area of a rectangular region is often given as "$A = lw$," where A represents the measure of the area, l represents the measure of a side, and w represents the measure of an adjacent side. What does this formula say?
    (d) Show that the above formula is applicable to a rectangle which measures 6 inches by $3\frac{1}{2}$ inches.

(e) Use the formula to find the area of a rectangle measuring $8\frac{1}{2}$ inches by $10\frac{1}{4}$ inches.

11. (a) If the area of a region is 36 square feet, what is its measurement in square yards?
    (b) If the area of a region is 5 square feet, what is its measurement in square inches?

12. (a) Criticize this statement: The area of a certain region is 12 inches.
    (b) Is the area of a rectangle zero? Explain.

13. (a) Use compasses to draw a representation of a circle with a radius of 6 inches.
    (b) Make a "grid" of square inches and estimate the area of the circle in (a).
    (c) Remember that the area of a circle is given by the product πr^2 (where $\pi \approx 3.14$). Compute the area of the circle, and compare with the approximation in part (b).

14. (a) What is the volume of a rectangular solid which is 10 inches long, 6 inches wide, and 4 inches high?
    (b) Explain the meaning of the formula $V = lwh$, for determining the volume of a rectangular solid.
    (c) Use the formula to determine the volume of a rectangular solid which measures 2.5 feet by 5.1 feet by 4.3 feet.

15. (a) Determine the area of a triangle whose base measures 5 inches and whose altitude measures 4 inches.
    (b) Draw a sketch of the triangle. Then show how another triangle congruent to it may be used to form a *parallelogram*. What is the area of the parallelogram?

16. (a) Using 3.14 as an approximation for π, determine the area of a circle whose radius is 10 inches.
    (b) Determine the area of a circle whose radius is 20 inches.
    (c) How do the areas in (a) and (b) compare?
    (d) If the radius of a circle is doubled, how is the area affected?

17. (a) Determine the volume of a cube each of whose edges measures 2 feet.
    (b) Determine the volume of a cube each of whose edges measures 4 feet.
    (c) How do the volumes in (a) and (b) compare?
    (d) If the edge of a cube is doubled, how is the volume affected?

18. Determine the volume of a sphere whose radius is 8 feet.

19. How long must the edge of a cube be if the volume is to be 27 cubic yards? Will doubling the edge double the volume?

20. (a) Determine the volume of a cone which has a height of 10 inches and whose base is a circle with radius 4 inches.
    (b) Determine the volume of a cylinder which has a height of 10 inches and whose base is a circle with radius 4 inches.
    (c) Compare the volumes of (a) and (b).

15.14 REFERENCE QUESTIONS

1. How does one construct line segments whose lengths cannot be measured exactly by ordinary whole numbers and fractions? For an answer to this question, and a general discussion of linear measurement, see

   Botts, Truman. "Linear Measurement and Imagination," *The Arithmetic Teacher*, 9: 376–382; 1962.

2. Why is the area of a rectangle found by multiplying the length by the width? For a rather rigorous mathematical discussion of this question, see

   Ringenberg, Lawrence. "The Area of a Rectangle," *The Mathematics Teacher*, LVI: 329–332; 1963.

16 APPLICATIONS OF MATHEMATICS

IN THIS CHAPTER *we shall extend the concept of a fraction to be the indicated quotient of any two real numbers, and show some of the applications of this concept.*

16.1 RATIO

On a number ray, $\overrightarrow{OX}$, by selecting a segment $\overline{OU}$, it was possible to calibrate the ray

(1) first, by assigning whole numbers 0, 1, 2, . . . , to the end points of successive congruent segments

(2) next, by subdividing these segments into equal segments and assigning rational numbers to the end points, and

(3) finally, by attaching real numbers, properly ordered, to the points left unassigned by (1) and (2).

We can now use a calibrated ray as a measuring device. We shall refer to it as the *number ray* or *rule* or, if we include the opposite ray with the opposite of all the real numbers, the *number line* or rule. We agree that any segment may be transferred to lie along the number ray, with one end point at the origin 0, and the other end point coinciding with a point for which the assigned real number is the measure of the segment.

Consider a number rule with U the unit segment. Let there be given two segments V and V' for which the measures are the rational numbers $\frac{a}{b}$ and $\frac{c}{d}$ respectively. That is:

$$m(V) = \frac{a}{b} \qquad m(V') = \frac{c}{d}$$

or

$$V = \frac{a}{b}U \qquad V' = \frac{c}{d}U$$

Then, to transform V' into V we proceed as follows:

$$bV = aU \qquad dV' = cU$$

$$bcV = acU \qquad adV' = acU$$

Hence

$$bcV = adV' \quad \text{or} \quad V = \frac{ad}{bc}V'.$$

Since

$$\frac{ad}{bc} = \frac{a}{b} \cdot \frac{d}{c} = \frac{a}{b} \div \frac{c}{d},$$

we can write (see extended definition of fraction in section 14.12)

$$V = \frac{\frac{a}{b}}{\frac{c}{d}}V'. \tag{I}$$

This last formula gives us a means of comparing segments V and V' by the use of their measures. If we operate on the segment V' by the fraction $\frac{ad}{bc}$, or $\frac{a}{b} \div \frac{c}{d}$, we obtain the segment V. However, it is more customary to write the formula I in the form

$$\frac{V}{V'} = \frac{\frac{a}{b}}{\frac{c}{d}} \quad \text{or} \quad \frac{V}{V'} = \frac{m(V)}{m(V')} \tag{II}$$

where the expression $\frac{V}{V'}$ is called the *ratio* of the two segments, and as such is the number which is the quotient of their measures. Thus we have the following:

DEFINITION: *If two segments V and V' have a common unit of measure, the* ratio *of V to V' is the quotient of their measures, $m(V) \div m(V')$.*

It is also evident that this quotient is the operator which transforms V' into V.

It is customary to say that in the form I or II, V' is the *base* for comparison, or V is compared to V'.

If the base were V and V' is compared to V, we would obtain the formulas

$$\frac{V'}{V} = \frac{m(V')}{m(V)} = \frac{\frac{c}{d}}{\frac{a}{b}} = \frac{cb}{da}. \tag{III}$$

Here V is transformed into V' by the operator or ratio $\left(\frac{c}{d} \cdot \frac{b}{a}\right)$.

In general, measurable things such as length, area, volume, time, velocity, and so on, are referred to as *magnitudes.* If we measure a given segment, or plane region, or region of space, or an interval of time, by some given unit of the thing we are measuring, we call the measurement, i.e. the number of units with the name of unit, the *quantity* or *magnitude* of the thing. Thus, to say the measure of a segment is 3 is of very little value, for it could be 3 inches, 3 yards, 3 feet, 3 centimeters, or 3 of any unit used to measure length. To say the *length* of the segment is *3 yards* is to give the *magnitude* or *quantity* of the segment. To say a jar holds 3 pints is to give the magnitude or quantity of its volume.

If any two magnitudes of the same kind have a common unit of measure, we can compare them in exactly the same way as we compared segments, that is by using the quotient of their measures, and we can write

$$\frac{M}{M'} = \frac{m(M)}{m(M')}.$$

EXAMPLE 1. Find the ratio of the contents of two jars, one holding 3 pints, the other 4 quarts.

Solution: $\frac{M_1}{M_2} = \frac{3}{8}$ or $\frac{M_1}{M_2} = \frac{1\frac{1}{2}}{4} = \frac{3}{8}$

since we first change the unit quarts into pints by multiplying by 2 or we change pints into quarts by dividing by 2. Note that we have a ratio only if the same unit of measure is used.

EXAMPLE 2. If on a map 1 inch represents 30 miles, what is the ratio of the map segment to the earth represented?

Solution: $\frac{1}{30 \cdot 5280 \cdot 12}$ or $\frac{1}{1{,}900{,}800}$

since we change the unit of measurement of miles to inches by multiplying by $5280 \cdot 12$ or 63,360.

In the foregoing account, our measures were restricted to rational numbers. However, we may extend the same idea to those measures that involve irrational numbers.

EXAMPLE 3. What is the ratio of a diagonal of a square, the length of each side of which is one inch, to a side of the square (Figure 16–1)?

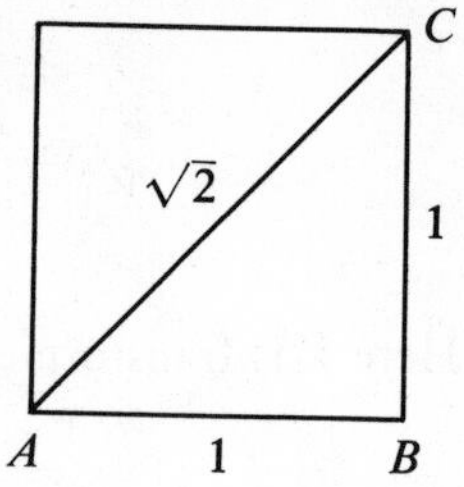

Solution: $\frac{\overline{AC}}{\overline{AB}} = \frac{m(\overline{AC})}{m(\overline{AB})} = \frac{\sqrt{2}}{1}$ or $\sqrt{2}$.

FIGURE 16–1

EXAMPLE 4. What is the ratio of the circumference C to the diameter d of a circle, using the same unit of length in both cases (Figure 16–2)?

Solution: Recall the method in section 15.6 for approximating the circumference of a circle. We find:

$$\frac{m(C)}{m(d)} \approx \frac{6.2832\ldots}{2} \quad \text{or} \quad 3.1416\ldots$$

This is a nonrepeating infinite decimal which we symbolize by the Greek letter π (pronounced "pie") and is therefore an irrational real number.

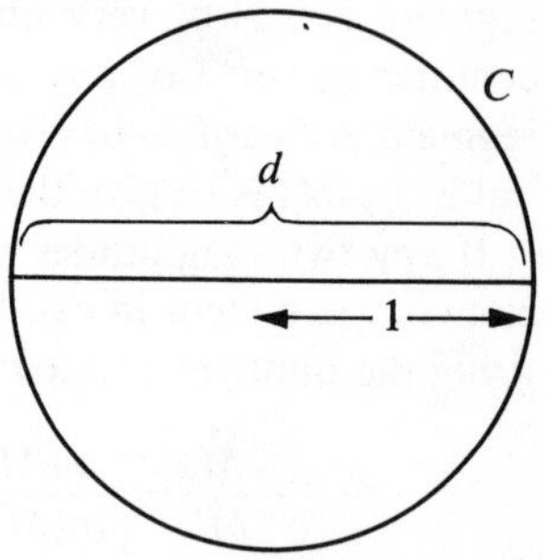

FIGURE 16–2

From the results of Example 4 we may develop the formula given in section 15.6:

The ratio of a circumference to a diameter of the circle is π; that is,

$$\frac{C}{d} = \pi \quad \text{or} \quad C = \pi d.$$

We use the equal sign here, because π is a numeral which is assigned to an exact point on the number scale, and 3.1416 is a rational approximation to this number π. A better approximation is 3.14159265, and there are approximations worked out correctly to over two thousand decimal places.

Note that in stating a ratio, we may express it (see Example 3) as an "indicated quotient," $\frac{\sqrt{2}}{1}$, or as a quotient, $\sqrt{2}$. The indicated quotient may be looked upon as a fraction (section 14.12). An indicated quotient of two whole numbers is a fraction that represents a rational number. An indicated quotient of two rational numbers is also a fraction that represents a rational number. But an indicated quotient of an irrational number and a rational number is a fraction, but the quotient is not a rational number. An indicated quotient of two irrational numbers is a fraction which may represent a rational or an irrational number. For example:

$$\frac{2}{3};\quad \frac{\frac{2}{3}}{\frac{3}{4}} = \frac{8}{9};\quad \frac{\sqrt{3}}{5},\quad \frac{\sqrt{3}}{\sqrt{2}};\quad \frac{\sqrt{12}}{\sqrt{27}} = \frac{2\sqrt{3}}{3\sqrt{3}} = \frac{2}{3}$$

rational (for $\frac{2}{3}$); rational (for $\frac{8}{9}$); irrational (for $\frac{\sqrt{3}}{5}$ and $\frac{\sqrt{3}}{\sqrt{2}}$); rational (for $\frac{2\sqrt{3}}{3\sqrt{3}}$)

The reason for expressing a ratio as an indicated quotient (fraction) rather than a single number is due to the use of the word "ratio" when more than two measures are to be compared. For example, if the lengths of three segments are

2 inches, $3\frac{1}{2}$ inches, and $4\frac{1}{2}$ inches,

we say these lengths are in a *continued ratio* and write

$$2 : 3\tfrac{1}{2} : 4\tfrac{1}{2}$$

and say the lengths are to each other as "two is to three and one half is to four and one half." If we find the sum of the three lengths (here it is 10), then we can compare each measure to the sum of the measures, and these three ratios are:

$$\frac{2}{10} \text{ or } \frac{4}{20},\quad \frac{3\frac{1}{2}}{10} \text{ or } \frac{7}{20},\quad \text{and}\quad \frac{4\frac{1}{2}}{10} \text{ or } \frac{9}{20}$$

Using the second ratio in each case, we can write the continued ratio as

$$4:7:9.$$

16.2 EXERCISES

1. A ratio is given by $\frac{5}{3}$. Give at least three other ratios that are equivalent to this ratio.
2. Find the ratio of
   (a) 3 feet to 5 yards.
   (b) 4 inches to 3 feet.
   (c) 4 inches to 10 centimeters.
   (d) 2 gallons to 3 pints.
3. If the measure of a magnitude A is $\frac{2}{5}$ and that of a magnitude B is $\frac{3}{4}$, both measures in the same unit, find
   (a) the ratio of A to B.
   (b) the operator that transforms A into B.
   (c) the operator that transforms B into A.
4. Approximate the ratio $\sqrt{3}$ to $\sqrt{2}$ to the nearest hundredth.
5. If the unit of measure is changed, will the ratio of two magnitudes be changed or remain the same as with the original unit? Explain your answer.

6. If $V = 2U$, $V' = 3U$, and $U' = \frac{1}{5}U$, find V and V' in terms of U', and the ratio of V to V' using the common unit U'.

7. Generalize Exercise 6, using $V = aU$, $V' = bU$, $U' = kU$, a, b, k all real numbers.

8. Can you have a ratio of
   (a) 5 days to 3 boys?
   (b) 6 weeks to one year?
   (c) 7 miles to two quarts?
   (d) unlike magnitudes?
   (e) like magnitudes?

9. Three boys have respectively \$2, \$5, and \$3.
   (a) What is the ratio of their money?
   (b) What is the ratio of each boy's money to their total money?

10. Two continued ratios are given as
    (1) $3 : 4\frac{1}{2} : 6 : 6\frac{1}{2}$;
    (2) $7\frac{1}{2} : 11\frac{1}{4} : 15 : 16\frac{1}{4}$
    (a) Give a reason why these ratios should be called equivalent.
    (b) Give a general definition of equivalent continued ratios.

16.3 RATIO AND PROPORTION

Ratio was defined in terms of the measures of two segments, or of two magnitudes with the same unit of measure. We can, however, think of any two numbers as being possible measures, and hence define their quotient to be a ratio. This we shall do, and say:

DEFINITION: *A* ratio *of numbers a to b is the quotient $\frac{a}{b}$, which is a number r.*

From the definition of division it follows that

$$\frac{a}{b} = r \Leftrightarrow a = br.$$

We call b the *base* of the ratio. The ratio of b to a is $\frac{b}{a}$ and here a is the base.

If the ratio $\frac{b}{a} = s$, then s is the reciprocal of r because

$$r \cdot s = \frac{a}{b} \cdot \frac{b}{a} = 1.$$

(Recall that the base is the denominator of the ratio.)

If $\frac{a}{b} = r$ and $\frac{c}{d} = r$, then $a = br$ and $c = dr$.

Hence: $ad = bdr$ and $bc = bdr$

or $ad = bc$.

Hence we can write

$$\frac{a}{b} = \frac{c}{d} \Leftrightarrow ad = bc.$$

A statement that two ratios are equal is called a *proportion*. Thus

$\frac{a}{b} = \frac{c}{d}$ is a proportion in which the *terms* are a, b, c, d.

It is customary to call the terms a and d the *extremes* and b and c the *means* of this proportion. Thus we have from the formula above:

Two ratios are in proportion if and only if the product of the means is equal to the product of the extremes.

Using this definition of a proportion, it is possible to form new proportions from a given one. Let us consider the proportion

$$\frac{3}{4} = \frac{6}{8}. \tag{IV}$$

Since these ratios are equal, their reciprocals are equal and we have the proportion

$$\frac{4}{3} = \frac{8}{6}. \tag{V}$$

Note that in (V) the means and extremes are interchanged with those in (IV).

If we add 1 to each fraction in (IV) and express the result as the equality of two ratios, we obtain

$$1 + \frac{3}{4} = 1 + \frac{6}{8} \quad \text{or} \quad \frac{4 + 3}{4} = \frac{8 + 6}{8}, \text{ i.e. } \frac{7}{4} = \frac{14}{8}. \tag{VI}$$

Note that the last result can be obtained from (IV) by adding the denominator to the numerator and comparing the sum to the denominator for each ratio. In a similar way by subtracting each ratio from 1 we obtain

$$\frac{4 - 3}{4} = \frac{8 - 6}{8} \quad \text{or} \quad \frac{1}{4} = \frac{2}{8}. \tag{VII}$$

Finally, if we add the numerators and the denominators in (IV), and form the ratio of the sums, the ratio is equal to the given ratio:

$$\frac{3 + 6}{4 + 8} = \frac{9}{12} = \frac{3}{4} \tag{VIII}$$

Note that the ratios in (V), (VI), and (VII) are different from that in (IV), while the ratio in (VIII) remains the same as in (IV).

All these derived proportions are true generally and we state this as a theorem:

THEOREM: *If* $\frac{a}{b} = \frac{c}{d}$, *and a and c are not zero, then*

(a) *the extremes and means may be exchanged to form the proportion* $\frac{b}{a} = \frac{d}{c}$.

(b) *the sum or difference of the terms of the ratios is in the same ratio to the numerators or the denominators:*

$$\frac{a+b}{b} = \frac{c+d}{d}; \quad \frac{a+b}{a} = \frac{c+d}{c}$$

$$\frac{a-b}{b} = \frac{c-d}{d}; \quad \frac{a-b}{a} = \frac{c-d}{c} \quad (a > b, c > d)$$

(c) *the ratio of the sum of the numerators to the sum of the denominators is equal to the given ratio:* $\frac{a+c}{b+d} = \frac{a}{b}$.

EXAMPLE 5. Given the proportion $\frac{8}{5} = \frac{24}{15}$, find five other proportions that can be derived from it.

Solution: We could use the theorem above for one solution. We can also write the proportion as

(a) $\frac{5+3}{5} = \frac{15+9}{15}$ or $1 + \frac{3}{5} = 1 + \frac{9}{15}$ or $\frac{3}{5} = \frac{9}{15}$

from which we derive

(b) $\frac{5}{3} = \frac{15}{9}$, by inversion of (a), (c) $\frac{20}{12} = \frac{5}{3}$, by addition of (b),
(d) $\frac{2}{3} = \frac{6}{9}$, by subtraction of (b), (e) $\frac{3}{2} = \frac{9}{6}$, by inverting (d), etc.

If we write the measures of the sides of triangle I (Figure 16–3) in a continued ratio we have:

$$3 : 4 : 5$$

Similarly, for triangle II we have:

$$4\tfrac{1}{2} : 6 : 7\tfrac{1}{2}$$

Comparing the corresponding terms of each ratio, we find the ratios

$$\frac{3}{4\frac{1}{2}}, \frac{4}{6}, \frac{5}{7\frac{1}{2}},$$

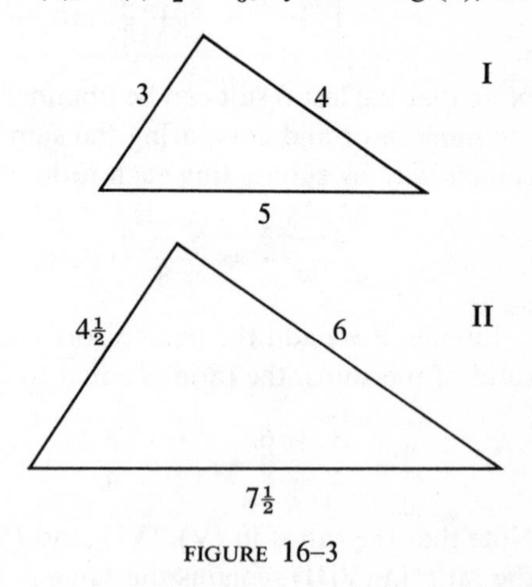

FIGURE 16–3

all of which are equal to $\frac{2}{3}$. Thus each measure of a side in triangle II can be transformed into the measure of the corresponding side of triangle I by multiplying it by the operator $\frac{2}{3}$. Whenever a situation like this occurs, we say the measures of the first set are *proportional* to the corresponding measures of the second set.

More generally, let there be two sets of measures, each set given in a fixed order, as:

$$\{a_1, a_2, a_3, \ldots, a_n\}$$
$$\{b_1, b_2, b_3, \ldots, b_n\}$$

If there is a number k, such that

$$a_1 = kb_1, \quad a_2 = kb_2, \quad a_3 = kb_3, \ldots, \quad a_n = kb_n,$$

then the measures of the two sets are said to be in *continued proportion* and we write

$$\frac{a_1}{b_1} = \frac{a_2}{b_2} = \frac{a_3}{b_3} = \cdots = \frac{a_n}{b_n} = k.$$

Note also that using the properties of proportions, we can write

$$\frac{a_1}{a_2} = \frac{b_1}{b_2}; \frac{a_1}{a_3} = \frac{b_1}{b_3}; \text{ but } \frac{a_1}{a_2} \neq \frac{a_1}{a_3} \neq k.$$

The *constant ratio* is that ratio which is of a term of one set to the corresponding term of the other set.

Thus, in the sets of measures of the sides of triangles I and II (Figure 16–3)

$$\frac{3}{4\frac{1}{2}} = \frac{4}{6} = \frac{5}{7\frac{1}{2}} = \frac{2}{3}; \text{ but } \frac{3}{4} = \frac{4\frac{1}{2}}{6} \text{ is not the ratio } \frac{2}{3}.$$

The important ratio in comparing measures is the constant or the ratio of corresponding terms in the two sets.

16.4 EXERCISES

1. Which of the following statements of equalities are proportions?

   (a) $\frac{3}{5} = \frac{21}{35}$ (b) $2 = 3 - 1$ (c) $\frac{3}{2} = \frac{4}{3}$ (d) $\frac{1\frac{2}{3}}{3\frac{1}{2}} = \frac{10}{21}$

2. Form two different proportions from the terms of $\frac{4}{7} = \frac{12}{21}$. (The proportions are different if the ratios in one are not equal to the ratios in the other.)
3. The length measures of two rods are $m(R_1) = 8$ and $m(R_2) = 15$. Their weight measures are $w(R_1) = 36$ and $w(R_2) = 67.5$. Are the length and weight measures in proportion?

4. Two fractions $\frac{3}{8}$ and $\frac{x}{7}$ are in proportion. Find the value of x.

5. The circumferences of two circles are proportional to their radii. If the radii measure $3\frac{1}{2}$ and $4\frac{3}{4}$ inches respectively, find the circumference of the larger circle if that of the smaller is 7π.

6. In Exercise 5, could you find the circumferences without knowing the ratio of the circumference to the diameter of the circle?

7. Prove: If $\frac{a}{b} = \frac{c}{d}$, then $\frac{a+b}{b} = \frac{c+d}{d}$.

8. Prove: If $\frac{a}{b} = \frac{c}{d}$, then, if $a > b$, $\frac{a-b}{a} = \frac{c-d}{c}$.

9. Prove: If $\frac{a}{b} = \frac{c}{d}$, then $\frac{a+c}{b+d} = \frac{a}{b}$.

10. Prove: If $\frac{a}{b} = \frac{c}{d} = \frac{e}{f}$, then $\frac{a+c+e}{b+d+f} = \frac{a}{b}$.

11. A continued ratio is 3 : 4 : 6 : 7. Another continued ratio is $8 : x : y : z$. If the two ratios form a continued proportion, find the values of x, y, and z.

12. If $\frac{a_1}{b_1} = \frac{a_2}{b_2} = \frac{a_3}{b_3}$, $a_1 \neq a_2 \neq a_3$, show that

    (a) $\frac{a_1}{a_2} \neq \frac{a_1}{a_3}$.

    (b) $\frac{a_1}{a_2} = \frac{b_1}{b_2}$ and $\frac{a_1}{a_3} = \frac{b_1}{b_3}$.

13. (a) The sum of two measures is 5. The measures are whole numbers. In what ratios can the measures be?

    (b) The ratio of two measures is 2 : 3 or $\frac{2}{3}$. What sums can the measures be if the measures are whole numbers?

14. If $\frac{a}{b} < \frac{c}{d}$, prove $\frac{a+c}{b+d} < \frac{c}{d}$, and $\frac{a+c}{b+d} > \frac{a}{b}$.

15. The lengths of the sides of one triangle are proportional to those of a second triangle. If the sides of the first measure 2.3, 4.6 and 5.8, find the lengths of the sides of the second triangle if the measure of the side corresponding to 4.6 is 6.9.

16. Define:

    (a) ratio
    (b) equal ratios
    (c) unequal ratios
    (d) continued ratio
    (e) proportion
    (f) continued proportion
    (g) magnitude
    (h) quantity
    (i) measure
    (j) measurement
    (k) unit of measure

Any ratio can be expressed either approximately or exactly as an indicated quotient in which the denominator is 100. Thus,

$$\frac{2}{5} = \frac{40}{100};\ \frac{3}{8} = \frac{37\frac{1}{2}}{100};\ \frac{1}{3} \approx \frac{33}{100};\ \frac{1}{3} = \frac{33\frac{1}{3}}{100};\ \text{etc.}$$

The study of ratios in which the denominator is 100 is called the study of *percent.*

DEFINITION: *A percent, or one percent, is one one-hundredth.*

The common symbol for percent is "%."

$$3\% \text{ means } 3 \cdot \frac{1}{100} \text{ or } 0.03$$

$$100\% \text{ means } 100 \cdot \frac{1}{100} \text{ or } 1.00$$

$$250\% \text{ means } 250 \cdot \frac{1}{100} \text{ or } 2.50$$

We now have many ways of writing a ratio. For example, the ratio $\frac{7}{20}$ may be given as

$$\frac{7}{20} = \frac{35}{100} = 35\% = 35 \cdot \frac{1}{100} = 0.35.$$

Similarly,

$$\frac{2}{3} = \frac{66\frac{2}{3}}{100} = 66\tfrac{2}{3}\% \approx 0.67.$$

In the study of percent we shall use the above definition.

Percents arise most frequently in the comparison of two measures. On a test a person's score is 16 and the total possible score is 25. We then say the ratio of these two measures is 16 : 25 or $\frac{16}{25}$ and change the ratio to the percent form $\frac{64}{100}$ which we read as "64 percent" and write as "64%." Thus to compare two quantities we form the ratio of their measures and change it to a fraction with denominator 100; then the numerator tells us the *percent* the first measure is compared to the second measure as a base.

EXAMPLE 6. A man borrowed $250 for one year, and repaid $266. What was the percent of interest paid?

Solution: The interest paid was $266 - 250 = 16$. The ratio of this to the money borrowed is $\frac{16}{250}$. Changing this fraction to one with denominator 100 gives $\frac{6.4}{100}$. Hence the interest for the year was 6.4%.

Since a ratio can be looked upon as an operator which changes the base into the other measure, we can find this measure, given the base and the ratio. Suppose the ratio of the measures of two magnitudes is $\frac{a}{b}$, this means

$$\frac{m(M_1)}{m(M_2)} = \frac{a}{b} \qquad \text{or} \qquad m(M_1) = \frac{a}{b} \cdot m(M_2),$$

and if $\frac{a}{b} = \frac{c}{100}$ or $c\%$, it means

$$m(M_1) = c\% \cdot m(M_2).$$

EXAMPLE 7. The length of a road to be constructed was 240 miles. At a certain time 30 percent of the road had been completed. How many miles of road had been constructed?

Solution: Let x be the number of miles of road constructed. Then

$$\frac{m(R_1)}{m(R_2)} = \frac{x}{240} = \frac{30}{100}$$

or

$$x = 0.30(240) = 72.$$

Thirty percent operates on 240 to transform it into 72, which represents the number of miles completed.

It is customary, in ordinary usage, to refer to the measure M_1 in the paragraph above as the *percentage*. Thus, the ratio $\frac{\text{Percentage}}{\text{Base}}$ is the ratio of the measure of M_1 to that of the base M_2. If this ratio is expressed as a fraction with denominator 100, then it is the percent. We say the percent is the ratio of the percentage to the base:

$$\frac{\text{Percentage}}{\text{Base}} = \frac{\text{Percent}}{1}$$

It is quite evident that in the latter form, we can interchange the means, to obtain

$$\frac{\text{Percentage}}{\text{Percent}} = \frac{\text{Base}}{1}.$$

Hence if a percentage (one measure) and the percent (the ratio of the measures) are known, we can determine the base by finding the quotient "percentage ÷ percent."

EXAMPLE 8. A man lost 15% of his weight and then weighed 170 pounds. What was his original weight?

Solution: We are asked to find a number (base) for which 85% of it (100% − 15% = 85%) will be 170. The problem can be stated:

$$\frac{170}{0.85} = \text{base} \qquad \text{or} \qquad \frac{170}{x} = \frac{85}{100} = \frac{0.85}{1}$$

By division we find the base is 200; hence the man originally weighed 200 pounds.

The above examples illustrate that any problem involving percents and measures can be solved, if we know two of the three numbers, base, percentage, and the percent. The one relation

$$\frac{\text{Percentage}}{\text{Base}} = \text{Percent},$$

where "percent" is the ratio of the percentage to the base, is sufficient for describing the solution. We can also write

$$\frac{m(M_1)}{m(M_2)} = \frac{a}{100}$$

where a is the number of percents or number of hundredths.

A frequent error made in the use of percent is to misinterpret 0.30% for 30%.

The first is $0.30 \cdot \frac{1}{100} = \frac{30}{100} \cdot \frac{1}{100} = \frac{30}{10{,}000}$ or $\frac{3}{1000}$.

The second is $30 \cdot \frac{1}{100} = \frac{30}{100}$ or $\frac{3}{10}$.

The second number is 100 times the first number.

Note that we can have *any number* of percent. Thus:

$$\begin{aligned}
\text{one percent} &= 1\% = \tfrac{1}{100} = 0.01 \\
0.1 \text{ percent} &= 0.1\% = \tfrac{1}{10} \times \tfrac{1}{100} = \tfrac{1}{1000} = 0.001 \\
230 \text{ percent} &= 230\% = 230 \times \tfrac{1}{100} = 2.30 \\
100 \text{ percent} &= 100\% = 100 \times \tfrac{1}{100} = 1.00
\end{aligned}$$

EXAMPLE 9. What is 50%? 500%? 0.5%? 0.05%? 5000%?

Solution: $\frac{1}{2}$; 5.00; $\frac{1}{200}$; $\frac{1}{2000}$; 50.00.

16.6 EXERCISES

1. Express each of the following in percent form:
(a) $\frac{1}{2}$ (b) $\frac{1}{20}$ (c) $\frac{2}{125}$ (d) 3 (e) 1.4 (f) 0.005
2. Express each of the following in simplest rational number form:
(a) 30% (b) $\frac{1}{2}$% (c) 50% (d) 330% (e) $33\frac{1}{3}$% (f) $0.33\frac{1}{3}$%

3. Express each of the following comparisons as a percent:
   (a) 30 correct of 40 attempts
   (b) 20 hits in 80 attempts (at bat, in baseball)
   (c) $150 collected for a desired $100 fund
   (d) $30 interest on a loan of $300
   (e) a gain of 5 pounds from a weight of 150 pounds
   (f) a loss of $40 on an investment of $80
   (g) one drop in 800 drops
   (h) two feet from 8 yards of cloth
   (i) three minutes every day
4. Express each of the following to the nearest tenth of a percent:
   (a) $\frac{1}{3}$ (b) $\frac{3}{7}$ (c) $\frac{5}{12}$ (d) $\frac{2}{9}$ (e) $2\frac{2}{3}$ (f) $\frac{1}{300}$
5. The base of a comparison of two magnitudes is 65. The ratio of the magnitudes is 30%. Find the percentage.
6. The percentage is 274. The ratio is 30%. Find the base.
7. A measure was 72. This was increased to 80. Find the percent of increase.
8. A measure is 72. It was decreased from 80. Find the percent of decrease. Why is the answer to Exercise 8 different from that of Exercise 7?
9. A sales tax on a purchase is 5% of the price paid. A man buys a $50.00 article at a 5 percent discount but he must pay the sales tax. What is his total payment?
10. Write each of the following as a proportion in which one ratio expresses a percent.
   (a) 5% of 68 is y. (b) 5% of y is 68.
   (c) y% of 68 is 5. (d) y is in the ratio to 68 as 1 is to 20.

16.7 SIMILARITY, RATIO, PROPORTION

In Figure 16–4, the drawing was started with triangle CBA, the length of whose sides were 3, 4, and 5. The sides $\overline{AC}$ and $\overline{AB}$ were extended until the measures of the sides were doubled, that is,

$$m(AC') = 2 \cdot m(AC)$$

and

$$m(AB') = 2 \cdot m(AB).$$

If the segment $\overline{C'B'}$ is drawn, its measure will be double that of $\overline{CB}$, and the lengths of the sides of triangle $C'AB'$ will be 6, 8, 10. We can look upon the triangles as being generated through a *transformation of the plane*. In this case the plane is operated upon by any real number in the direction $\overrightarrow{AB}$ with A as an origin; at the same time the plane is operated upon by the same number in the direction $\overrightarrow{AC}$. The plane is thus stretched the same amount along two distinct lines. When this happens we intuitively feel that the plane is stretched the same amount in the

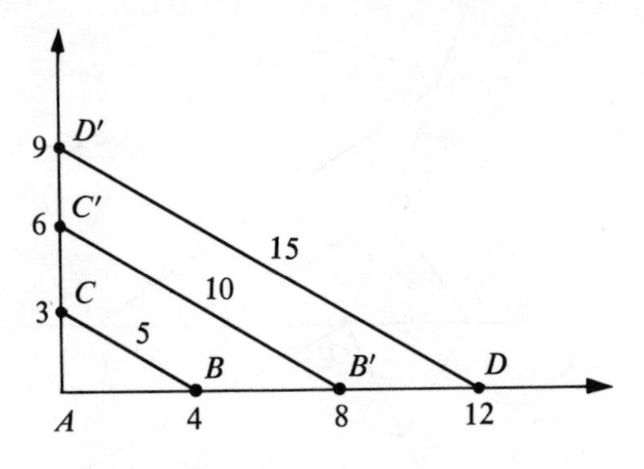

FIGURE 16–4

direction of all lines emanating from point A, and indeed we shall accept this as the case. Since the angle at A, common to all these triangles, does not change in this stretching, the line opposite the angle, that is, BC, is operated upon by the same real number, and hence stretches in the same ratio to the initial length as the segments on $\overrightarrow{AC}$ and $\overrightarrow{AB}$ do. Similarly, if the sides AC and AB had been stretched so that the original measures were multiplied by 3, then the side CB would also be stretched to 3 times its measure and the lengths of the sides of triangle $D'AD$ would be 9, 12, and 15.

These stretchings or transformations mean

$$CB \parallel C'B' \parallel D'D \ \ldots .$$

Hence the other corresponding angles of each of the transformed triangles have the same measure. We say the triangles are *similar*.

The continued ratio of the sides of any one of these triangles is a multiple of any of the others. Thus any two continued ratios are in continued proportion. For example, for 3 : 4 : 5 and 6 : 8 : 10 we have

$$\frac{3}{6} = \frac{4}{8} = \frac{5}{10}$$

or the length of any side of the second triangle is twice the length of the corresponding side of the first. For 3 : 4 : 5 and 9 : 12 : 15 we have $\frac{3}{9} = \frac{4}{12} = \frac{5}{15}$ or the length of any side of the second triangle is three times the length of the corresponding side of the first. Similarly 6 : 8 : 10 and 9 : 12 : 15 form the continued proportion $\frac{6}{9} = \frac{8}{12} = \frac{10}{15}$ or the first length is $\frac{2}{3}$ the corresponding second length.

In Figure 16–5 the drawing was started with polygon $ABCDE$ and *any* point O inside the polygon. Rays were drawn from O through each vertex of the polygon.

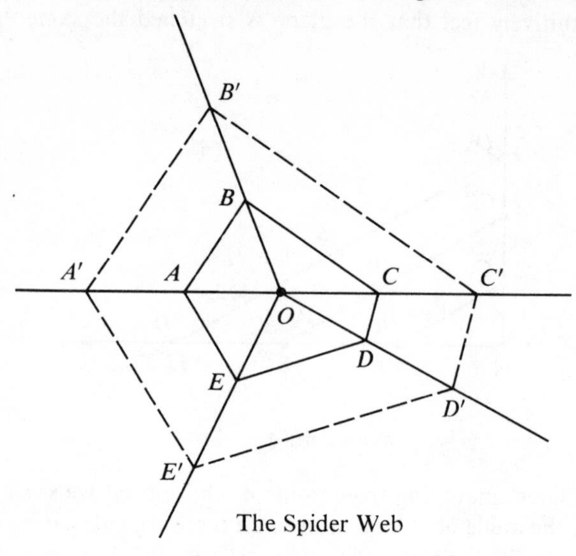

The Spider Web

FIGURE 16–5

The lengths $\overline{OA}$, $\overline{OB}$, . . . are each multiplied by the same number to determine points A', B', ... Then the polygon $A'B'C'D'E'$ is *similar* to polygon $ABCDE$, and the lengths of the sides of $A'B'C'D'E'$ are the lengths of the corresponding sides of $ABCDE$ multiplied by the same number. If OA' is twice OA, then $A'B'$ is twice AB, $B'C'$ is twice BC, and so on. This number (2 in the illustration just given) is called the *ratio of similitude.* Note that the sides of the polygons are parallel and hence the corresponding angles are congruent, that is, have equal measures.

Notice that in Figures 16–4 and 16–5 the corresponding sides are in continued proportion and the corresponding angles are congruent. It may be shown in geometry that in these two cases if the corresponding sides are in continued proportion, then the corresponding angles are congruent, and vice versa. However, there are pairs of polygons for which this statement is not true. For example, given a square and a rectangle that is not a square, it can be shown that even though the corresponding angles are congruent, the corresponding sides are not in continued ratio; that is, the rectangle cannot be constructed from the square as the polygons were constructed in the preceding figures. We, therefore, make the following general definition:

DEFINITION: *Two polygons are* similar *if the lengths of the corresponding sides are in continued proportion and the measures of corresponding angles are equal.*

In general, if two geometric figures are similar, then to each point of one figure there is a corresponding point of the other figure. If the segment formed by any two points of one of the figures is compared with the segment formed by the corresponding points of the other figure, then the ratio of the measures of these two segments is equal to the ratio of similitude of the two figures. In Figure 16–6, the ratio of similitude is 3 : 2 and the ratio of the measures of $\overline{AB}$ and $\overline{A'B'}$ is also 3 : 2 (6 : 4). A photographic enlargement is nothing else but a similar configuration in a given ratio of similitude.

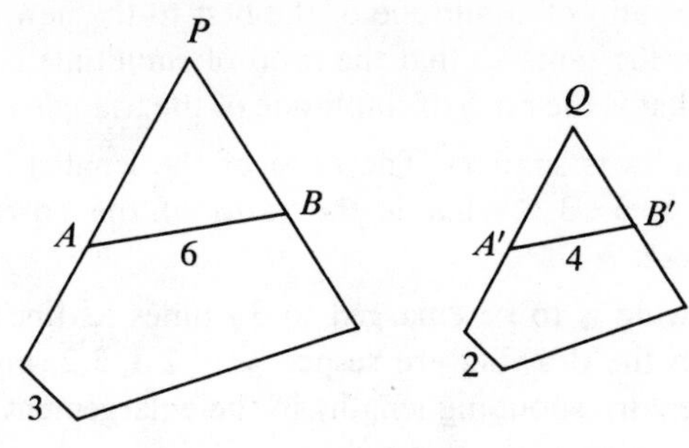

FIGURE 16–6

EXAMPLE 10. Polygon A is similar to polygon B. The lengths of the sides of polygon A are in the ratio 3 : 6 : 7 : 12 : 14. The side of polygon B corresponding to the length 6 of A has a length of 9. Find the corresponding lengths of the other sides of B.

Solution: The ratio of similitude of B to A is 9 : 6 or $\frac{3}{2}$. Hence each side of B has a length $\frac{3}{2}$ times the corresponding length in polygon A. Thus the lengths of the sides of B are

$\frac{3}{2} \cdot 3;\ \ \frac{3}{2} \cdot 6;\ \ \frac{3}{2} \cdot 7;\ \ \frac{3}{2} \cdot 12;\ \ \frac{3}{2} \cdot 14;$

or

$4\frac{1}{2}$, 9, $10\frac{1}{2}$, 18, 21.

EXAMPLE 11. A vertical tree casts a shadow 60 feet long at the same time that a vertical pole 4 feet long casts a shadow 10 feet long (Figure 16–7). How high is the tree?

FIGURE 16–7

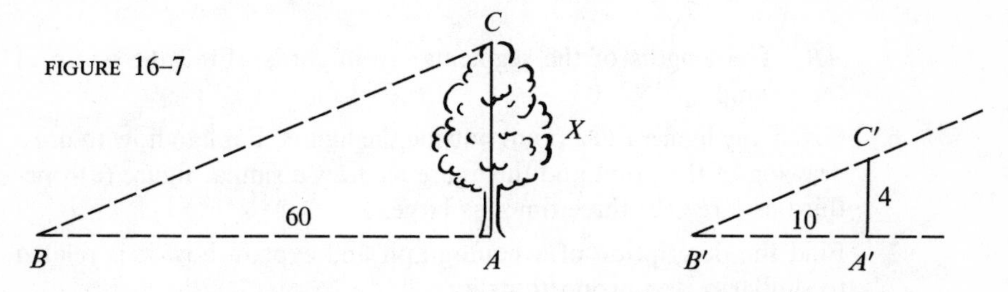

Solution: Since the sun's rays are parallel, the triangle BAC is similar to the triangle $B'A'C'$ and their sides are proportional. Hence, if x is the height of the tree,

$$\frac{60}{10} = \frac{x}{4};\quad 240 = 10x;\quad 10 \cdot 24 = 10 \cdot x;\quad \text{or}\quad x = 24$$

and the height of the tree is 24 feet.

16.8 EXERCISES

1. Draw a picture of a triangle.
   (a) Using the triangle as a base construct a similar triangle so that the ratio of similitude of the first to the new triangle is $\frac{3}{2}$.
   (b) Do the same so that the ratio of similitude is $\frac{2}{3}$.
   (c) What is the ratio of similitude of the triangle in (b) to that in (a)?
2. All circles is similar. The ratio of the lengths of the radii of two circles is 5 : 3. What is the ratio of the corresponding circumferences?
3. A drawing is to be enlarged to $3\frac{1}{2}$ times its linear size. Three key lines in the drawing are respectively 2.3, 3.2, and 4 inches. What are the corresponding lengths in the enlargement?
4. Draw a pentagon and select any point in the interior region. Using this point as a *center of similitude* construct similar polygons for which the ratios of similitude to the drawn polygon are respectively $\frac{1}{2}$, $\frac{2}{3}$, 1, $\frac{3}{2}$, and 2.
5. In Figure 16–8 M is a swamp. Line segments were measured as shown in the figure where $\overline{ED}$ is parallel to the width of the swamp

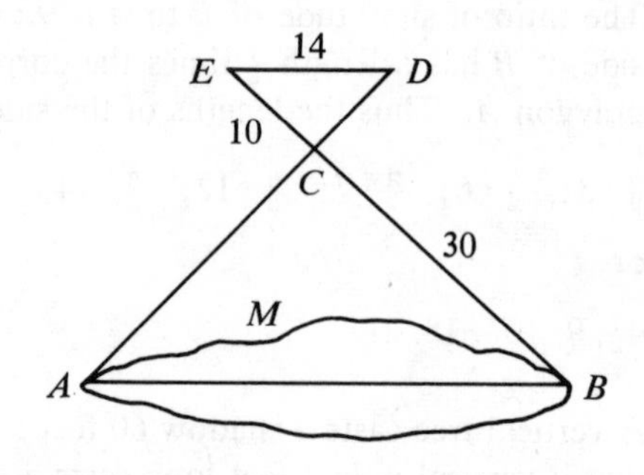

FIGURE 16–8

$\overline{AB}$. The lengths of the segments are in yards. Find the width of the swamp.

6. Given any figure and a point outside the figure. Explain how to use a drawing of the point and the figure to draw a similar figure (a) one-third as large (b) three times as large.
7. Find the description of a pantograph and explain how it is related to similarity and proportionality.
8. A square is similar to any other square. By drawing two squares with the ratio of similitude 1 : 2, show that the ratio of the square regions is 1 : 4, or the square of the ratio of the side lengths.

9. In Figure 16–9 the sides of $\triangle ABC$ are calibrated into thirds, and the points are connected as shown.

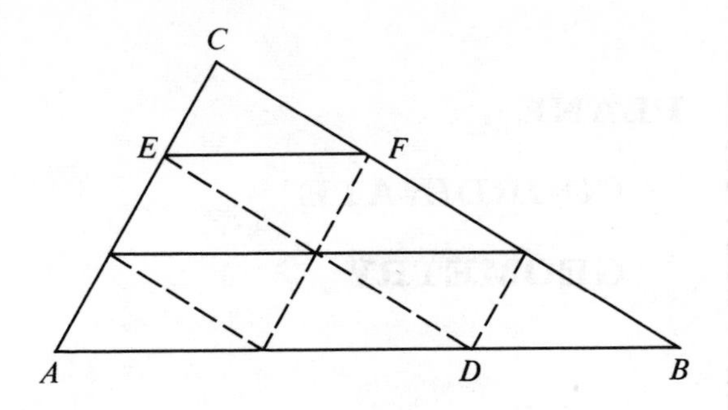

FIGURE 16–9

(a) $\triangle ADE$ and $\triangle ABC$ are similar. Find their ratio of similitude.

(b) Find the ratio of the area of $\triangle ADE$ to that of $\triangle ABC$, using $\triangle ECF$ as unit.

(c) Compare the ratio of similitude of the triangles with the ratio of the areas.

(d) Draw a conclusion concerning the ratio of areas of similar polygons.

10. If an enlargement is in the ratio of 7 : 2 to the original snapshot, what is the ratio of the areas of the pictures?

16.9 REFERENCE QUESTIONS

1. May any common percentage problem be solved by use of a proportion? (See discussion in this chapter.) For another discussion of this question, see

   Wendt, Arnold. "Per Cent without Cases," *The Arithmetic Teacher*, 6: 209–214; 1959.

2. Is a fraction an "indicated quotient"? For a discussion bearing upon this question, see

   National Council of Teachers of Mathematics. *Topics in Mathematics for Elementary School Teachers* (29th yearbook). Washington, D.C.: NCTM, 1964. Pp. 272–277.

17 PLANE COORDINATE GEOMETRY

FOR MANY YEARS, *the subjects of algebra and geometry were considered and studied as separate disciplines, almost totally unrelated to each other. Until the seventeenth century, the study of geometry was confined for the most part to a study of the work of the ancient Greeks. In the seventeenth century, however, a mathematician named René Descartes (1596–1690) developed a new method, called coordinate geometry. Coordinate geometry (or analytic geometry) may be described roughly as the application of algebraic principles to the study of geometric relationships, and it is only in recent years that it has begun to play a significant role in the mathematics curriculum of the schools. In this chapter, we take a look at some elementary topics from coordinate geometry.*

17.1 COORDINATES ON A LINE

As we saw in Chapter 14, there is a one-to-one correspondence between the set of real numbers and the set of points on a line. One way to establish this correspondence is to select two arbitrary points on a line—call them O and I—and assign to them the real numbers 0 and 1, respectively. (See Figure 17–1.) While

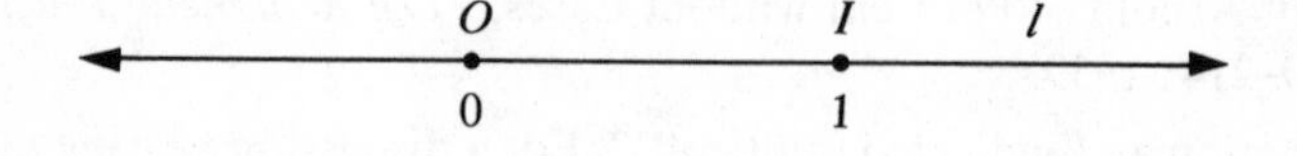

FIGURE 17–1

the choice of points is completely arbitrary, it is customary to choose I "to the right of" O in dealing with a horizontal line. The numbers 0 and 1 are called the *coordinates* of the points O and I; once they have been assigned, a unique coordinate is determined for each point of the line. Conversely, given any real number, there is a unique point of the line whose coordinate this number is.

The preceding statements are clarified by reference to a figure such as Figure 17–2. If point A is specified, the coordinate of A can be determined; here, it appears

S C O I R A B

$-\sqrt{2}$ -1 0 1 $\sqrt{2}$ 2 3 $\frac{7}{2}$

FIGURE 17–2

that the coordinate of A is 2. Also, the coordinate of B is $\frac{7}{2}$, and the coordinate of C is -1. And on the other hand, if the real number $\sqrt{2}$ is specified, there is a point of the line corresponding to this number; in the figure, this point is labeled R. Also, the point whose coordinate is $-\sqrt{2}$ has been labeled S.

We may say then that the line has been "coordinatized," and a coordinatized line is frequently called a *number line*. Physically, one might liken a number line to a sort of "infinite ruler," extending indefinitely to left and right. Observe that points "to the left of" 0 are assigned negative coordinates, while points "to the right of" 0 are assigned positive coordinates. Observe also that for any two distinct points of a number line, the point to the *left* has the smaller number as its coordinate. The meaning of this statement may be checked by referring to any two of the points in Figure 17–2. The statement is also illustrated by Figure 17–3. Point M has coordinate x, and point N has coordinate y; since M is "to the left of" (or "comes before") point N, we shall agree that $x < y$.

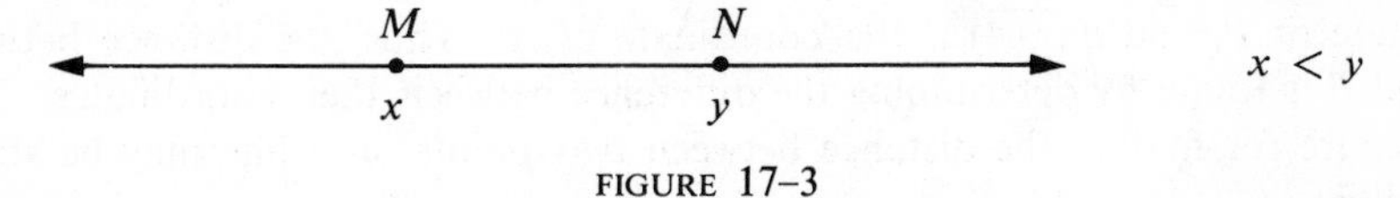

FIGURE 17–3

The discussion above has been based upon a horizontal number line, and indeed this is the customary presentation. Such a horizontal orientation is certainly not mandatory, however, and Figure 17–4 illustrates number lines oriented in various ways in the plane. Note especially Figure 17–4a, in which the line is in a vertical position; in such a case, it is customary to agree that positive coordinates be assigned to points "above" 0 and negative coordinates to points "below" 0. Thus, in this case if one point is "above" another, it will have a larger coordinate.

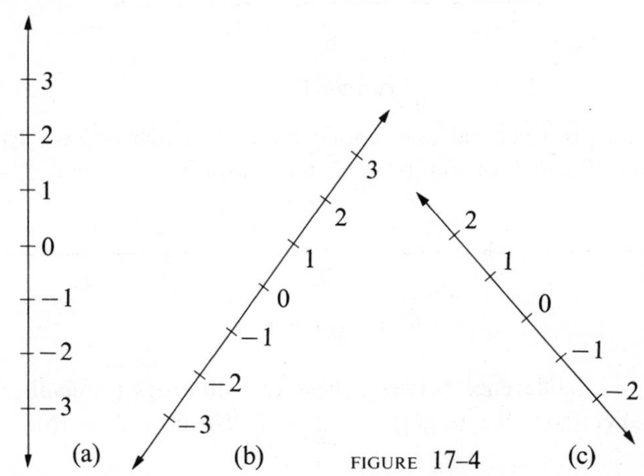

FIGURE 17–4

The concept of distance between two points is indispensable to coordinate geometry, and in this section we consider distance between two points of a coordinatized line. In Figure 17–5, the distance between O and A is 3, sometimes

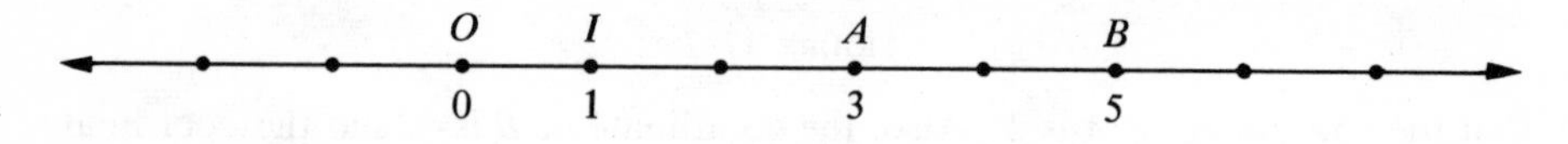

FIGURE 17–5

written as "$d(O, A) = 3$." In effect, we are saying that $m(\overline{OA}) = 3$, where $\overline{OI}$ serves as the unit of measurement.

In considering the distance between A and B, we simply consider $m(\overline{AB})$. Proceeding intuitively, we note the following:

A is between O and B.

$m(\overline{OA}) + m(\overline{AB}) = m(\overline{OB})$

Thus, $m(\overline{AB}) = m(\overline{OB}) - m(\overline{OA})$. However, $m(\overline{OB}) = 5$ and $m(\overline{OA}) = 3$; therefore, $m(\overline{AB}) = 2$. We see then that the distance between A and B is 2—symbolically, $d(A, B) = 2$. The procedure followed here amounted to performing the following subtraction: $m(\overline{OB}) - m(\overline{OA})$. However, $m(\overline{OB})$ is the coordinate of B, and $m(\overline{OA})$ is the coordinate of A. Thus, the distance between A and B is found by determining the difference between their coordinates. This procedure for finding the distance between two points on a line may be stated as follows:

If P_1 and P_2 are points on a line, with coordinates x_1 and x_2, respectively, and $x_2 > x_1$, then

$$d(P_1, P_2) = x_2 - x_1.$$

Figure 17–6 serves as an illustration of the statement.

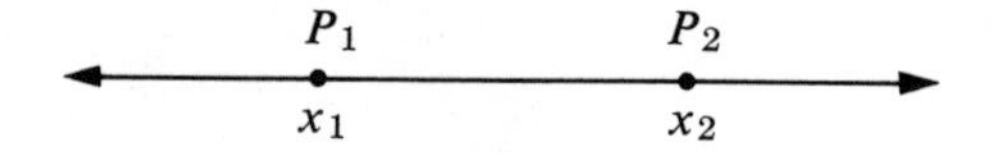

FIGURE 17–6

The procedure is a general one, applicable to any two points. Consider, for instance, points E and F of Figure 17–7, with negative coordinates -6 and -2,

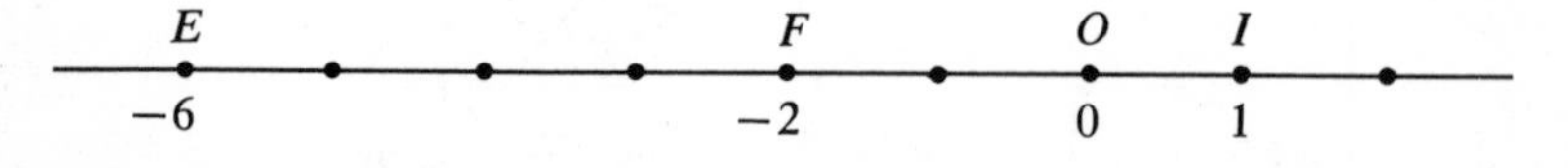

FIGURE 17–7

respectively. The difference between these two numbers (remembering to subtract the smaller from the larger) is $-2 - (-6)$, or $-2 + (6)$, or 4.

Some additional examples follow:

EXAMPLE 1. If x has coordinate 97, and y has coordinate 43, what is the distance between x and y?

Solution: The distance is $97 - 43$, or 54.

EXAMPLE 2. What is the distance between the point with coordinate 2, and the point with coordinate -10?

Solution: $2 - (-10) = 2 + 10 = 12.$

(The reader is familiar with the concept of *absolute value* and he should be aware of the fact that the distance between two points with coordinates x_1 and x_2 is $|x_1 - x_2|$, regardless of which of the two numbers x_1 and x_2 is greater.)

17.3 COORDINATES IN A PLANE

In Figure 17–8, the three points A, B, and C do not all lie on one line; thus we cannot assign each of them a real number coordinate as we did with collinear points in the preceding section. The three points do, of course, lie in one plane; and so we direct our attention to the problem of assigning coordinates to points of a plane (that is, coordinatizing the plane).

• B

• C

• A

FIGURE 17–8

First, let us introduce two "reference lines" in the plane, as illustrated in Figure 17–9. The reference lines in this case are *perpendicular* (intersecting at right angles) as is customary in coordinate geometry. (The reader should note that this is not essential, but the following discussion uses the language appropriate for perpendicular axes.) These reference lines are referred to as *axes*, the horizontal line being the *x-axis*, and the vertical line being the *y-axis*. Since the

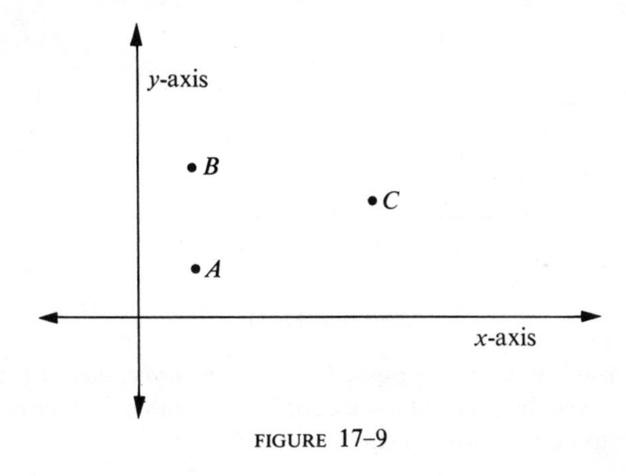

FIGURE 17–9

axes are lines, each of them may be coordinatized, as indicated in Figure 17–10; note that we are careful to make the unit segment on the y-axis congruent to

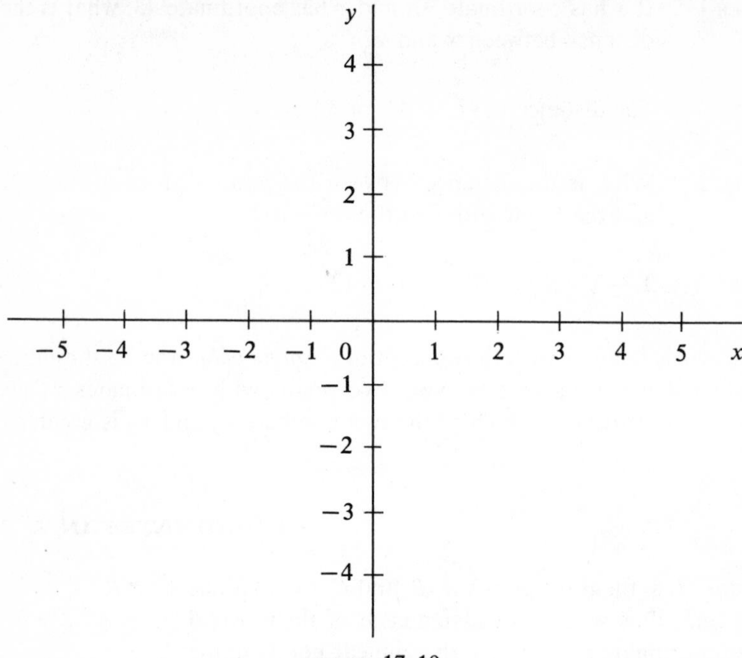

FIGURE 17–10

the unit segment on the x-axis. Also note that the intersection of the two axes serves as the zero point for each; in the plane, this point is called the *origin.*

Consider now a point P in the plane and perpendicular axes. Through P, there is a unique (that is, one and only one) line perpendicular to the x-axis. This perpendicular is indicated by the dotted line in Figure 17–11. The perpendicular

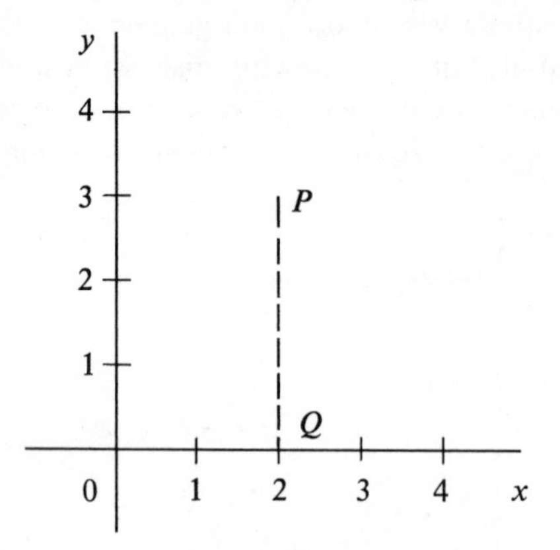

FIGURE 17–11

intersects the x-axis in a unique point Q, called the *projection* of P on the x-axis. Being on the x-axis, the point Q has a coordinate; in this case the coordinate is 2. Thus 2 is said to be the *x-coordinate* of point P.

The *y-coordinate* of P is determined in precisely the same manner, this time using the dotted line through P and perpendicular to the y-axis to determine the projection of P on the y-axis—call it point R. On the y-axis, R has the coordinate 3, and 3 is the y-coordinate of point P.

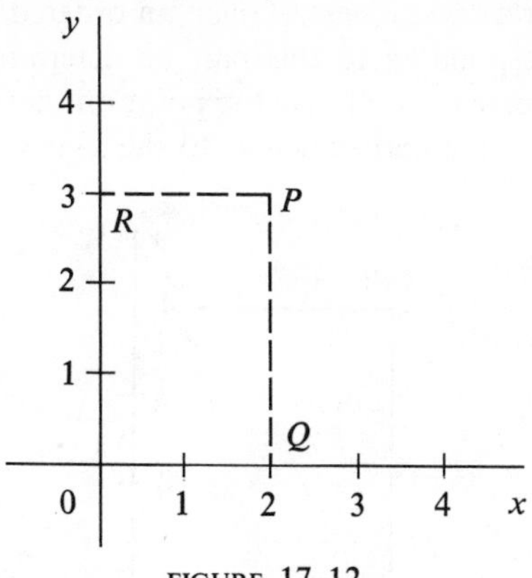

FIGURE 17–12

The essential idea of the preceding development is that a pair of numbers is assigned to a point in a plane. To point up the need for a pair of numbers, note (in Figure 17–13) that point G has the same x-coordinate, 2, as has point P.

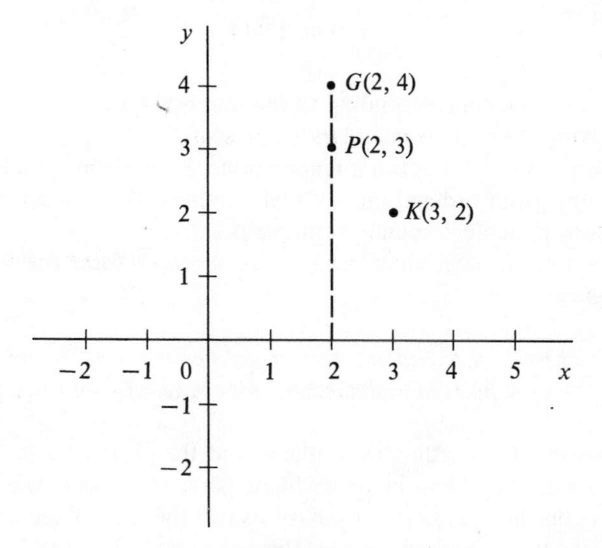

FIGURE 17–13

Hence, if just the x-coordinate 2 were specified, the point P would not be sufficiently described. (There are, in fact, an infinite number of points having an x-coordinate of 2.) However, of all points having x-coordinate 2, only point P has the y-coordinate 3. Therefore, the pair of numbers (2, 3) completely determines the point P. By agreement the x-coordinate is written first. Thus, the point with coordinates (3, 2) is *not* the same as the point with coordinates (2, 3). (Refer to points K and P of Figure 17–13.) For this reason, (2, 3) is called an *ordered pair* of numbers, and to each point of a plane an ordered pair of numbers, called coordinates of the point, may be assigned. (While the phrase "ordered pair" may be precisely defined in terms of sets, we use it here simply in the clear intuitive sense of meaning "x-coordinate first, y-coordinate second.")

We turn now to the reverse process. Given an ordered pair of numbers (x, y), how can a point corresponding to this pair be determined? To illustrate the process, let us use the pair $(-3, 4)$. At the point on the x-axis corresponding to the number -3, erect a line perpendicular to the x-axis (see Figure 17–14). At

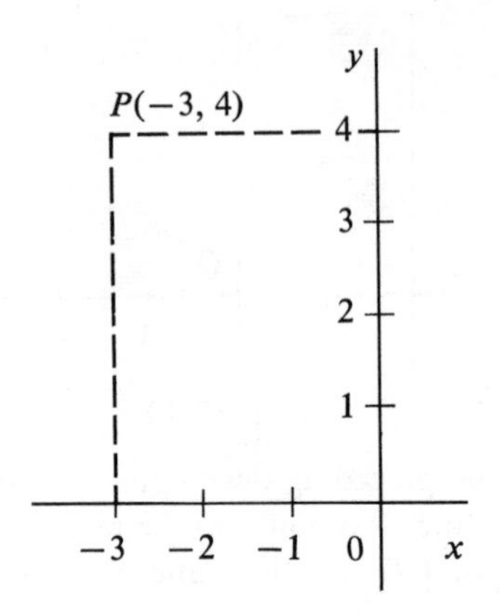

FIGURE 17–14

the point on the y-axis corresponding to the number 4, erect a perpendicular to the y-axis. Now these perpendiculars (represented by the dotted lines in the figure) are unique and intersect in a unique point P. And this procedure may be followed for any given ordered pair of real numbers; thus, to any ordered pair of real numbers, there corresponds a unique point.

On the basis of the preceding paragraphs, we now form the following important statement:

> *There is a one-to-one correspondence between the set of all ordered pairs of real numbers and the set of points in a plane.*

Thus, it is possible to coordinatize a plane, and the phrase "coordinate plane" is frequently used. Any point in a coordinate plane then has a pair of real numbers (x, y) as coordinates; it is customary to call the first of these numbers (x) the *abscissa*, and the second number (y) the *ordinate*. In Figure 17–15, a number of points, together with their coordinates, are shown. Special note should be made of points such as C which are on one of the axes themselves. It is true that, considering the x-axis as a number line, C has coordinate 3; however, considering C as a point of the plane, it—like all other points—has a pair of coordinates, in this case $(3, 0)$. The reader should make sure that he knows the difference between the point with coordinates $(3, 0)$ and the point with coordinates $(0, 3)$. Also, it is important to note that the coordinates of the origin are $(0, 0)$.

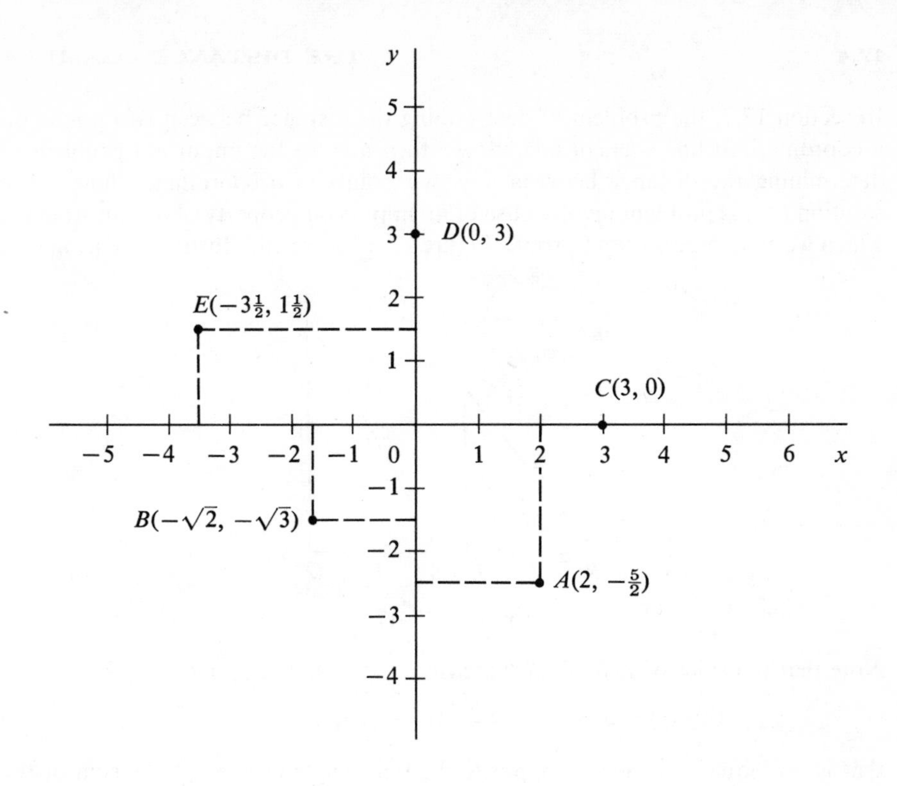

FIGURE 17–15

In an earlier chapter, separations of a plane were discussed; and, in the case of a coordinate plane, the axes separate the plane into four regions, called *quadrants*. These quadrants are usually referred to by number, as indicated by the Roman numerals in Figure 17–16. Consider a point P with coordinates (x, y) in the second quadrant; in this case, $x < 0$ and $y > 0$. The reader should make sure that he can describe the coordinates of points in the other quadrants in a similar way. (See Exercises, section 17.5.)

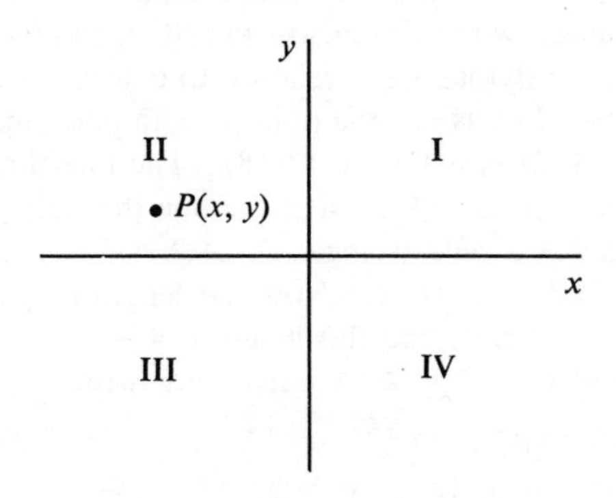

FIGURE 17–16

In section 17.2, the problem of determining the distance between two points on a coordinatized line was considered; we turn now to the important problem of determining the distance between any two points of a coordinate plane. The solution of this problem involves use of an important property of a right triangle, which we state here without proof. Figure 17–17 serves to illustrate the property.

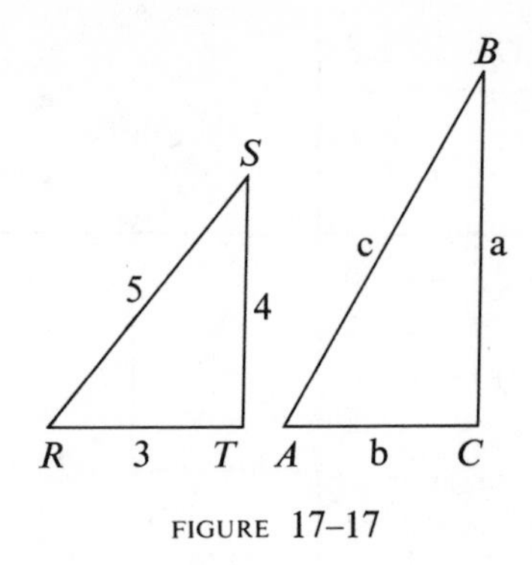

FIGURE 17–17

Note that the sides of $\triangle RST$ have measures of 3, 4, and 5, and

$$3^2 + 4^2 = 5^2 \qquad (9 + 16 = 25);$$

that is, the square of the side opposite the right angle is equal to the sum of the squares of the other two sides. (By "squaring a side," of course, we mean "squaring the measure" of that side.) This equality is a property of any right triangle. Thus, if c is the measure of the side opposite the right angle of a right triangle, and a and b are the measures of the other two sides, then

$$c^2 = a^2 + b^2.$$

This important property is known as the *Pythagorean relation* named after the Greek mathematician Pythagoras.

The converse of the property is also valid. Thus, if the sides of a triangle measure 6, 8, and 10, the triangle is a right triangle since $10^2 = 6^2 + 8^2$. On the other hand, a triangle with sides measuring 10, 6, and 9 is *not* a right triangle.

Now we shall use the Pythagorean relation to determine the distance between two points of a plane. Let us use the point P with coordinates (4, 6) and point Q with coordinates (1, 2) (see Figure 17–18). The line through P and perpendicular to the x-axis intersects at point A the line through Q and perpendicular to the y-axis; in this way a right triangle, $\triangle PAQ$, is formed. The coordinates of A are easily determined to be (4, 2). Now the length of $\overline{QA}$ is the same as the length of $\overline{Q_1A_1}$ on the x-axis; and this length is $4 - 1$, or 3. In the same way, $m(\overline{PA}) = m(\overline{P_1A_2}) = 6 - 2 = 4$. We may now write:

$$\begin{aligned}(PQ)^2 &= 3^2 + 4^2\\ (PQ)^2 &= 9 + 16 = 25\\ PQ &= 5\end{aligned}$$

We are here using PQ to represent $m(\overline{PQ})$, or $d(P, Q)$; thus the distance between the points is 5.

The problem above may be generalized by considering two points P_1 and P_2, with coordinates (x_1, y_1) and (x_2, y_2), respectively (see Figure 17–19). For the

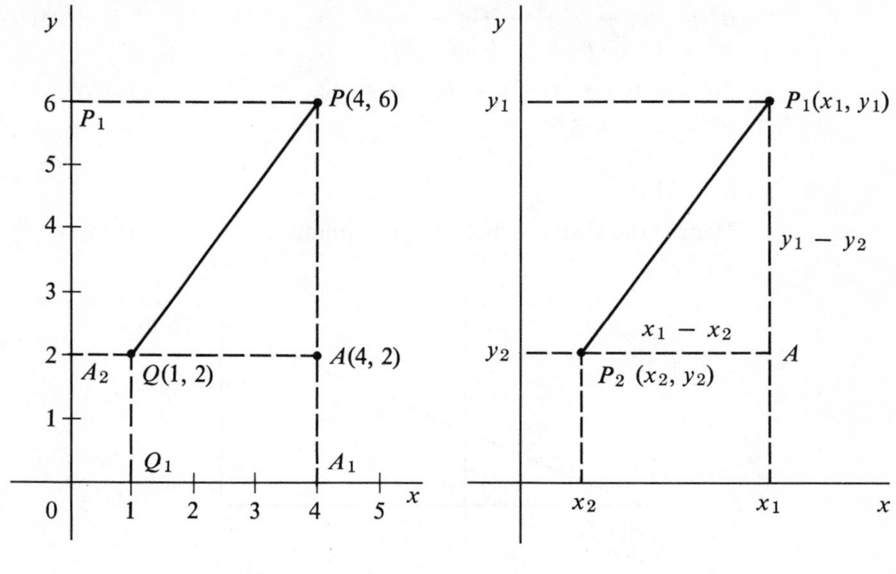

FIGURE 17–18 FIGURE 17–19

time being, we shall assume both points to be in the first quadrant, with $x_1 > x_2$ and $y_1 > y_2$. A right triangle P_1AP_2 may be formed as in the previous specific problem. Then $m(\overline{P_2A}) = x_1 - x_2$, and $m(\overline{P_1A}) = y_1 - y_2$. Using these results together with the Pythagorean relation, we have:

$$(P_1P_2)^2 = (x_1 - x_2)^2 + (y_1 - y_2)^2$$

$$P_1P_2 = \sqrt{(x_1 - x_2)^2 + (y_1 - y_2)^2}$$

In order to simplify the above derivation, certain assumptions were made concerning the coordinates of P_1 and P_2. Actually, such restrictions are unnecessary, as subsequent examples will illustrate. We have then the so-called "distance formula" which may be stated as follows:

If P_1 and P_2 are points in a plane with coordinates (x_1, y_1) and (x_2, y_2), respectively, and if d represents the distance between these points, then

$$d^2 = (x_1 - x_2)^2 + (y_1 - y_2)^2$$

or

$$d = \sqrt{(x_1 - x_2)^2 + (y_1 - y_2)^2}.$$

Note that the formula involves only the positive square root since we shall consider distance to be always positive.

EXAMPLE 3. R has coordinates $(-5, 3)$ and S has coordinates $(7, 8)$. Determine $d(R, S)$.

Solution: Let $x_1 = 7$, $y_1 = 8$, $x_2 = -5$, $y_2 = 3$.

$$d^2 = (x_1 - x_2)^2 + (y_1 - y_2)^2$$
$$d^2 = (7 - (-5))^2 + (8 - 3)^2$$

Note that $7 - (-5) = 7 + 5 = 12$.

$$d^2 = 12^2 + 5^2$$
$$d^2 = 169$$
$$d = 13$$

Hence, the distance between the points is 13 (see Figure 17–20).

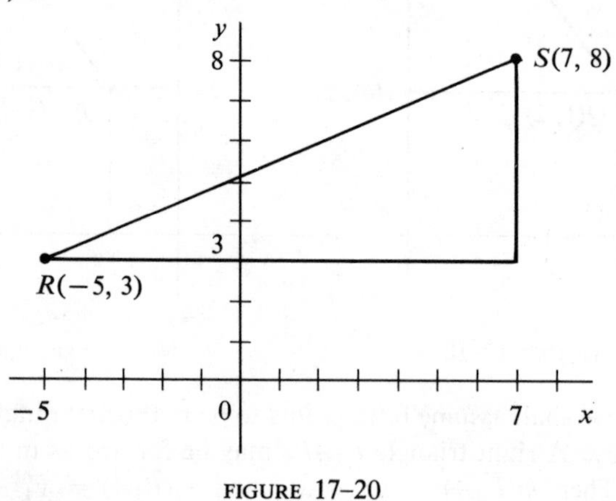

FIGURE 17–20

EXAMPLE 4. Here we determine again the distance between R with coordinates $(-5, 3)$ and S with coordinates $(7, 8)$.

Solution: This time we let $x_1 = -5$, $y_1 = 3$, $x_2 = 7$, and $y_2 = 8$.

$$d^2 = (x_1 - x_2)^2 + (y_1 - y_2)^2$$
$$d^2 = (-5 - 7)^2 + (3 - 8)^2$$

Note that $-5 - 7 = (-5) + (-7) = -12$;
$3 - 8 = 3 + (-8) = -5$.

$$d^2 = (-12)^2 + (-5)^2$$
$$d^2 = 144 + 25$$
$$d^2 = 169$$
$$d = 13$$

Thus, we see that in finding the distance between two points, it makes no difference which coordinates are designated as (x_1, y_1). A reexamination of the two examples above will reveal that in one case we obtain 12^2 and 5^2, and in the other case $(-12)^2$ and $(-5)^2$. These results are, however, the same since $12^2 = (-12)^2 = 144$ and $5^2 = (-5)^2 = 25$. (The reader needs to recall here that the product of two negative numbers is a positive number.)

EXAMPLE 5. Find the distance between the point with coordinates $(0, -6)$ and the point with coordinates $(5, 0)$.

Solution:

$$d^2 = (x_1 - x_2)^2 + (y_1 - y_2)^2$$
$$d^2 = (0 - 5)^2 + (-6 - 0)^2$$
$$d^2 = (-5)^2 + (-6)^2$$
$$d^2 = 25 + 36$$
$$d^2 = 61$$
$$d = \sqrt{61}$$

In some of the problems that follow, we employ the language "point (x, y)" as an elliptical expression for "point with coordinates (x, y)." Thus, we might say in Example 5 above that we found the distance between $(0, -6)$ and $(5, 0)$.

17.5 EXERCISES

1. Find the distance between two points on the number line if the coordinates of the two points are:

   (a) 10 and 3 (b) 10 and -3 (c) -10 and -3
   (d) 6 and 0 (e) -6 and 0 (f) 164 and 64
   (g) 164 and -64 (h) 1000 and -1000 (i) $7\frac{1}{2}$ and $-2\frac{3}{4}$
   (j) a and b $(a > b)$

2. A and B are two points on a number line, and $d(A, B) = 6\frac{1}{2}$. What is the coordinate of B if the coordinate of A is 4, and B is

   (a) to the right of A? (b) to the left of A?

3. Draw (preferably on graph paper) a pair of perpendicular axes; indicate the scale on each; locate and label the following points:

   (a) $(5, 2)$ (b) $(2, 5)$ (c) $(5, -2)$
   (d) $(-2, 5)$ (e) $(-5, -2)$ (f) $(-2, -5)$
   (g) $(-5, 2)$ (h) $(2, -5)$ (i) $(4, 0)$
   (j) $(-4, 0)$ (k) $(0, 4)$ (l) $(0, -4)$
   (m) $(6\frac{1}{2}, \sqrt{2})$ (n) $(-\sqrt{2}, -2\frac{1}{4})$ (o) $(\sqrt{3}, -3)$

4. If (x, y) represents the coordinates of point P, in which quadrant of the plane is P if

   (a) $x > 0$ and $y > 0$. (b) $x > 0$ and $y < 0$.
   (c) $x < 0$ and $y > 0$. (d) $x < 0$ and $y < 0$.

5. Describe the set of points in the plane which have positive abscissas. (Recall that "abscissa" is a name for the x-coordinate.)

6. (a) Describe the set of points whose coordinates are of the form $(a, 0)$ where a is a real number.
   (b) Describe the set of points whose coordinates are of the form $(0, a)$ where a is a real number.
   (c) What are the coordinates of the origin?

7. (a) Explain why the coordinates of a point in the plane are described as an "ordered pair" rather than as simply a "pair."
   (b) Is $(8, 2) = (2, 8)$?
   (c) Is $\{8, 2\} = \{2, 8\}$?
   (d) Is $\{a, b\} = \{b, a\}$?
   (e) Is it ever the case that $(a, b) = (b, a)$?

8. (a) Determine the length of the side opposite the right angle of a right triangle if the other two sides measure 9 and 12?
   (b) If the three sides of a triangle have measures of 10, 11, and 14, is the triangle a right triangle?

9. (a) Determine the distance between the points (2, 5) and (10, 14).
   (b) Draw a sketch of the coordinate plane, showing the right triangle involved in the computation of this distance.

10. Determine the distance between the following pairs of points:

(a) (5, 5) and (10, 10)	(b) $(-3, 4)$ and (4, 1)
(c) $(-6, 0)$ and (0, 6)	(d) $(-4, -8)$ and (0, 0)
(e) (0, 0) and (4, 8)	(f) (100, 212) and (102, 215)
(g) (x_1, x_2) and (y_1, y_2)	(h) (a, b) and (c, d)

11. Use the distance formula to show that the triangle with vertices (2, 4), (7, 10) and (12, 4) is an *isosceles* triangle (that is, has two sides of equal length).

12. (a) Describe the set of all points whose distance from the origin is 5.
    (b) Does (3, 4) belong to this set?
    (c) Does $(-3, 4)$ belong to this set?
    (d) Does (2, 2) belong to this set?

17.6 SLOPE OF A LINE

Consider the points (1, 2) and (3, 6); these points determine a line, as we saw in Chapter 6, and this line is indicated in Figure 17–21. The difference between the ordinates of the two given points on the line is $6 - 2$, or 4; and the difference between the two abscissas is $3 - 1$, or 2. Often, the difference in ordinates is denoted by the symbol "Δy" (read "delta y") and the difference in abscissas is denoted by "Δx." Hence, in the example just cited, $\Delta y = 4$ and $\Delta x = 2$. Then the ratio of Δy to Δx is $\frac{\Delta y}{\Delta x}$, or $\frac{4}{2}$, or 2. Notice how Δx and Δy are illustrated in Figure 17–21; it might be said that "as

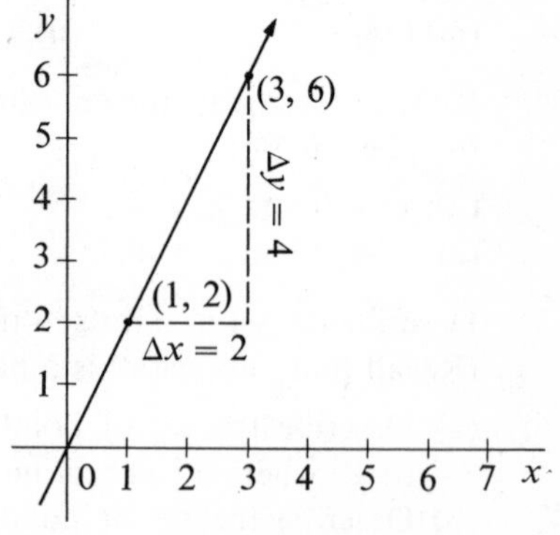

FIGURE 17–21

x increases from 1 to 3, y increases from 2 to 6," or "an increase of 2 in the value of x results in an increase of 4 in the value of y."

We obtained the value 2 for $\dfrac{\Delta y}{\Delta x}$ by considering the two points (1, 2) and (3, 6); there are of course an infinite number of points on the line determined by these two points, and we turn now to the problem of evaluating $\dfrac{\Delta y}{\Delta x}$ for various pairs of points on the line. From Figure 17–22, it appears (as is indeed the case) that the following points are also on the line under discussion:

$$A(4, 8), \quad B(-1, -2), \quad C(-2, -4)$$

Let us now use the points A and B, and evaluate $\dfrac{\Delta y}{\Delta x}$. In this case,

$$\Delta y = 8 - (-2) = 10,$$
$$\Delta x = 4 - (-1) = 5,$$

and

$$\frac{\Delta y}{\Delta x} = \frac{10}{5} = 2,$$

the same value obtained before. In Figure 17–22, we see that we have just evaluated the ratio $\dfrac{AE}{BE}$ and found it to be the same as the ratio $\dfrac{ST}{RT}$. (In fact, the triangles ABE and SRT are *similar*, and the ratios of corresponding sides are equal.) If the points B and C are used to compute $\dfrac{\Delta y}{\Delta x}$, we obtain

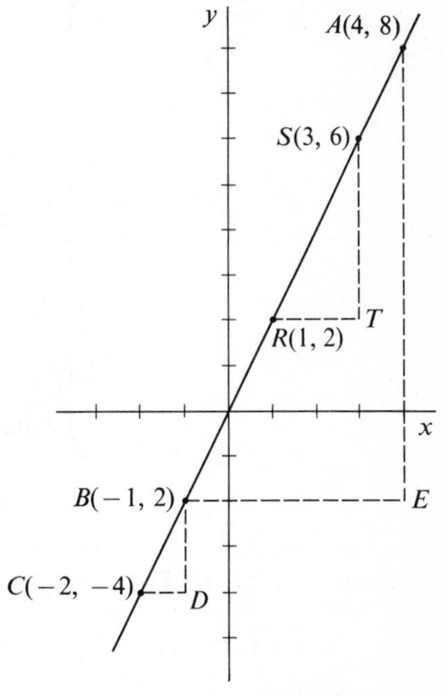

FIGURE 17–22

$$\frac{-2 - (-4)}{-1 - (-2)} = \frac{-2 + 4}{-1 + 2} = \frac{2}{1} = 2$$

the same value as before (see $\triangle BCD$ in the figure). In fact, no matter which two points of this line are used, the value of $\dfrac{\Delta y}{\Delta x}$ is 2. For it is a property of a line that the ratio $\dfrac{\Delta y}{\Delta x}$ is constant (that is, the same for every pair of points on the line). In the light of this property, we make the following definition:

DEFINITION: *If (x_1, y_1) and (x_2, y_2) are two distinct points of a line, then the ratio $\dfrac{y_2 - y_1}{x_2 - x_1}$ is called the* slope *of the line.*

In this definition, of course, $y_2 - y_1 = \Delta y$ and $x_2 - x_1 = \Delta x$ so that we might also say that the slope of a line is given by the expression $\dfrac{\Delta y}{\Delta x}$. The concept of slope is an all-important one in analytic geometry and calculus, and we shall attempt to clarify it further by means of specific examples.

EXAMPLE 6. What is the slope of the line determined by $P_1(3, 7)$ and $P_2(2, 4)$ (see Figure 17–23)?

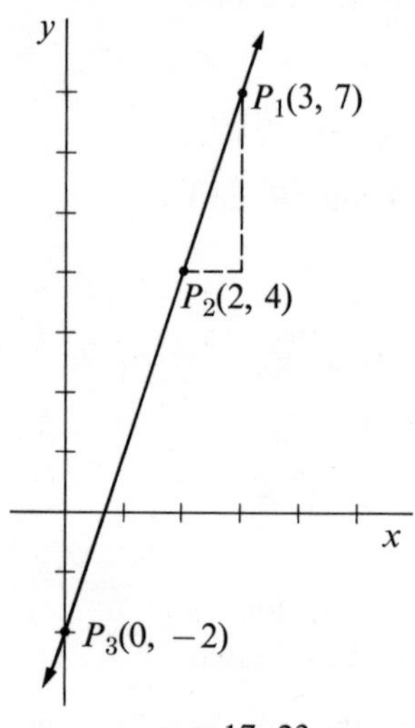

FIGURE 17–23

Solution: Let $(3, 7) = (x_2, y_2)$ and $(2, 4) = (x_1, y_1)$. Then

$$y_2 - y_1 = 7 - 4 = 3$$

and

$$x_2 - x_1 = 3 - 2 = 1.$$

Thus we have

$$\frac{y_2 - y_1}{x_2 - x_1} = \frac{3}{1} = 3,$$

and the slope of the line is 3. This means that an increase of 1 unit in x corresponds to an increase of 3 units in y.

In Example 6, the reader should show the result is unchanged if (2, 4) is designated as (x_2, y_2) and (3, 7) as (x_1, y_1). Also, it should be shown the same result is obtained by using $P_3(0, -2)$—which is also on the line—and P_1, or P_3 and P_2.

In the examples so far, the slope has been a positive number; in the next example, we shall see what is meant by a negative slope.

EXAMPLE 7. What is the slope of the line containing the points (2, −1) and (−2, 5) (see Figure 17–24)?

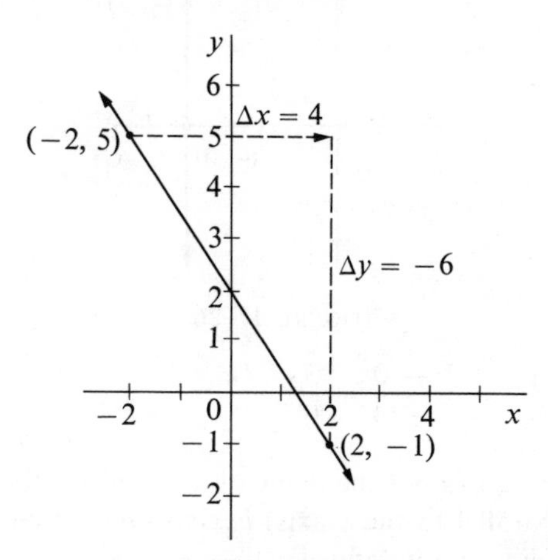

FIGURE 17–24

Solution:

$$\frac{y_2 - y_1}{x_2 - x_1} = \frac{5 - (-1)}{-2 - 2} = \frac{6}{-4} = -\frac{3}{2}$$

Thus, the ratio $\frac{\Delta y}{\Delta x}$ is negative, which means that an increase in x results in a *decrease* in the value of y. Specifically, in this case, for every two units increase in the value of x, the value of y is decreased three units. Equivalently, if $\Delta x = 1$, $\Delta y = -\frac{3}{2}$; if $\Delta x = 4$, $\Delta y = -6$ (see Figure 17–24).

EXAMPLE 8. What is the slope of the line containing (0, 4) and (3, 4) (see Figure 17–25)?

Solution: Here,

$$\frac{y_2 - y_1}{x_2 - x_1} = \frac{4 - 4}{3 - 0}$$

$$= \frac{0}{3} = 0.$$

Thus, the slope of this line (parallel to the x-axis) is zero.

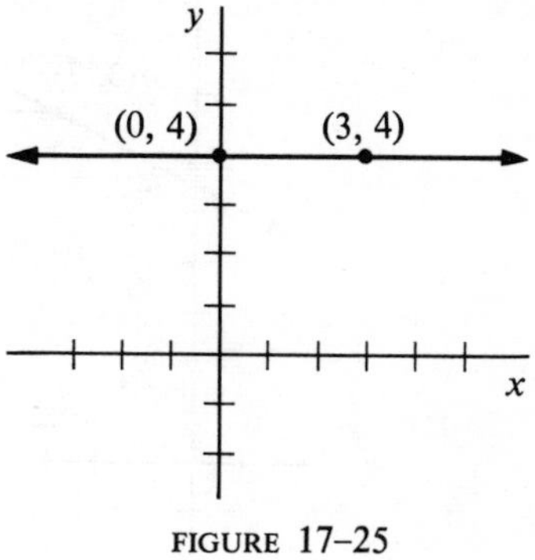

FIGURE 17–25

EXAMPLE 9. What is the slope of the line containing (4, 0) and (4, 3) (see Figure 17–26)?

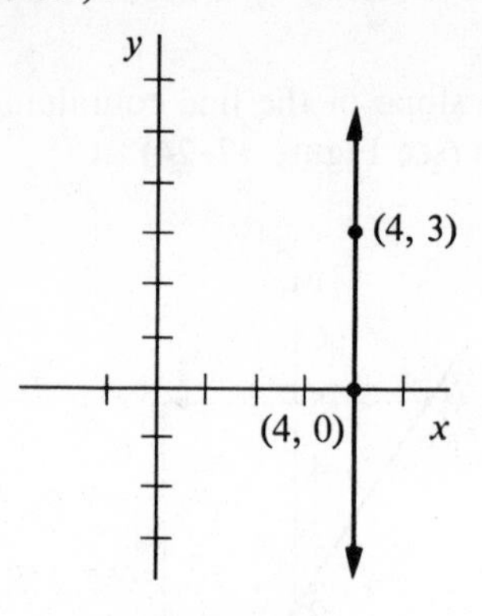

FIGURE 17–26

Solution:
$$\frac{y_2 - y_1}{x_2 - x_1} = \frac{3 - 0}{4 - 4} = \frac{3}{0}$$

However, $\frac{3}{0}$ is not the name of any real number; hence this line (parallel to the y-axis) *has no slope*—that is, the slope of the line is not defined.

Examples 8 and 9 serve to emphasize the distinction between "slope zero" and "no slope." To say that the slope of a line is 0 is to say that its slope is defined, and the value is 0; to say that a line has no slope is to say that the slope of the line is simply not defined, and so has no value.

The symbol "m_{AB}" is sometimes used to denote the slope of the line determined by points A and B; this symbol is used in Example 10.

EXAMPLE 10. If $m_{AB} = \frac{1}{2}$ and A has coordinates (3, 7), what is the ordinate of B if the abscissa of B is 9 (see Figure 17–27)?

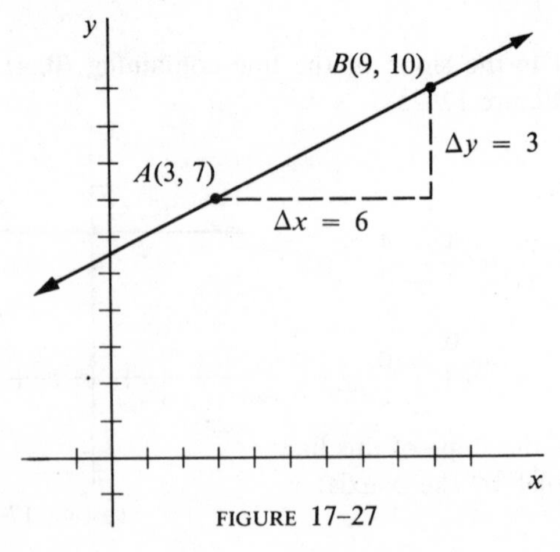

FIGURE 17–27

Solution: $\Delta x = 6$. Since $m_{AB} = \frac{1}{2}$, we know that

$$\frac{\Delta y}{\Delta x} = \frac{1}{2}$$

and

$$\frac{\Delta y}{6} = \frac{1}{2}.$$

So, $\Delta y = 3$. The ordinate of A is 7, so the ordinate of B is $7 + 3$, or 10. (9, 10) then are the coordinates of B.

17.7 PARALLEL LINES

In coordinate geometry, there is a simple test for parallel lines:

Two lines are parallel if and only if they have equal slopes.

That is, if two lines are parallel, they have equal slopes; and, conversely, if two lines have equal slopes, they are parallel. (This definition admits the possibility of a line being parallel to itself.)

A few examples of this test for parallel lines should serve both to clarify and justify it.

EXAMPLE 11. Given the following four points $A(3, 2)$, $B(5, 6)$, $C(6, 3)$, and $D(8, 7)$. Are lines $\overleftrightarrow{AB}$ and $\overleftrightarrow{CD}$ parallel (see Figure 17–28)?

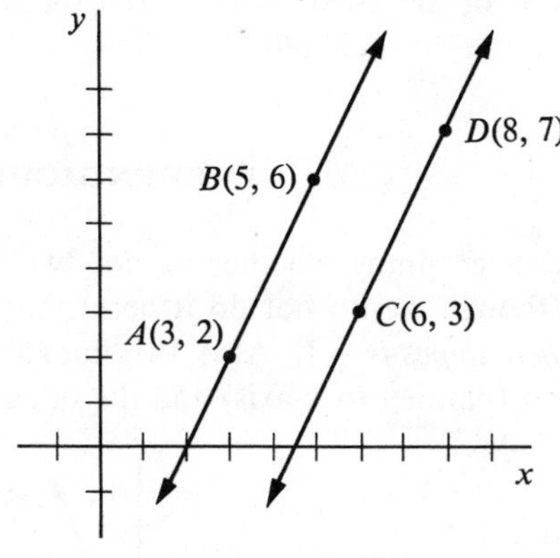

FIGURE 17–28

Solution:

$$m_{AB} = \frac{6 - 2}{5 - 3} = \frac{4}{2} = 2$$

$$m_{CD} = \frac{7 - 3}{8 - 6} = \frac{4}{2} = 2$$

$m_{AB} = m_{CD}$. Therefore, lines $\overleftrightarrow{AB}$ and $\overleftrightarrow{CD}$ are parallel.

EXAMPLE 12. If a line $\overleftrightarrow{RS}$ through $R(5, 2)$ is to be parallel to a line with slope -2, what are the coordinates of S if S is on the y-axis?

Solution: Consider the points R and S. R has abscissa 5. S is on the y-axis; hence, the abscissa of S is 0. Thus, $\Delta x = 5 - 0$. The ordinate of R is 2; the ordinate of S is to be determined.

$$\frac{\Delta y}{\Delta x} = \frac{2 - y}{5 - 0} = \frac{2 - y}{5}$$

But $\frac{2 - y}{5} = -2$ since the slope of $\overleftrightarrow{RS}$ is to be -2.

$$2 - y = -10 \qquad -y = -12 \qquad y = 12$$

Therefore, the coordinates of S are $(0, 12)$.

EXAMPLE 13. What is the slope of a line which is parallel to the x-axis?

Solution: $(3, 0)$ and $(5, 0)$ are two points on the x-axis (any two points on the axis may be selected). Therefore, the slope of the x-axis is

$$\frac{y_2 - y_1}{x_2 - x_1} = \frac{0 - 0}{5 - 3} = \frac{0}{2} = 0.$$

Therefore, the slope of the x-axis is zero; and the slope of any line parallel to the x-axis is zero.

17.8 PERPENDICULAR LINES

There is also a simple test for determining whether or not two lines are perpendicular. It can be shown (though we do not do it here) that *two lines are perpendicular if the product of their slopes is* -1. Also, two lines are perpendicular if one line has a slope of zero (parallel to x-axis) and the other has no slope (parallel to y-axis).

EXAMPLE 14. Is the line through $A(1, 5)$ and $B(-2, -1)$ perpendicular to the line through $C(2, 2)$ and $D(4, 1)$ (see Figure 17–29)?

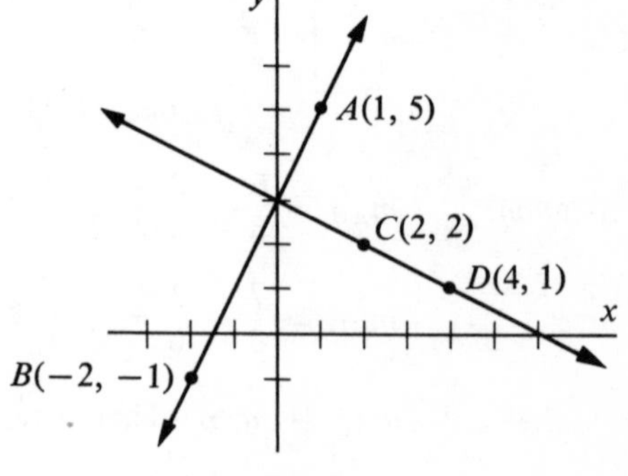

FIGURE 17–29

Solution: $m_{AB} = \dfrac{-1 - 5}{-2 - 1} = \dfrac{-6}{-3} = 2$

$$m_{CD} = \frac{1 - 2}{4 - 2} = \frac{-1}{2} = -\frac{1}{2}$$

$$(m_{AB})(m_{CD}) = (2)\left(-\frac{1}{2}\right) = -1$$

Since the product of the slopes is -1, the lines are perpendicular.

Two numbers whose product is -1 are said to be *negative reciprocals* (their product is -1 rather than 1). Consequently, one may say that two lines are perpendicular if their slopes are negative reciprocals.

EXAMPLE 15. What is the slope of any line which is perpendicular to the line containing $R(8, 2)$ and $S(1, 6)$?

Solution: $m_{RS} = \dfrac{6 - 2}{1 - 7} = \dfrac{4}{-6} = -\dfrac{2}{3}$

So, the slope of a line perpendicular to $\overleftrightarrow{RS}$ must be $\frac{3}{2}$ since $(-\frac{2}{3})(\frac{3}{2}) = -1$.

17.9 EXERCISES

1. Each of the following pairs of points determine a line. Find the slope of each line:

   (a) (5, 2) and (7, 4) (b) (5, 4) and (7, 2)
   (c) (0, 6) and (3, 0) (d) (0, 3) and (6, 0)
   (e) (−2, 8) and (4, 3) (f) (8, 0) and (−3, 0)
   (g) (−5, −2) and (−1, 6) (h) (4, −3) and (−3, 4)
   (i) (0, 6) and (0, −6) (j) (a, b) and (c, d) $(b \neq d)$

2. Given that the slope of a line is 2,
   (a) how does the value of y change if the value of x is increased by 1?
   (b) if (4, 3) is on the line, what is the ordinate on the line having abscissa 9?
   (c) how does the value of y change if the value of x is decreased by 1?
   (d) if (4, 3) is on the line, what is the ordinate of the point on the line having abscissa 1?

3. A certain line contains point (4, 4) and has slope -2.
   (a) What are the coordinates of the point at which the line intersects the x-axis?
   (b) What are the coordinates of the point at which the line intersects the y-axis?

4. A certain line contains point $(-2, 3)$ and has slope $\frac{1}{2}$. Determine the coordinates of the following points on the line:
   (a) the point with abscissa 2   (b) the point with abscissa -8
   (c) the point with ordinate 4   (d) the point with ordinate 1
5. Give the coordinates of five different points which are on the line
   (a) containing the origin and having slope 5.
   (b) containing the origin and having slope $\frac{1}{5}$.
   (c) containing the origin and having slope -5.
   (d) containing the origin and having slope $-\frac{1}{5}$.
6. (a) What is the slope of the line determined by (a, c) and (b, c)?
   (b) What is the slope of the line determined by (r, s) and (r, t)?
7. Given $A(0, 0)$, $B(2, 5)$, $C(8, 5)$, $D(6, 0)$,
   (a) plot the four points.
   (b) draw the following segments: $\overline{AB}$, $\overline{BC}$, $\overline{CD}$, $\overline{DA}$.
   (c) show, by use of slopes, that $\overline{AB}$ and $\overline{CD}$ are parallel (two segments are parallel if the lines containing them are parallel).
   (d) show that $\overline{BC}$ and $\overline{DA}$ are parallel.
8. Given $E(0, 0)$, $F(10, 0)$, $G(14, 14)$, and $H(4, 6)$, determine whether the following pairs of segments are parallel or perpendicular or neither:
   (a) $\overline{EH}$ and $\overline{FG}$ (b) $\overline{EG}$ and $\overline{FH}$
   (c) $\overline{HG}$ and $\overline{EF}$ (d) $\overline{EH}$ and $\overline{HF}$
9. The points $(-3, 8)$ and $(4, -2)$ determine a line l.
   (a) What is the slope of a line parallel to l?
   (b) What is the slope of a line perpendicular to l?

★10. Use the concept of slope to show that the points $(2, 0)$, $(4, 4)$, and $(6, 8)$ are collinear.

17.10 SENTENCES AND SETS OF POINTS; LINES

It is apparent that the ordered pairs $(2, 2)$, $(-6, -6)$, and $(-1, -1)$ share a common characteristic. Specifically, the two coordinates in each pair are equal; that is, for each pair (x, y), $y = x$. It is also apparent that there are an infinite number of other pairs possessing this characteristic—$(0, 0)$, $(1, 1)$, $(-2\frac{1}{2}, -2\frac{1}{2})$, to name a few. Since it is impossible to list all of these pairs, it is best to indicate them in this way:

$$\{(x, y) : y = x\},$$

read "the set of all ordered pairs (x, y) such that $y = x$." (We are tacitly assuming, of course, that x and y are real numbers.) Some of the elements—

ordered pairs—of this set have been indicated by plotting the points in the coordinate plane which correspond to them (Figure 17–30). Studying the points,

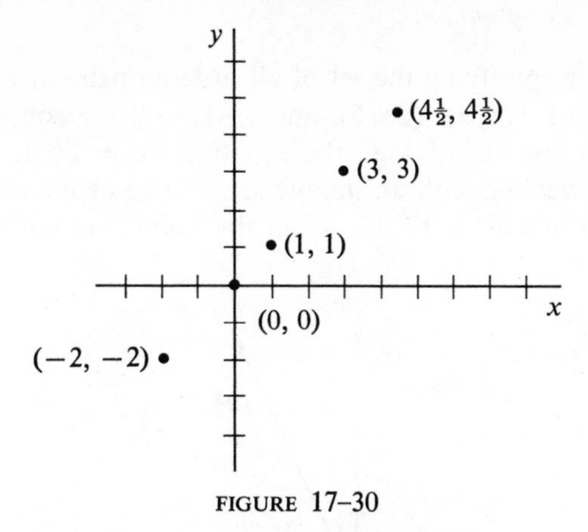

FIGURE 17–30

one immediately notices that they seem to be collinear; and indeed, although we do not prove it here, this is indeed the case. In fact, the line containing these points (see Figure 17–31) contains all those points—and only those points—

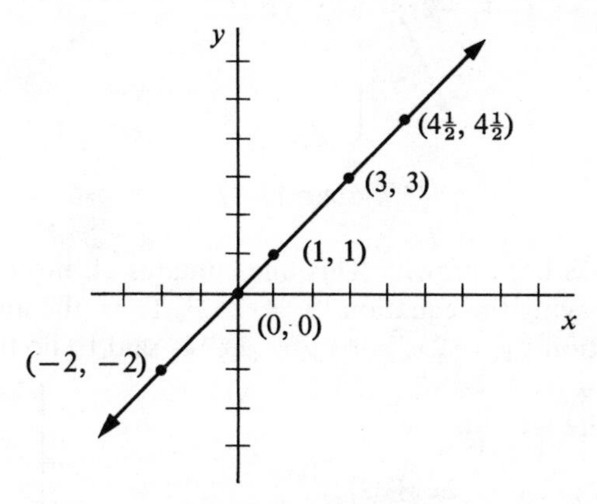

FIGURE 17–31

corresponding to ordered pairs (x, y) in which $y = x$. For this reason, we say that the line in Figure 17–31 is the *graph* of the set

$$\{(x, y) : y = x\}.$$

More succinctly, we may say that the line is the graph of the equation "$y = x$." Note that we have in effect identified an equation with a set of points in the following way:

1. Every ordered pair (x, y) having the property $y = x$ determines a point on the line.
2. Every point on the line has coordinates (x, y) which satisfy the equation "$y = x$."

As another illustration, we might consider the set

$$\{(x, y) : y = 2x\}.$$

In this case, we are specifying the set of all ordered pairs in which the ordinate is twice the abscissa. $(1, 2)$, $(2\frac{1}{2}, 5)$, and $(-1, -2)$ are some of the pairs belonging to this set (or "satisfying" the equation "$y = 2x$"); and it is obvious that we are again dealing with an infinite set. Some of the elements of this set have been plotted in Figure 17–32; again the points are collinear and the line

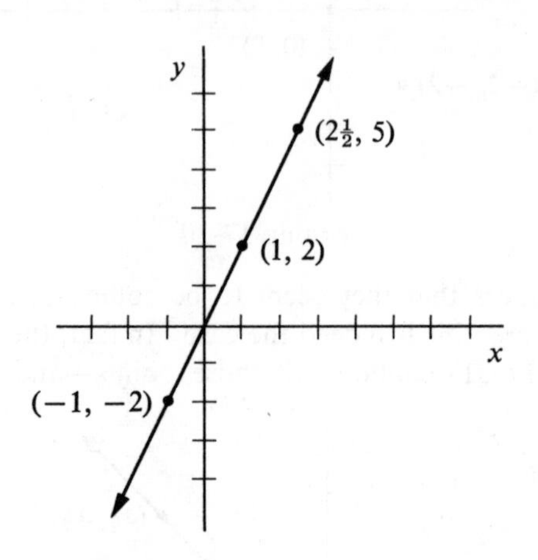

FIGURE 17–32

containing them has been drawn. This line contains all those points—and only those points—satisfying the equation "$y = 2x$." Thus, the line is said to be the graph of the equation "$y = 2x$," or "$y = 2x$" is said to be the equation of the line.

If we consider the set

$$\{(x, y) : y = 2x + 3\},$$

we see that the elements of this set can be obtained from the elements of

$$\{(x, y) : y = 2x\}$$

by adding 3 to each ordinate. Thus, whereas $(1, 2)$, $(2\frac{1}{2}, 5)$, and $(-1, -2)$ satisfy the equation "$y = 2x$," $(1, 5)$, $(2\frac{1}{2}, 8)$ and $(-1, 1)$ satisfy "$y = 2x + 3$." As we might expect, then, the graph of "$y = 2x + 3$" is a line which may be considered as the graph of "$y = 2x$" translated upward 3 units (for each x on this new line, the y value is 3 more than it was on the old line.) Both lines are shown in Figure 17–33.

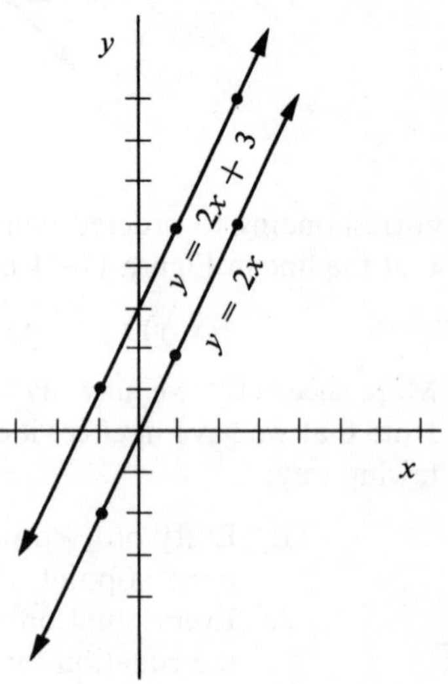

FIGURE 17–33

We make use of the foregoing illustration to introduce an important generalization.

The graph of any equation of the form

$$y = ax + b$$

where a and b are real numbers, is a line. In fact, we often speak of the "line $y = ax + b$" when referring to the graph of such an equation. In the equation "$y = 2x + 3$" the value of a is 2, and the value of b is 3.

For clarification of the generalization, we turn now to further examples of equations of the form "$y = ax + b$," often called *linear* equations.

EXAMPLE 16. Is "$y = 4x - 2$" a linear equation? If so, draw the graph. What is the slope of the line (see Figure 17–34)?

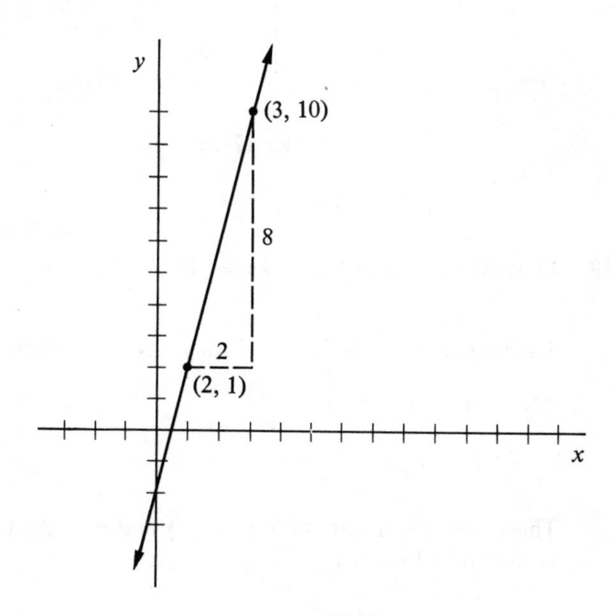

FIGURE 17–34

Solution: If x is 1, y is 2 $(y = 4(1) - 2)$. Thus, the pair (1, 2) satisfies the equation. Similarly, (3, 10) satisfies the equation. The equation is linear since it is of the form "$y = ax + b$" with $a = 4$, $b = -2$. Therefore, the graph can be drawn by drawing the line determined by points (1, 2) and (3, 10). As shown in the figure, the slope of the line is

$$\frac{10 - 2}{3 - 1} \text{ or } 4.$$

EXAMPLE 17. Draw the graph of "$y = 3$."

Solution: This may be considered as a linear equation "$y = ax + b$," with $a = 0$, $b = 3$. More simply, it is the set of all pairs with ordinate 3. Note from Figure 17–35 that the graph is a line parallel to the x-axis.

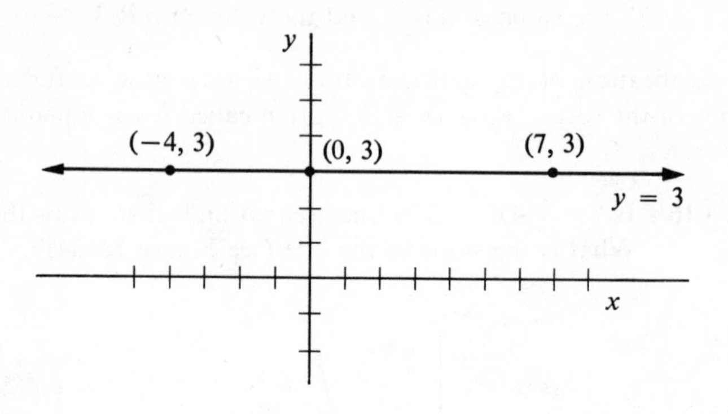

FIGURE 17–35

EXAMPLE 18. Draw the graph of "$x + 2y = 4$."

Solution: The equation "$x + 2y = 4$" may also be written as

"$2y = 4 - x$" or

"$y = 2 - \frac{1}{2}x$."

Therefore, it is linear, with $a = -\frac{1}{2}$ and $b = 2$. The graph is shown in Figure 17–36.

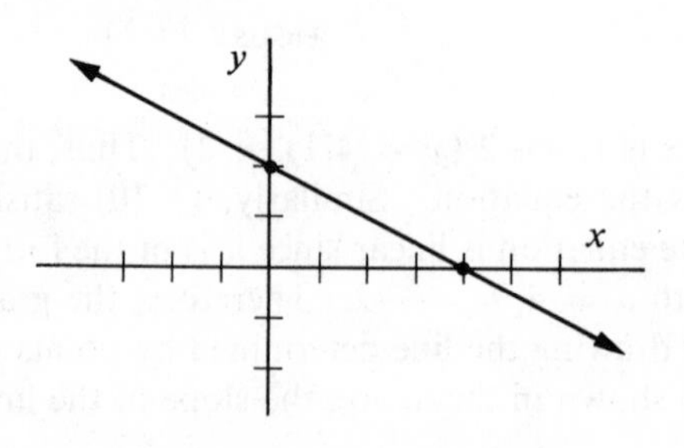

FIGURE 17–36

In Figure 17–37 is a representation of a circle with radius 5 and center at the origin; we seek the equation of this circle. Let $P(x, y)$ represent a point on the circle. Then, as shown in the figure, a right triangle OPA is determined; x and

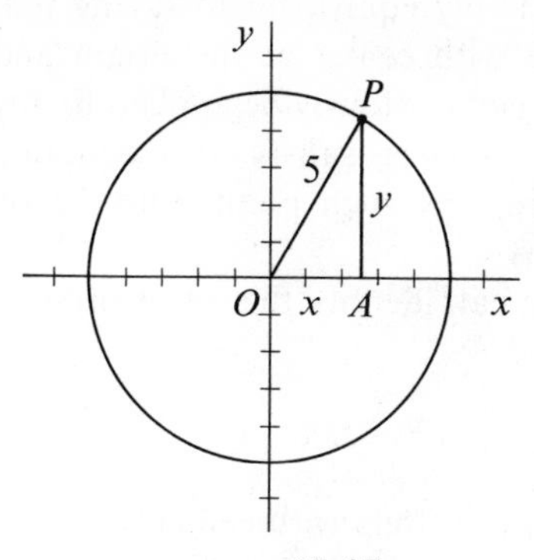

FIGURE 17–37

y—the coordinates of P—are the measures of two sides of this triangle, and 5—the radius of the circle—is the measure of the hypotenuse (side opposite the right angle). Therefore, by the Pythagorean relation (section 17.4), we have

$$x^2 + y^2 = 5^2$$

or

$$x^2 + y^2 = 25.$$

Now, this equation is applicable to the coordinates (x, y) of any point on the circle; Figure 17–38 shows a number of such points, together with the appro-

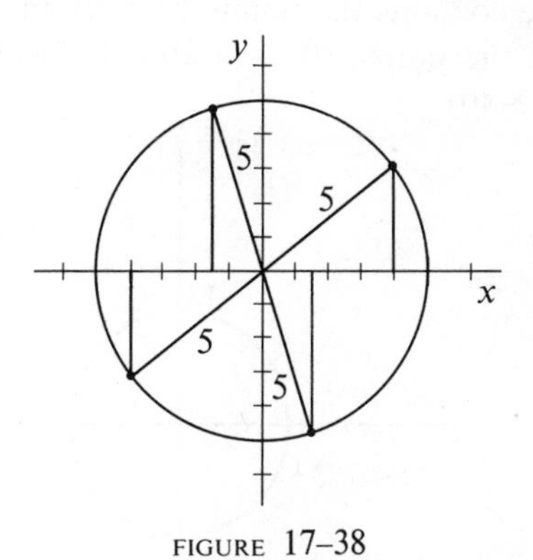

FIGURE 17–38

priate right triangle. The essential argument then is that for *any* point (x, y) on the circle, $x^2 + y^2 = 25$.

We may also reverse the preceding argument. In order to establish this procedure, let us consider the point (3, 4). Certainly $3^2 + 4^2 = 25$; that is, the point (3, 4) is one whose coordinates satisfy the equation $x^2 + y^2 = 25$. Hence, as shown in Figure 17–39, the right triangle OPA must have hypotenuse OP with measure 5. But this is simply equivalent to saying that $P(x, y)$ lies on the circle with center at the origin and radius 5. This argument can obviously be applied to any point (x, y) whose coordinates satisfy the equation $x^2 + y^2 = 25$; therefore, any such point must lie on the specified circle.

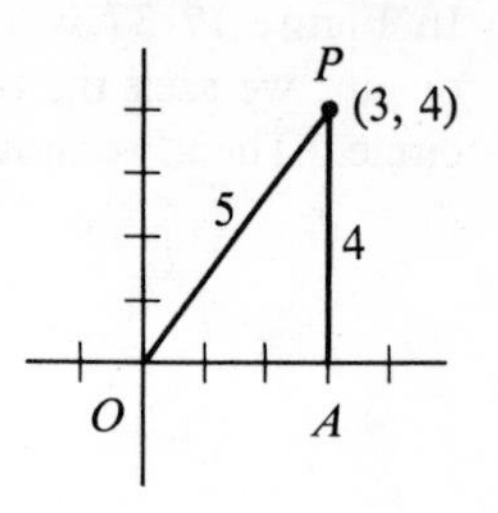

FIGURE 17–39

It follows then that we can identify the set of ordered pairs of real numbers

$$\{(x, y) : x^2 + y^2 = 25\}$$

with the set of points on the circle with center at the origin and radius 5; there is a one-to-one correspondence between the two sets. "$x^2 + y^2 = 25$" is said to be the *equation of the circle;* and the circle is called the *graph of the equation.*

Similarly, it can be shown that "$x^2 + y^2 = 16$" is the equation of a circle with center at the origin and radius 4. (The reader should carry through this argument for himself.) In fact, any equation of the form

$$x^2 + y^2 = r^2$$

is the equation of a circle with center at the origin and radius r ($r > 0$).

EXAMPLE 19. What is the graph of "$x^2 + y^2 - 1 = 0$"? This equation is of the form $x^2 + y^2 = r^2$, where $r = 1$. Hence, the graph is a circle with center (0, 0) and radius 1. Note that the circle contains the points $(-1, 0)$ and $(1, 0)$ on the x-axis and the points $(0, -1)$ and $(0, 1)$ on the y-axis (see Figure 17–40).

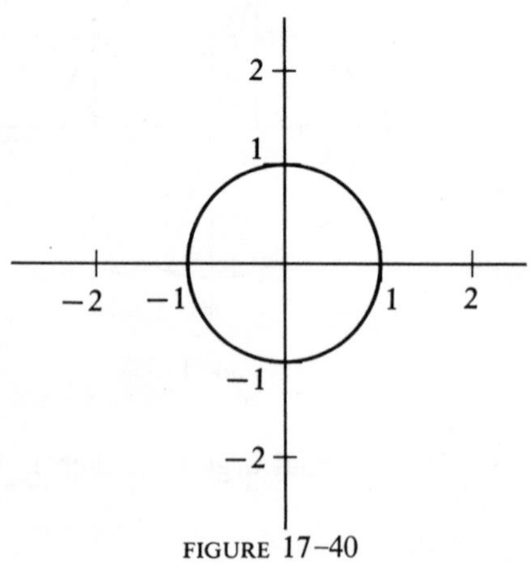

FIGURE 17–40

EXAMPLE 20. What is the equation of the circle with center (0, 0) and radius $\sqrt{2}$?

Solution: The equation must be of the form $x^2 + y^2 = r^2$, with $r = \sqrt{2}$. If $r = \sqrt{2}$, $r^2 = 2$. So, the required equation is $x^2 + y^2 = 2$.

EXAMPLE 21. Does the point $P(3, 1)$ lie on the circle with center (0, 0) and radius 4?

Solution: Any point (x, y) on this circle must satisfy the equation $x^2 + y^2 = 16$.

$$3^2 + 1^2 \neq 16$$

Therefore, the point (3, 1) is not on the given circle.

17.12 EXERCISES

1. For each of the following equations, list three ordered pairs satisfying the equation; then, using graph paper, plot the points corresponding to the pairs, and draw the line which is the graph of the equation:

(a) $y = x$ (b) $y = x + 2$ (c) $y = x - 2$
(d) $y = x + 3\frac{1}{2}$ (e) $y = 2x$ (f) $y = 2x + 3$
(g) $y = 2x - 1$ (h) $y = -x$ (i) $y = x + 4$
(j) $y = -x - 2$ (k) $y = \frac{1}{2}x$ (l) $y = \frac{1}{2}x + 3$
(m) $y = \frac{1}{2}x - 5$ (n) $y = \frac{1}{2}x + \frac{1}{2}$

2. (a) Determine the slope of each of the lines in problem 1. How does the slope of the line appear in the equation of the line?
(b) Each of the following equations is the equation of a line. Give the slope of the line by merely inspecting the equation:

$$y = 5x + 2; \quad y = -3x + 2; \quad y = ax + b$$

3. (a) For each of the lines in problem 1, determine the coordinates of the point at which it crosses the y-axis. How may these coordinates be determined from the equation of the line?
(b) For each of the following equations, give the coordinates of the point at which its graph crosses the y-axis:

$$y = 3x + 5; \quad y = 2x - \tfrac{1}{2}; \quad y = ax + b$$

4. Draw the graphs of the following equations (see Example 17 of section 17.10):

   (a) $y = 4$ (b) $y = -1$ (c) $y = \frac{3}{2}$
   (d) $y = 0$ (e) $x = 4$ (f) $x = -1$
   (g) $x = \frac{3}{2}$ (h) $x = 0$

5. (a) What is the form of the equation of a line parallel to the x-axis?
   (b) What is the form of the equation of a line parallel to the y-axis?
   (c) What is the equation of the x-axis?
   (d) What is the equation of the y-axis?

6. Draw the graphs of the following equations:

   (a) $x + y = 8$ ★(b) $2x + 3y = 12$

★7. Is the equation "$y = x^2$" a linear equation? Draw the graph of this equation, showing that it is not a straight line. (Hint: In plotting points, be sure to use some in which the value of x is negative.)

8. Use graph paper to draw the graphs of the following equations:

   (a) $x^2 + y^2 = 4$ (b) $x^2 + y^2 = 36$
   (c) $x^2 + y^2 - 100 = 0$ (d) $y^2 + x^2 = 49$
   (e) $x^2 + y^2 = \frac{9}{4}$ (f) $x^2 + y^2 = 0$
   ★(g) $x^2 + y^2 = -4$

9. Write the equations of the following circles:

   (a) center $(0, 0)$; radius 12
   (b) center $(0, 0)$; radius $\frac{7}{8}$
   (c) center $(0, 0)$; radius $\sqrt{5}$
   (d) center $(0, 0)$; radius 50
   (e) center $(0, 0)$; radius n

10. Determine three ordered pairs belonging to the following sets:

   (a) $\{(x, y) : x^2 + y^2 = 25\}$ (b) $\{(x, y) : x^2 + y^2 = 100\}$
   (c) $\{(x, y) : x^2 + y^2 = 169\}$ (d) $\{(x, y) : x^2 + y^2 = 1\}$

17.13 REGIONS

In section 17.10, it was observed that the graph of "$y = x$" is a line. Let us now consider the set

$$\{(x, y) : y > x\}.$$

Specifically, we shall consider the graph of the sentence "$y > x$." There are, of course, an infinite number of ordered pairs satisfying this sentence; to cite a few of them, there are (1, 2), (1, 5), (3, 6), (0, 5), (−1, 2), (−2, −1), (−2, 2), and (−2, 3), and the points corresponding to these pairs have been plotted in Figure 17–41. One notices immediately that each of these points lies in the half plane "above" the line "$y = x$." In fact, all the pairs satisfying the inequality

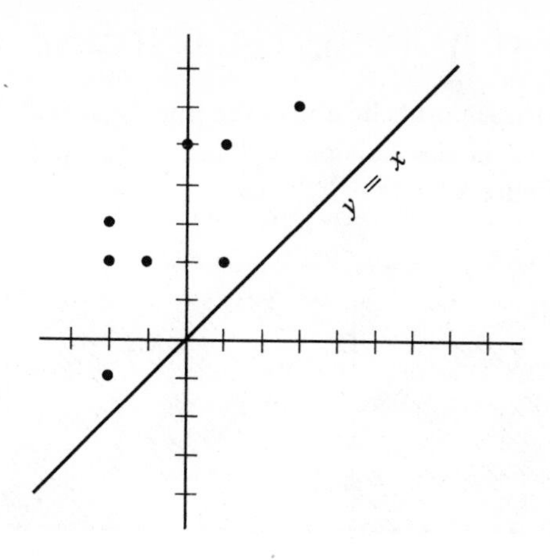

FIGURE 17–41

"$y > x$" correspond to points above the line "$y = x$." And all of the points above the line "$x = y$" have coordinates which satisfy the inequality "$y > x$." Thus, the graph of the sentence "$y > x$" is a region of the plane—namely, the half plane determined by, and lying above, the line "$y = x$." The graph is shown

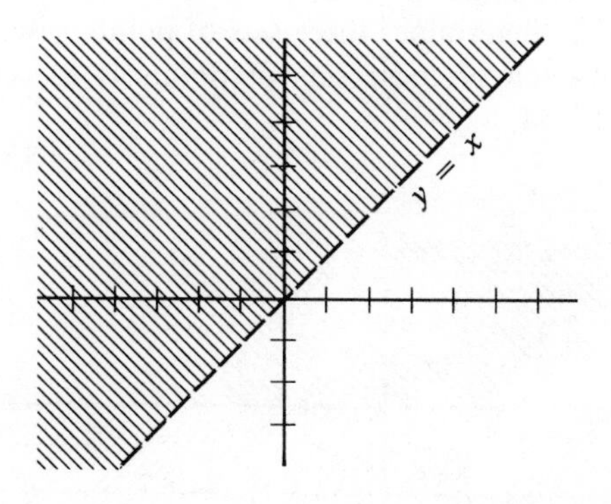

FIGURE 17–42

(by shading the appropriate region) in Figure 17–42; observe that the line $y = x$ itself is dotted in order to emphasize that the points of this line are not a part of the graph.

EXAMPLE 22. Sketch the graph of the sentence "$y > 2$."

Solution: Any ordered pair (x, y) in which the ordinate is greater than 2 satisfies this sentence. Examples of such pairs are

$$(0, 3),\quad (4, 3),\quad (3, 2\tfrac{1}{2}),\quad (-1, 4),\quad (-2, 6),\quad (-5, 5).$$

All of these points lie above the line "$y = 2$." The graph of "$y > 2$" is the half plane lying above the line "$y = 2$" (see Figure 17–43).

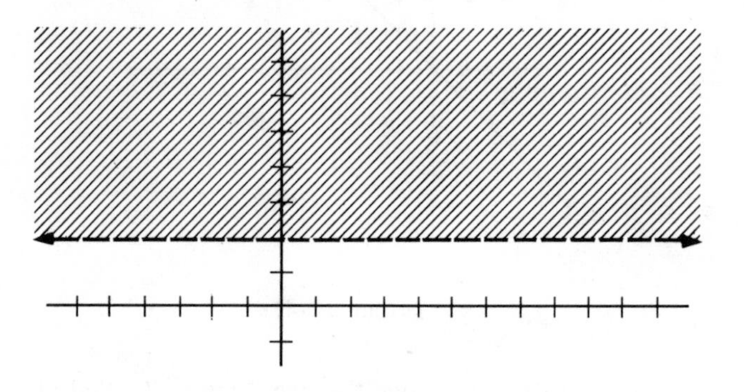

FIGURE 17–43

Continuing with the above example, you might have guessed that the sentence of the half plane below the line "$y = 2$" is "$y < 2$"—and that is indeed the case. Thus, the line "$y = 2$" determines three sets of points—two half planes and the line itself—and with each of these sets of points is associated a sentence, as indicated in Figure 17–44.

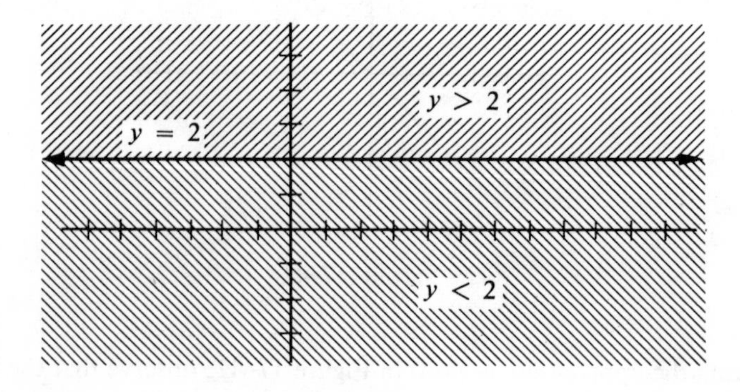

FIGURE 17–44

Although it lies somewhat beyond the province of this text, one significant use of coordinate geometry lies in proving geometric theorems. For illustrative purposes, an outline of such a proof is considered here. Suppose it is required to prove the following:

THEOREM: *The diagonals of a square are perpendicular to each other.*

Proof: Let the measure of each side of the square be a. Then the square can be considered in the coordinate plane in the following way. Let one vertex, A, be at the origin and one side $\overline{AD}$ be a subset of the positive ray of the x-axis. The coordinates of D will then be $(a, 0)$. Why? If we take side $\overline{AB}$ as a subset of the positive ray of the y-axis, the coordinates of B will be $(0, a)$. Why? Also the coordinates of the fourth vertex of the square, C, will be (a, a). Why? (See Figure 17–45.)

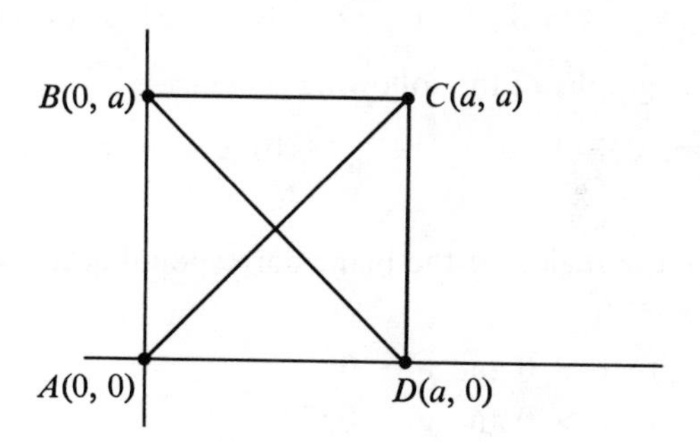

FIGURE 17–45

The slope of the diagonal $\overline{AC}$ is

$$\frac{a-0}{a-0} = \frac{a}{a} = 1.$$

The slope of diagonal BD is

$$\frac{a-0}{0-a} = \frac{a}{-a} = -1.$$

Since $(1)(-1) = -1$, we see that the slope of diagonal $\overline{BD}$ is the negative reciprocal of diagonal $\overline{AC}$. Therefore, as was to be proven, the diagonals of the square are perpendicular.

17.15 EXERCISES

1. (a) List ten different elements of the set
   $\{(x, y) : y < x\}$.

   (b) On graph paper, shade the region of the plane corresponding to the set in (a).

2. Use graph paper to show the regions of the plane corresponding to the following sentences:

   (a) $y > 1$ (b) $y > -1$ (c) $x > 1$
   (d) $x > -1$ (e) $y < 2$ (f) $y < -2$
   (g) $x < 2$ (h) $x < -2$

3. (a) Draw the graph of $y = x + 2$.
   (b) Draw the graph of $y > x + 2$.
   (c) Draw the graph of $y < x + 2$.
   (d) Describe the following set:

   $$\{(x, y) : y = x + 2\} \cup \{(x, y) : y > x + 2\} \cup \{(x, y) : y < x + 2\}$$

4. Draw the graphs of the following sentences:

   (a) $y > 2x + 3$ (b) $x < -x + 2$
   (c) $x + y < 8$ (d) $x + y < -8$

5. Describe the region of the plane corresponding to each of the following sets:

   (a) $\{(x, y) : x > 0 \text{ and } y > 0\}$
   (b) $\{(x, y) : x > 0 \text{ and } y < 0\}$
   (c) $\{(x, y) : x < 0 \text{ and } y > 0\}$
   (d) $\{(x, y) : x < 0 \text{ and } y < 0\}$

6. What is the equation of the y-axis?
   What is the equation of the x-axis?

7. If the expression $|x| = c$ means $x = c$ or $x = -c$, draw the graph of the sentence $|y - x| = 5$. Hint: This is the union of two lines.

8. Draw the graph of the region that satisfies both the sentences $y > x - 5$ and $y < x + 5$. Hint: The solution is an intersection of two regions.

9. Draw the graph of the region that satisfies both $x^2 + y^2 < 25$ and $y > 3$.

★10. Draw the graphs of the following sentences:

   (a) $y > x^2$ (b) $y < x^2$
   (c) $x^2 + y^2 < 4$ (d) $x^2 + y^2 > 4$

17.16 REFERENCE QUESTIONS

1. Coordinate geometry may be developed by using a finite "lattice" of points rather than the entire plane. For a discussion of such a development, see

   National Council of Teachers of Mathematics. *The Growth of Mathematical Ideas, K–12* (24th yearbook). Washington, D.C.: NCTM, 1959. Pp. 82–85.

2. How can the ideas of ordered pairs and graphs be translated to the level of the elementary classroom? See

   Driscoll, Lucy E. "Ordered Pairs, Patterns, and Graphs in Fourth Grade," *The Arithmetic Teacher*, 8: 127–130; 1961.

ANSWERS TO EXERCISES

Answers to most odd-numbered problems are given here. Answers to even-numbered problems are furnished in a separate booklet.

Exercises 1.4 Page 6

3. $\{x : x \text{ is a classroom in school } A\}$. There are rooms (e.g., the office) which are not in the set.

5. (a) $\{1, 2, 3, 4, 5\}$ (b) $\{6, 7, 8, 9\}$ (c) $\{1, 2, 3, 4\}$ (d) $\{8, 9\}$ (e) $\{6, 7, 8\}$ (f) $\{1, 2\}$ (g) $\{1, 2, 3, 4, 5, 6, 7, 8, 9\}$ (h) $\emptyset$ (i) $\{1, 2, 3, 4, 5, 6, 7, 8, 9\}$

7. (a), (e), and (h) are true.

9. $\{0, 1, 2, 3, 4, 5, 6, 7, 8, 9\}$

11. $\{2, 3, 4, 23, 24, 32, 34, 42, 43, 234, 243, 324, 342, 423, 432\}$

13. $\{1, 4, 9, 16, 25, 36, 49, 64, 81, 100\}$

15. $\{\text{team } A \text{ wins, team } B \text{ wins, tie}\}$

17. $\{x : x \text{ is in the English alphabet and } x \text{ is a vowel}\}$

19. $\{x : x \text{ is a consonant and acts sometimes as a vowel}\}$

21. $\{x : x \text{ is a symbol used to write Roman numerals}\}$

23. 0 is a number denoting the cardinality of the empty set; $\emptyset$ is not a number, but a set which contains no elements.

Exercises 1.6 Page 10

3. (a) $\{\emptyset, \{a\}, \{b\}, \{a, b\}\}$ (b) $\{\emptyset, \{a\}\}$
(c) There are sixteen subsets.
(d) If a set contains n elements, it has 2^n subsets.

9. Finite. The set could be counted, with the counting coming to an end.

11. $\{\frac{1}{1}, \frac{1}{2}, \frac{1}{3}, \frac{1}{4}, \frac{1}{5}, \frac{2}{1}, \frac{2}{2}, \frac{2}{3}, \frac{2}{4}, \frac{2}{5}, \frac{3}{1}, \frac{3}{2}, \frac{3}{3}, \frac{3}{4}, \frac{3}{5}, \frac{4}{1}, \frac{4}{2}, \frac{4}{3}, \frac{4}{4}, \frac{4}{5}, \frac{5}{1}, \frac{5}{2}, \frac{5}{3}, \frac{5}{4}, \frac{5}{5}\}$;
$\{\frac{1}{2}, \frac{1}{3}, \frac{1}{4}, \frac{1}{5}, \frac{2}{3}, \frac{2}{4}, \frac{2}{5}, \frac{3}{4}, \frac{3}{5}, \frac{4}{5}\}$

Exercises 1.9 Page 17

1. (a) $\{3, 5, 7\}$ (b) $\{1, 2, 3, 5, 7, 9\}$ (c) $\emptyset$ (d) $\{1, 2, 3, 4, 5, 6, 7, 8, 9\}$
(e) $\{2, 3, 4, 5, 6, 7, 8\}$ (f) $\{2\}$ (g) $\{1, 2, 3, 4, 5, 6, 7, 8, 9\}$
(h) $\{2, 3, 5, 7\}$ (i) $\{1, 2, 3, 4, 5, 6, 7, 8, 9\}$

3. Two sets may have an *intersection* which is the empty set; in this case, it may be said that the sets *do not intersect.*
5. (a) Contains all whole numbers except those giving a remainder 2 when divided by 3
   (b) Contains all whole numbers except those giving a remainder 1 when divided by 3
   (c) Contains all whole numbers (d) $\emptyset$
7. $A \cup B = B$; $A \cap B = A$
9. (a) The set of whole numbers whose units digit is 0, 2, 4, 6, or 8, which is the set of even numbers (b) The set of whole numbers whose units digit is 0, 4, or 8 and which are divisible by 4 (c) The set of whole numbers whose units digit is 2 or 6 and which are divisible by 4 (d) The set of all multiples of 4 (e) $\emptyset$

Exercises 1.12 Page 23

3.

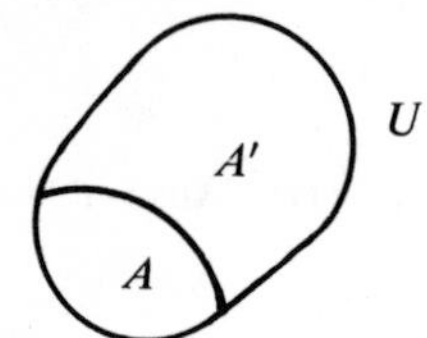

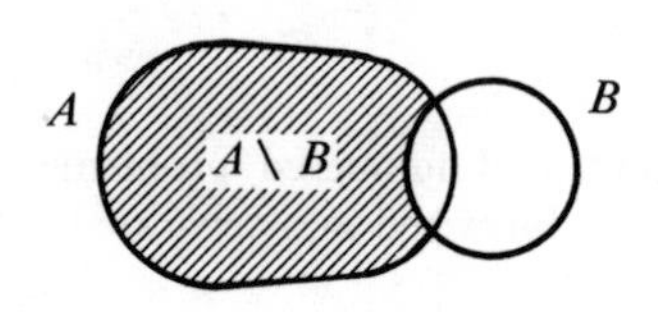

A' is related to subtraction in arithmetic.

5. $1 \leftrightarrow 1$
   $2 \leftrightarrow 4$
   $3 \leftrightarrow 9$
   $4 \leftrightarrow 16$
   etc.
7. There are 6 possible ways to map set A into set B. Set A cannot be mapped *onto* set B.
9. There are 6 possible mappings.
11. At least one seat would have to be assigned to two different people; this would not be an "into" mapping. The seats can be mapped into the audience; some of the persons would not be assigned to a seat.

Exercises 1.14 Page 28

1. (a) 676 (b) (2, 5), (9, 12), . . .
   (c) $\{(0, 0), (1, 1), (2, 4), (3, 9), (4, 16), (5, 25)\}$
3. Not precisely defined
5. It is reflexive and transitive. It is not an equivalence relation, since it is not symmetric.
7. It is an equivalence relation.

Exercises 2.4 Page 35

1. Two sets are equal if they contain precisely the same elements; two sets are equivalent if they contain the same number of elements.
3. A set is simply a collection of elements; a cardinal number is an abstract property of a set.
5. Yes
7. There are six possible bijections.

9. 24 mappings are possible.
13. 0; 1; 0; 1; 2
15. $\{\ \}$, $\{\{\ \}\}$, $\{\{\ \}, \{\{\ \}\}\}$, $\{\{\ \}, \{\{\ \}\}, \{\{\ \}, \{\{\ \}\}\}\}$,
$\{\{\ \}, \{\{\ \}\}, \{\{\ \}, \{\{\ \}\}\}, \{\{\ \}, \{\{\ \}\}, \{\{\ \}, \{\{\ \}\}\}\}\}$
17. If a and b are the numbers, then $a < b$, $a = b$, or $b < a$.

Exercises 2.8 Page 42

1. Both "third" and "eighth" refer to the position of an element in an ordered set.
3. You could, if you wished to begin counting by counting the empty set as the set having cardinality 0.
5. (a) Objects are grouped into sets of five, and these sets are then matched with the ordered set $\{5, 10, 15, 20, \ldots\}$.
   (b) Objects are grouped into sets of two, and these sets are then matched with the ordered set $\{2, 4, 6, 8, \ldots\}$.
7. The tally marks may be placed into one-to-one correspondence with the ordered set $\{1, 2, 3, 4, 5, \ldots\}$.

9. 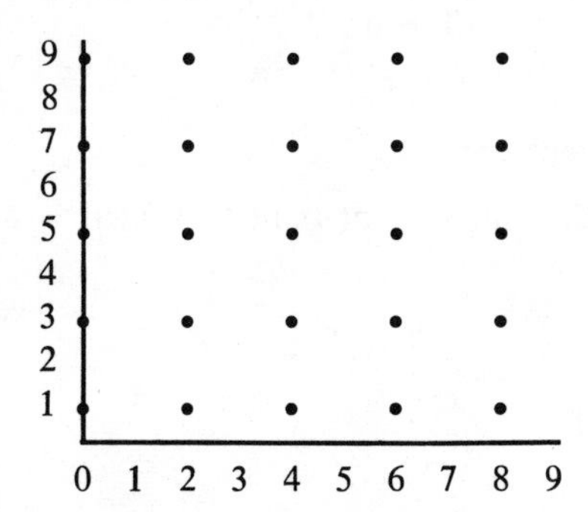

11. There are 6 outfits in the product set.
15. The two teams are equivalent sets, since they each have cardinality 5. If the two teams are matched in order, right guard to right guard, left guard to left guard, etc., the two sets are similar.
17. The cardinal number of the set is "six," since it can be matched one-to-one with any set having this cardinality, without regard to order in which the elements are taken. The ordinal number of the set is "six," since it can be matched with all sets of six elements arranged in a definite order.

Exercises 2.10 Page 46

1. (a) (2, 3), (2, 5), (2, 7), (4, 3), (4, 5), (4, 7), (6, 3), (6, 5), (6, 7)
   (b) (2, 3), (2, 5), (2, 7), (4, 5), (4, 7), (6, 7)
   (c) (2, 3), (4, 5), (6, 7)
5. The domain is the set of all whole numbers; the range is the set of whole numbers which are perfect squares.
7. (a) (II) and (IV) are functions. (b) The domain in each case is $\{1, 2, 3, 4, 5\}$. (c) The range in each case is $\{a, b, c, d, e\}$.
9. Yes. For example, $\{(1, 2)\}$ is a function with domain $\{1\}$ and range $\{2\}$.
11. Yes. For example, the relation would contain (2, 1), but would contain no other pair with first number 2.

Exercises 3.3 Page 52

7. Match the elements of a set containing b elements with the ordered set of cardinal numbers beginning with the number $a + 1$.
9. Let $2m$ and $2n$ represent any two even numbers. $2m + 2n = 2(m + n)$, which is an even number. Thus, the sum of two even numbers is even, and addition is always possible in the set. The addition is commutative and associative, since the even numbers are cardinal numbers. The identity element is 0.
11. (a) $x + r + s = (x + r) + s$
$= s + (x + r)$
$= s + (r + x)$
$= (s + r) + x$
$= s + r + x$
(b) $a + b + c + d = [(a + b) + c] + d$
$= (a + b) + (c + d)$
$= a + [b + (c + d)]$
$= a + [(c + d) + b]$
$= [a + (c + d)] + b$
$= [(a + c) + d] + b$
$= a + c + d + b$

Exercises 3.5 Page 55

1. (c) $n(E) - n(A) = n(B)$, $n(E) - n(B) = n(A)$, $n(A) + n(B) = n(E)$, $n(B) + n(A) = n(E)$

(d)

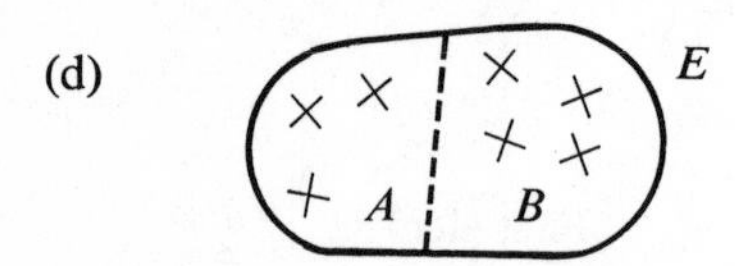

3. (a) The complement of $\{e, f, g\}$ with respect to $\{a, b, c, d\}$ must contain all elements of $\{a, b, c, d\}$ which are not elements of $\{e, f, g\}$. This is precisely the set $\{a, b, c, d\}$.
(b) The subset $\{b, c, d\}$ of the set $\{a, b, c, d\}$ is equivalent to the set $\{e, f, g\}$; and $\{a, b, c, d\} \setminus \{e, f, g\} = \{a\}$.
5. $a + (b - c) + c = a + b$ since $(b - c) + c = b$, by definition.
Thus, $[a + (b - c) + c] - c = (a + b) - c$
$a + (b - c) = (a + b) - c$

Exercises 3.9 Page 62

1. Consider forming the union of a empty sets (which are "equal sized"). The union of these sets is still the empty set. Hence, $0 \cdot a = 0$.
5. $a \cdot b \cdot c \cdot d = [(a \cdot b) \cdot c] \cdot d$
$= d \cdot [(a \cdot b) \cdot c]$ by commutativity of multiplication
$= d \cdot [a \cdot (b \cdot c)]$ by associativity of multiplication
$= d \cdot [a \cdot (c \cdot b)]$ by commutativity of multiplication
$= (d \cdot a) \cdot (c \cdot b)$ by associativity of multiplication
$= [(d \cdot a) \cdot c] \cdot b$ by associativity of multiplication
$= d \cdot a \cdot c \cdot b$
7. If $b - c = x$, then $b = x + c$. Now, $ab = a(x + c) = ax + ac$; $ab - ac = ax = a(b - c)$.

11. $(2 + 3)(2 + 3) = (2 + 3)(2) + (2 + 3)(3) = 2 \cdot 2 + 3 \cdot 2 + 2 \cdot 3 + 3 \cdot 3$
$= 2 \cdot 2 + 2 \cdot (2 \cdot 3) + 3 \cdot 3$

13. 10

15. Since $x = x \cdot 1$, if $x \cdot a = x$, then $x \cdot a = x \cdot 1$, and by the cancellation law, $a = 1$.

Exercises 3.11 Page 66

1. The set of counting numbers possesses properties P_1, P_2, P_5, P_6, P_7, and P_8, but no others.

3. $a = a \cdot 1$. Thus, if $c \cdot a = a$, then $c \cdot a = a \cdot 1 = 1 \cdot a$; and, by the cancellation law, $c = 1$.

5. (a) 10 and 1, or 5 and 2
   (b) Each of the numbers is 1.
   (c) One of the numbers is 0; the other may be any cardinal number (including 0).

7. Subtraction is an internal law of composition in this case.

Exercises 4.4 Page 74

1. (a) 81 (b) 125 (c) 0 (d) 1 (e) 1 (f) 3 (g) 16 (h) 16 (i) 1024
   (j) 16,807

3. 3^0 would occur as the first term in the sequence; hence, 3^0 is defined to be 1.

5. In both cases, the result is 16. In this special instance, $2^4 = 4^2$.

9. (a) 2^{12} (b) 3^6 (c) 1 (d) 1 (e) 1 (f) 4^6 (g) $2^4 \cdot 3^4$, or 6^4
   (h) $3^2 \cdot 2^2 \cdot 5^2$, or 30^2 (i) $2^2 \cdot 8^2 \cdot 10^2$, or 160^2 (j) 10^6 (k) 100^6

11. (a) $a^1 = a$, but it is not the case that $1^a = a$ (if $a \neq 1$); and identity elements must commute.
    (b) $(a \cdot b)^n = (a^n)(b^n)$, whereas $a \cdot b^n = (a)(b^n)$. $a + b \cdot c = a + (bc)$, whereas $(a + b) \cdot c = ac + bc$.

13. 0 1 2 3 4 ... n
    0 3 6 9 12 ... $3n$ $x \to 3x$

15. 0 1 2 3 4 ... n
    0 1 8 27 64 ... n^3 $x \to x^3$

17. $a^p = a^{n+k} = (a^n)(a^k)$. And $a^n < (a^n)(a^k)$, since $a^k > 1$.

19. $a^n = a^{p+0} = (a^p)(a^0) = a^p(1) = a^p$

21. In each case, $a^n = a^p$.

Exercises 4.6 Page 78

1. The following are statements: (*a*), (*b*), (*c*), (*e*), (*h*), (*i*).

5. {5}

7. {0, 1, 2, 3, 4}

9. {1, 2, 3, 4, 5, . . .}

11. {0, 1, 2, 3}

13. {20}

15. {0, 1, 2, 3, 4, 5, 6, 7}

17. $\emptyset$

19. {6, 7, 8, 9, 10, . . .}

21. The solution is the product of the cardinal numbers a and b.

23. No, since the rule for the operation does not cover the case where $a > b$. Thus, no result is available for 5–2, for example. However, if it is understood that the usual subtraction will be performed in such cases, then the set is closed to the operation.

Exercises 4.10 Page 85

1. The following have exact quotients: (a), (b), (d), (g), (h).
3. (a) If $b + x = a$, then $x = a - b$. If $b \cdot x = a$, then $x = a \div b$.
   (b) $a - 0 = a$, but $0 - a \neq a$; $a \div 1 = a$, but $1 \div a \neq a$;
   (c) $a - b$ has an exact answer if $a \geq b$; $a \div b$ has an exact answer if a is a multiple of b.
   (d) $a - b$ and $(a + k) - (b + k)$ have the same difference; $a \div b$ and $ak \div bk$ have the same quotient. (In both cases, $k \neq 0$.)
   (e) The difference increases; the quotient increases (or remains the same).
   (f) $2 - 3 = 0$, deficit 1; $2 \div 3 = 0$, remainder 2.
5. $b - 1$
9. No
11. 2
13. 5^{90}
15. Not possible
17. 0
19. 7
21. The total quotient is 6; the remainder 9.
23. $12 \div 4 = 3$, but $4 \div 12 \neq 3$.
   $24 \div (12 \div 2) = 24 \div 6 = 4$; $(24 \div 12) \div 2 = 2 \div 2 = 1$. These counterexamples show that exact division is neither commutative nor associative. The number one is not an identity element for division; $a \div 1 = a$, but, in general, $1 \div a \neq a$, and an identity element must commute.

Exercises 5.4 Page 92

1. (a) A number is an abstract concept, a property of a set. (b) A digit is a basic symbol used in a system of numeration. (c) A numeral is a systematic arrangement of digits used to name a number.
5. n
7. (a) 38002 (b) 452301 (c) $\overline{u_4u_3u_2u_1u_0}$
15. (a) 9 (not counting zero) (b) 90 (c) 900 (d) $9 \cdot 10^{n-1}$
17. 51
19. 193

Exercises 5.7 Page 99

1. (a) When the number ten is used as base (b) When a cardinal number other than ten is used as base
3. (a) The coefficient of x^5 (b) $\{0, 1, 2, 3, 4, 5\}$
   (c) $2 \cdot 10^5 + 4 \cdot 10^4 + 1 \cdot 10^3 + 5 \cdot 10^2 + 0 \cdot 10^1 + 3 \cdot 10^0{}_{(six)}$;
   $2 \cdot 10^4 + 1 \cdot 10^3 + 1 \cdot 10^2 + 3 \cdot 10^1 + 5 \cdot 10^0$
7. (a) $1242222_{(five)}$ (b) $12353_{(twelve)}$ (c) $60157_{(eight)}$
9. (b) 1030 (c) $3\bar{9}37_{(twenty)}$
11. The base is two. The largest number which can be represented is $1 \cdot 10^n + 1 \cdot 10^{n-1} + \ldots + 1 \cdot 10^1 + 1 \cdot 10^0{}_{(two)}$, and this is one less than $1 \cdot 10^{n+1}{}_{(two)}$.

Exercises 5.9 Page 106

1. (a) 10 added to minuend and subtrahend (b) 72 added to minuend and subtrahend, changing subtrahend to 100 (c) Standard algorism, by simple regrouping (d) 8 added to minuend and subtrahend

3. $10743_{(\text{nine})}$
5. $55_{(\text{seven})}$, remainder $255_{(\text{seven})}$
7. $14142_{(\text{six})}$
9. $3929tt_{(\text{eleven})}$
11. (a), (b), and (c) are even.
13. (a) $2565_{(\text{base } x)}$ (b) $x \geq 7$ (c) 1397
15. $(a_3 - 1)x^3 + (a_2 + x - 1)x^2 + (a_1 + x - 1)x^1 + (a_0 + x)x^0$

Exercises 6.6 Page 115

1. A set of points
3. The following are true: (a), (c), (e), (f), (g), (h), (k), (l).
5. $\dfrac{n(n-1)}{2}$
7. The following are true: (a), (b), (d), (e), (f), (i).

Exercises 6.12 Page 122

1. The following are true: (a), (d).
3. Yes
5. (a) Yes (b) No

Exercises 6.18 Page 130

1. (a) If three letters are used to name the angle, there are eight different names.
   (b) Vertex (c) The intersection of two half planes, the half plane on the "R side" of line ST and the half plane on the "T side" of line SR
3. The following are true: (b), (c), (d), (g), (h), (i), (k).
5. The following are convex: (b), (d), (f), (g), (h), (i), (j), (k), (m).
7. (a) Yes. The segment joining two points of a plane lies entirely in the plane.
   (b) No, not necessarily

Exercises 7.4 Page 136

1. (a) 4
   (b) {2, 8, 14, 20, 26, 32, 38, 44}
   (c) 6, 0, and $6k$ are not elements of S; all others are.
3. (a) Yes; $35 = 5 \cdot 7$
   (b) No; $5x = 32$ has no whole number solution.
   (c) Yes; $n \cdot 1 = n$ (d) Yes; $n \cdot 1 = n$
5. (a) 15 (b) 55 (c) 75 (d) $x + 15$, or $x - 15$.

Exercises 7.9 Page 140

1. The following are true: (a), (b), (c), (g), (h), (i), (j).
3. (a) 3
   (b) $C_0 = \{0, 3, 6, 9, \ldots 3k, \ldots\}$
   $C_1 = \{1, 4, 7, 10, \ldots 3k + 1, \ldots\}$
   $C_2 = \{2, 5, 8, 11, \ldots 3k + 2, \ldots\}$
   (c) Infinite number
   (e) Yes
5. (a) 25

Exercises 7.12 Page 143

1.

$\cdot$	C_0	C_1	C_2
C_0	C_0	C_0	C_0
C_1	C_0	C_1	C_2
C_2	C_0	C_2	C_1

(a) Yes (b) Yes (c) C_1

3. (a) C_1 (b) C_1 is its own inverse; C_3 is its own inverse; the other elements have no inverse. (c) No; some elements do not have inverses.
5. 0

Exercises 7.14 Page 145

1. (a) Yes (b) Yes (c) Yes, 0 (d) Yes; 1 and 3 are inverses; 0 is its own inverse; 2 is its own inverse. (e) Yes

Exercises 8.5 Page 151

1. (a) Four (b) $3 \cdot 10^3 + 2 \cdot 10^2 + 6 \cdot 10^1 + 5 \cdot 10^0$ (c) Four
(d) $u_3 \cdot 10^3 + u_2 \cdot 10^2 + u_1 \cdot 10^1 + u_0 \cdot 10^0$ (e) $n + 1$
(f) $u_n \cdot 10^n + u_{n-1} \cdot 10^{n-1} + \ldots + u_2 \cdot 10^2 + u_1 \cdot 10^1 + u_0 \cdot 10^0$
3. $a = b$

Exercises 8.9 Page 155

1. (a) $20 \equiv 56 \pmod 3$, since 36 is a multiple of 3.
(b) $50 \equiv 140 \pmod 3$, since 90 is a multiple of 3.
(c) If $a \equiv b \pmod n$, then $ac \equiv bc \pmod n$.

Exercises 8.12 Page 160

1. Yes; $9 - 9 = 0$, and 0 is divisible by 11.
3. (a), (f), (g), (i) are divisible by 11.

Exercises 9.6 Page 166

1. (a) and (h) are false.
3. Only (c) is false.
5. Only (c) is false.
7. 2 and 3, 3 and 5, 5 and 7, 11 and 13, 17 and 19, 29 and 31, 41 and 43, 59 and 61, 71 and 73

Exercises 9.11 Page 174

1. (a), (c), and (f) are false.
3. (a) 7 (b) 11 (c) 97

Exercises 9.14 Page 177

1. In each case, there is a remainder of 1.
3. (Answers may vary.) (a) $7 + 7$ (b) $11 + 5$ (c) $11 + 7$ (d) $17 + 3$
(e) $47 + 3$ (f) $59 + 5$ (g) $97 + 3$ (h) $163 + 5$

Exercises 10.4 Page 183

1. 1
3. (b)

5. (a) 4 (b) 1 (c) 4 (d) 55 (e) 21 (f) 75 (g) 1 (h) 27 (i) 8 (j) 21
(k) 1

Exercises 10.8 Page 188

1. (a) 24 (b) 10 (c) 168 (d) 91 (e) 20 (f) 144 (g) 144 (h) 1600
(i) 6912 (j) 6400 (k) 128 (l) 128
3. The product ab
5. (a) 96 and 8 (b) 144 and 72 (c) 252 and 21 (d) 864 and 1 (e) 224 and 4

Exercises 11.2 Page 192

5.

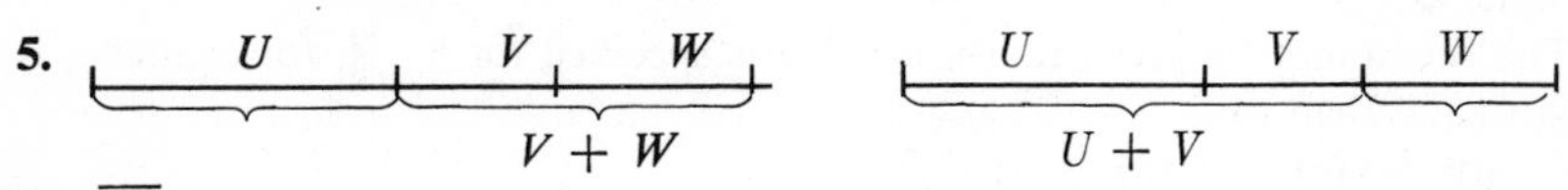

11. $\overline{CB}$

Exercises 11.5 Page 196

1. $2U$ $2U$ $2U$

U U U U U U

3. W W W W W W W

$3W$ $4W$

5. (a) $4 \cdot (0 \cdot U) = (4 \cdot 0) \cdot U = 0 \cdot U = \mathbb{O}$
(b) Let $V = 4U$. Then $0 \cdot (4U) = 0 \cdot V = \mathbb{O}$.
(c) No
(d) $\mathbb{O}$

Exercises 11.7 Page 199

1. O ________________ A

$2^{-1}\overline{OA}$

$4^{-1}\overline{OA}$

$5^{-1}\overline{OA}$

3. 4, 3, 2, 1 $= 1^{-1}, 2^{-1}, 3^{-1}, 4^{-1}$, 0 in decreasing order

Exercises 11.12 Page 206

1. If A is between O and B, and $V = \overline{OA}$ and $V' = \overline{AB}$, then $V + V' = \overline{OB}$.
If $V > V'$, $V - V'$ is the segment X such that $X + V' = V$.
aV is the segment obtained by using V as an addend a times.
$\frac{a}{b} V$ is the segment X such that $bX = aV$.
5. A segment $\overline{AA}$, whose end points are actually the same point, consists simply of that point.
7. A fraction is an ordered pair of whole numbers, the second of which is not zero.
13. The largest possible common unit segment is $\frac{V}{3}\left(= \frac{V'}{2}\right)$.
15. There are n fractions for which the sum of numerator and denominator is n.

Exercises 12.3 Page 213

1. 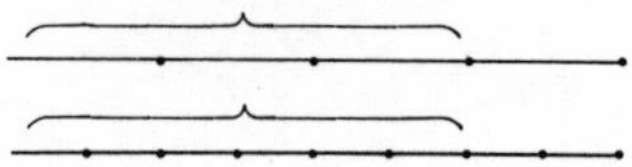

3. 0

5. (a) $\left\{\frac{4}{7}, \frac{8}{14}, \frac{12}{21}, \ldots, \frac{4k}{7k}, \ldots\right\}$
   (b) $\left\{\frac{2}{3}, \frac{4}{6}, \frac{6}{9}, \ldots, \frac{2k}{3k}, \ldots\right\}$
   (c) Same as (a)
   (d) The set cannot be given unless a value is specified for x. $\frac{2}{3}$, for example, is not equivalent to $\frac{3}{4}$.

7. (a) $\frac{0}{7}$ (b) $\frac{1}{6}$ (c) $\frac{7}{11}$ (d) $\frac{1}{1}$ (e) $\frac{257}{43}$

Exercises 12.8 Page 220

7. $18 \times 135 < 42 \times 60$

9. $\frac{7}{12}, \frac{5}{8}, \frac{13}{20}, \frac{2}{3}$, in increasing order

11. $\frac{a}{b} < \frac{a}{c}$ if $b > c$.

13. (a) $x = 0$ (least) (b) $x = 1$ (greatest) (c) $x = 0$ (least) (d) $x = 0$ (least)
    (e) $x = 1$ (greatest)

15. If $a < b$ and $\frac{a}{b}$ is irreducible, then $\frac{a+b}{ab}, \frac{b-a}{ab}, \frac{ab}{a^2+b^2}$, and $\frac{a+b}{a^2+ab+b^2}$ are irreducible

Exercises 13.6 Page 234

3. $\frac{36}{20}$

5. $\frac{1}{2} \times \frac{4}{6}, \frac{2}{4} \times \frac{2}{3}, \frac{2}{4} \times \frac{4}{6}$, etc.

9. (a) $\frac{6}{1}$ (b) 6 (c) $\frac{45}{1}$ (d) 45 (e) $\frac{1}{1}$ (f) 96 (g) $\frac{231}{1}$ (h) 231

11. $$\frac{a}{b} \times \frac{c}{d} \times \frac{e}{f} = \left(\frac{a}{b} \times \frac{c}{d}\right) \times \frac{e}{f} = \frac{e}{f} \times \left(\frac{a}{b} \times \frac{c}{d}\right) = \frac{e}{f} \times \left(\frac{c}{d} \times \frac{a}{b}\right)$$
    $$= \left(\frac{e}{f} \times \frac{c}{d}\right) \times \frac{a}{b}$$

Exercises 13.12 Page 242

1. (a) $\frac{1}{1}, \frac{1}{1}, \frac{1}{1}, \frac{1}{1}$
   (b) $\frac{5}{3}, \frac{2}{9}, \frac{31}{23}, \frac{47}{98}, \frac{b}{a}$
   (c) $\frac{0}{1} \times \frac{a}{b} = \frac{0}{b} \neq \frac{1}{1}$
   (d) $\frac{0}{1}$ is a rational number, and $\frac{1}{0}$ is not its inverse.

3. (a) $\frac{1}{1}$ (b) $\frac{4}{9}$ (c) $\frac{4}{1}$ (d) $\frac{1}{1}$ (e) $\frac{0}{1}$ (f) $\frac{0}{1}$ (g) $\frac{8}{1}$ (h) 8 (i) $\frac{5}{1}$ (j) 5 (k) $\frac{es}{fr}$

5. Since $ad < bc$, $afde < becf$. Therefore, $\frac{af}{be} < \frac{cf}{de}$.

7. (a) $\frac{2}{3} < \frac{3}{4}$ (b) $\frac{11}{23} < \frac{19}{37}$ (c) $\frac{0}{5} < \frac{4}{5}$ (d) $\frac{18}{36} = \frac{27}{54}$ (e) $\frac{11}{48} < \frac{8}{33}$
(f) $\frac{201}{400} < \frac{101}{200}$ (g) $\frac{17}{9} < \frac{15}{7}$ (h) $\frac{x}{y} < \frac{x+1}{y}$

Exercises 13.18 Page 251

1. (a) $\frac{5}{4}$

Exercises 13.23 Page 259

1. (a) $\frac{1}{6}$ (b) $\frac{22}{35}$ (c) $\frac{5}{28}$ (d) Not possible (e) $\frac{5}{6}$ (f) Not possible
(g) Not possible (h) Not possible (i) Not possible (j) $\frac{r}{s}$ (k) $\frac{r-t}{s}$
3. $5 + 3 = 8$; $\frac{5}{1} + \frac{3}{1} = \frac{8}{1}$; $5 \times 3 = 15$; $\frac{5}{1} \times \frac{3}{1} = \frac{15}{1}$
5. $a = 0$ or $c = 0$
7. $\frac{a}{b} < \frac{c}{d} \Rightarrow \frac{a}{b} + \frac{x}{y} < \frac{c}{d} + \frac{x}{y}$; $\frac{a}{b} + \frac{x}{y} < \frac{c}{d} + \frac{x}{y} \Rightarrow \frac{a}{b} < \frac{c}{d}$;
$\frac{a}{b} = \frac{c}{d} \Rightarrow \frac{a}{b} + \frac{x}{y} = \frac{c}{d} + \frac{x}{y}$; $\frac{a}{b} + \frac{x}{y} = \frac{c}{d} + \frac{x}{y} \Rightarrow \frac{a}{b} = \frac{c}{d}$
9. (a) $x = 5\frac{2}{3}$ (b) $x = 3\frac{1}{2}$ (c) $x = 6$
(d) $x > 2\frac{1}{2}$ (e) $x < 1\frac{4}{5}$ (f) $x = 5\frac{1}{10}$
(g) $x < \frac{11}{4}$

Exercises 14.3 Page 266

1. $\frac{8}{14}$, $\frac{9}{16}$, and $\frac{10}{18}$ are examples.
3. $\frac{a}{b} < \frac{ad + bc}{2bd} < \frac{c}{d}$, since $2abd = abd + abd < abd + bbc$, and $add + bcd < bcd + bcd = 2bcd$.
5. (a) .45 (b) 1.175 (c) .216
7. (a) $\frac{375}{500}$, $\frac{40}{500}$, $\frac{175}{500}$, $\frac{44}{500}$ (b) $\frac{40}{200}$, $\frac{1268}{200}$, $\frac{9}{200}$
9. If $\frac{1}{3} = \frac{n}{10^a}$, then $3n = 10^a = 2^a \cdot 5^a$. But this is not possible, since 3 is a factor of the left member but not of the right member.

Exercises 14.7 Page 275

1. (a) $\frac{8}{45}$ (b) .67 and .27 (c) .1809; the two results agree to two decimal places, .18.
3. (a) $.\dot{4}\dot{2}\dot{8}\dot{5}\dot{7}\dot{1}$ (b) $.\dot{5}\dot{7}\dot{1}\dot{4}\dot{2}\dot{8}$ (c) $1 = .99999\dot{9}$
5. Assuming a and b have no common factors, b has no prime factors other than 2 and 5.
9. $\frac{23}{55}$

11. $\frac{24}{10} < \frac{27}{11} < \frac{25}{10}$; $\frac{245}{100} < \frac{27}{11} < \frac{246}{100}$; $\frac{2454}{1000} < \frac{27}{11} < \frac{2455}{1000}$

13. $.\dot{0}\dot{7}\dot{6}\dot{9}\dot{2}\dot{3}$; $.\dot{1}\dot{5}\dot{3}\dot{8}\dot{4}\dot{6}$; $.\dot{3}\dot{8}\dot{4}\dot{6}\dot{1}\dot{5}$; $.\dot{7}\dot{6}\dot{9}\dot{2}\dot{3}\dot{0}$

Exercises 14.11 Page 284

1. (a) 1 (b) $\frac{45}{99}$ (c) $\frac{234}{999}$
3. (a) and (c)
5. (a) 2.2361 (b) 3.3166 (c) 147.7938 (d) 1.7724
7. Assume $\sqrt{5} = \frac{a}{b}$, where $\frac{a}{b}$ is irreducible. Then $5b^2 = a^2$; so 5 is a factor of a. Let $a = 5t$. Then $5b^2 = 25t^2$, and $b^2 = 5t^2$; so 5 is also a factor of b, contradicting the assumption that $\frac{a}{b}$ is irreducible.
9. $2a = a + a < a + b < b + b = 2b$
11. (a) $23409 = 3^6 \cdot 17^2$, so $\sqrt{23409} = 3^3 \cdot 17$.

    (b) $\frac{1764}{100} = \frac{9 \cdot 4 \cdot 49}{10 \cdot 10}$, so $\sqrt{17.64} = \frac{42}{10} = 4.2$.

    (c) $\frac{5184}{2401} = \frac{3 \times 3 \times 24 \times 24}{49 \times 49}$, so $\sqrt{\frac{5184}{2401}} = \frac{3 \times 24}{49}$.

Exercises 14.14 Page 291

1. (a) $3\frac{52}{55}$; $3\frac{39}{55}$ (b) 3.9453; 3.70880546 (c) $3\frac{52}{55}$; $3\frac{39}{55}$
   (d) The numbers in part (b) are decimal rationals; the numbers in parts (a) and (c) are not.
3. (a) -5 (b) 6 (c) $-2.\dot{3}$ (d) $4.44\dot{4}$ (e) -3 (f) 3 (g) 2 (h) $\sqrt{3}$ (i) 14.421,
7. (a) 10 (b) -6 (c) $6\sqrt{2}$ (d) $-\frac{1}{9}$
9. Yes; 4.732

Exercises 15.7 Page 304

1. (a) Counting (b) Yes (c) {1, 2, 3} (d) Set of whole numbers (e) $\boxed{\cdots}$
   (f) A segment
3. (a) 6 (b) 4 (c) 3 (d) $3\frac{0}{2}$ (e) $3\frac{1}{16}$
5. (a) 4 (b) 1 (c) 2 (d) 6 (e) 8
7. (a) 2 feet, $\frac{2}{3}$ yd., 60.96 centimeters (b) 30 decimeters, 300 cm.
   (c) 1 kilometer = .62 mile (approximately)
11. The following are true: (a), (c), (d), (f).

Exercises 15.13 Page 316

3. No. Most protractors are precise only to the nearest $\frac{1}{2}$°.
5. (a) One (b) Infinite number
9. (a) A rectangle is a quadrilateral having four right angles.
   (b) A square is a rectangle all of whose sides are congruent.
11. (a) 4 (b) 720
13. (c) 113.04 square inches
15. (a) 10 square inches
17. (a) 8 cubic feet (b) 64 cubic feet (d) If the edge is doubled, the volume is multiplied by 8.
19. 3 yards. No, it will multiply the volume by 8.

Exercises 16.2 Page 323

1. $\frac{10}{6}, \frac{15}{9}, \frac{20}{12}$
3. (a) $\frac{8}{15}$ (b) $\frac{15}{8}$ (c) $\frac{8}{15}$
5. It will remain the same; a quotient is unchanged if dividend and divisor are multiplied by the same number.
7. $V = \frac{a}{k} U'$; $V' = \frac{b}{k} U'$; $\frac{a}{b}$
9. (a) $2 : 5 : 3$ (b) $\frac{2}{10}$, $\frac{5}{10}$, and $\frac{3}{10}$

Exercises 16.4 Page 327

1. (a), (b), and (d)
3. Yes
5. 9.5π
7. Since $ad = bc$, $ad + bd = bc + bd$. Therefore, $(a + b)d = b(c + d)$.
11. $x = 10\frac{2}{3}$, $y = 16$, $z = 18\frac{2}{3}$
13. (a) $\frac{1}{4}, \frac{2}{3}, \frac{3}{2}, \frac{4}{1}$ (b) $\{5, 10, 15, 20, \ldots\}$
15. 3.45, 6.9, and 8.7

Exercises 16.6 Page 331

1. (a) 50% (b) 5% (c) 1.6% (d) 300% (e) 140% (f) .5%
3. (a) 75% (b) 25% (c) 150% (d) 10% (e) $3\frac{1}{3}$% (f) 50% (g) .125% (h) $8\frac{1}{3}$% (i) $2\frac{1}{12}$%
5. 19.5
7. $11\frac{1}{9}$%
9. $50.00

Exercises 16.8 Page 336

1. (c) $\frac{9}{4}$
3. 8.05 inches, 11.2 inches, 14 inches
5. 42 yards
9. (a) $\frac{2}{3}$ (b) $\frac{4}{9}$ (d) The ratio of the areas is the square of the ratio of similitude.

Exercises 17.5 Page 349

1. (a) 7 (b) 13 (c) 7 (d) 6 (e) 6 (f) 100 (g) 228 (h) 2000 (i) $10\frac{1}{4}$ (j) $a - b$
5. The half plane to the right of the Y-axis
7. (a) $(a, b) \neq (b, a)$ (b) No (c) Yes (d) Yes (e) Yes, if $a = b$
9. (a) $\sqrt{145}$
11. The distance between (2, 4) and (7, 10) is equal to the distance between (7, 10) and (12, 4).

Exercises 17.9 Page 357

1. (a) 1 (b) -1 (c) -2 (d) $-\frac{1}{2}$ (e) $-\frac{5}{6}$ (f) 0 (g) 2 (h) -1 (i) No slope (j) $\frac{b - d}{a - c}$ if $a \neq c$.
3. (a) (6, 0) (b) (0, 12)
7. (c) $\frac{5 - 0}{2 - 0} = \frac{0 - 5}{6 - 8}$ (d) $\frac{5 - 5}{2 - 8} = \frac{0 - 0}{0 - 6}$
9. (a) $-\frac{10}{7}$ (b) $\frac{7}{10}$

Exercises 17.12 Page 365

3. (a) The constant term tells the point on the Y-axis at which the line crosses the axis.
   (b) 5, $-\frac{1}{2}$, b
5. (a) $y = k$ (b) $x = k$ (c) $y = 0$ (d) $x = 0$
7. The equation is not linear. The graph is a parabola.
9. (a) $x^2 + y^2 = 144$ (b) $64x^2 + 64y^2 = 49$ (c) $x^2 + y^2 = 5$
   (d) $x^2 + y^2 = 2500$ (e) $x^2 + y^2 = n^2$

INDEX

234567890